Fundamentals of
EXPERIMENTAL DESIGN

Jerome L. Myers

Professor of Psychology and Statistics
University of Massachusetts

ALLYN AND BACON, BOSTON, 1966

PREFACE

To be useful a book on experimental design must clearly present designs and appropriate data analyses, supplemented by specific instances of application and by numerical examples. One purpose of this volume is such a presentation. However, recipes for designs and analyses are in themselves not sufficient for the training of independent researchers. It is hoped that the development of this book will provide a basis for selecting among designs and analyses and for extending the principles presented to designs and analyses which are not discussed here. In short, this book is concerned not merely with what is done but also with why it is done.

The reader should be familiar with material usually covered in a one-semester introductory statistics course—such topics as the binomial, normal, chi-square, and t distributions, and bivariate regression and correlation. No previous exposure to the analysis of variance is assumed. Ideally, the reader should have some foundation in such general inferential topics as estimation, Type I and Type II errors, power, and confidence intervals. A brief review of these topics is contained in Chapter 2. Notational usage, which is also considered to be part of a well-taught introductory course, is reviewed in Chapter 3. No mathematics beyond college algebra is required.

In organizing a book of this sort, the writer may exhaustively discuss a design within a single chapter, at that point treating the wide variety of data manipulations which he deems pertinent. A somewhat different strategy is followed here: Each design chapter covers the model and calculations related to the overall F tests which dominate our experimental literature. Changes in the model and in the computations are followed and the pertinent inferential problems noted as new design principles are added—matching, repeated measurements, nesting of variables, and counterbalancing. With a firm grasp (hopefully) of how the statistical model is developed and of the computations which it leads to, the reader should then be ready to turn to other data manipulations which may be performed on the designs which have been previously treated. Therefore, the later chapters consider the concepts and calculations relevant to such diverse topics as confidence intervals, covariance adjustment, range tests, and trend analyses.

Since this is meant to be a basic experimental design book rather than a handbook of designs and analyses, a number of topics have been excluded. The criteria for inclusion were whether or not the material was considered fundamental for the development of subsequent topics (as well as topics which have not been included), and the likelihood that the material might be of use to the researcher. Those topics that have been included in the book have generally received extensive consideration. It is hoped that the resulting book will provide a reasonably sound foundation in experimental design and analysis.

The author is indebted to the literary executor of the late Sir Ronald A. Fisher, F.R.S., Cambridge; to Dr. Frank Yates, F.R.S., Rothamsted; and to Messrs. Oliver & Boyd Ltd., Edinburgh, for permission to reproduce Tables A-3, A-4, and parts of A-5 from their book *Statistical Tables for Biological, Agricultural and Medical Research.*

There are many people who have made a contribution to the development of this volume. I particularly wish to express my gratitude to my secretary, Mrs. Dorothy Thayer, whose contribution in preparing the manuscript is incalculable; to Miss Virginia Kochanowski for drawing the figures; to several anonymous reviewers for their comments; and to Dr. Mary M. Suydam, who painstakingly read the manuscript. A multilithed edition was used as a text for my graduate course in experimental design; I am indebted to the many students who detected errors and who suggested improvements in exposition. A special note of gratitude is due my wife and co-worker, Dr. Nancy A. Myers, not only for reading and commenting on the manuscript, but also for encouraging me throughout the writing process.

J. L. M.

CONTENTS

PLANNING THE EXPERIMENT

1

1.1 INTRODUCTION

A psychological experiment is undertaken in order to determine the factors which influence a certain behavior and the extent and direction of their influence. The experimenter seeks answers to such questions as, What are the relative effects of these three drugs upon the number of errors made in learning a maze? Which of these training methods is more effective? What changes in auditory acuity occur as a function of these changes in sound intensity? If an experiment is to answer such questions adequately, the investigator must first specify those factors whose effects are to be studied (*independent variables*); minimize the operation of factors which are not of interest at the time (*irrelevant variables*); carefully select a measure, or measures, of the behavior which he is investigating (*dependent variables*); and choose those whose behavior is to be measured (*subjects*). Planning these four basic aspects of an experiment is the first and most critical step in obtaining answers about behavior. Therefore, this first chapter presents a general discussion of these considerations. Although much of this discussion may appear obvious to the well-trained and experienced researcher, it is hoped that the student of experimental design will profit from this review of the many things to be considered in planning an experiment.

1.2 THE INDEPENDENT VARIABLE

Once the experimenter has decided upon the independent variable or variables that are to be studied, he must choose the actual treatments: the levels—specific types or amounts—of the independent variable which will be tested in the experiment. He must decide which drugs, which training

1

methods, which sound intensities will be compared.   In considering this class of decisions, it is helpful to distinguish between two types of independent variables, quantitative and qualitative, and to discuss these separately.

1.2.1 Quantitative variables

A quantitative independent variable is a variable whose levels differ in amount.   Examples of such a variable are amount of reward, intensity of shock, and number of practice trials.   Generally, the experimenter is not interested in the specific numerical levels chosen for inclusion in the experiment.   For example, in a study of the effects of inter-trial interval upon the speed of learning lists of words, the experimenter may choose 2, 4, and 6 sec. as his levels for interval length.   Probably 1.8, 3.8, and 5.8 sec. would be just as adequate for his purpose, but he tends to think in terms of whole numbers. The levels of a quantitative independent variable are usually of interest only to the extent that they permit the experimenter to determine whether any change in the quantity manipulated results in a change in behavior, and, if so, what are the characteristics (e.g., the shape, slope, and position) of the function relating the independent and dependent variables.   This being the case, the levels of the independent variable should be chosen to cover a wide enough range to detect any behavioral change which might result, and in sufficient number and close enough together so that the shape of the function will be clearly defined.

In any single experiment it may be difficult to achieve the ideal of broadly covering the continuum of the independent variable with many levels, close together.   It is not always possible to decide without some pilot experimentation how many and how close the levels should be, and the limitations of time, money, and subjects may make the ideal difficult to realize.   Therefore, it will often be best in initial experiments to determine generally whether any behavioral change occurs as the independent variable is manipulated and to attain a rough description of the shape of the function relating the independent and dependent variables.   If desirable, subsequent experiments can be designed to yield a more precise definition of the function.

For example, suppose that an experimenter is interested in the relationship between x and y of Figure 1-1.   Assuming that there are other independent variables which he also wishes to investigate, he may not be able to include as many levels of x as would seem ideal.   In his first experiment, he might include the levels x_1, x_3, and x_5, thus learning that variations in x do result in variations in y and obtaining some idea of the slope of the function and the minimum range of x over which y varies.   In subsequent experiments levels might be chosen between x_2 and x_4, giving a more specific picture of the function.

Note that the decision about the selection of levels depends upon the results of previous research.   However, such decisions may also be influenced by theoretical considerations.   For example, suppose that the experimenter is trying to decide which of two theories is correct, one of which predicts gradual changes in y (in Fig. 1-1) with changes in x, while the other predicts a "staircase" effect, stepwise changes in the function.   In this case, an exami-

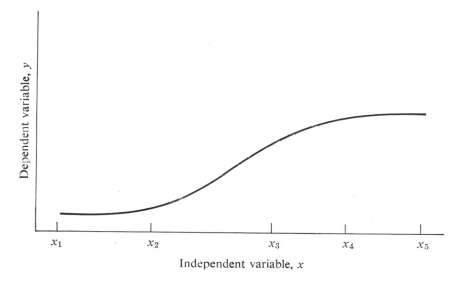

FIGURE 1-1   A function relating dependent and independent variables

nation of a broad range of levels of x might be sacrificed in order to concentrate more levels within a narrow range.

While on the topic of quantitative independent variables, one might note some of the inferential pitfalls that occur, particularly when only a few levels of the variable are included in an experiment.   Suppose that the variable x of Figure 1-1 is under investigation and that the relationship between independent and dependent variable is that depicted in the figure.   If no other information were available, and if only x_1 and x_2 or x_4 and x_5 were selected for investigation, the data might lead the experimenter to conclude that the independent variable, x, does not influence behavior.   If the experimenter happened to choose x_1, x_3, and x_4, he might conclude that performance and x were related by a linear function.   The first instance is an example of extrapolation beyond the range of levels selected, and the second instance is an example of interpolation between the levels selected.   It is wise to recognize the tentative status of inferences which go beyond the levels that have been included in the experiment.

1.2.2 Qualitative variables

A qualitative independent variable is one whose "levels"* differ in type. Examples of such a variable are type of punishment, method of training, and type of instructions. The particular "levels"—the specific types—of the variable which are included in the experiment are usually of direct interest to the experimenter, in contrast to the numerical levels of quantitative variables, which, as previously mentioned, are often less important in themselves than for the information they provide about some function relating the independent and dependent variables. Qualitative treatments are chosen because previous research, theoretical predictions, or practical considerations dictate their choice. For example, two particular methods of teaching reading may be chosen for experimental comparison because (a) previous experimentation suggests that these are the two most efficient procedures available, (b) the results of the comparison should differentiate between two educational theories in which the experimenter is interested, or (c) other methods require so much time and money that they are impractical to experiment with and would not be used in practice even if effective.

1.2.3 Control levels

A consideration common to both qualitative and quantitative variables is the selection of *control* levels. These are treatments which may not be of interest in themselves but which provide additional information about the effects of one or more other treatments. Suppose that one wished to compare the effects of teaching, and of not teaching, reading in kindergarten upon reading scores obtained at the end of first grade. The experiment demands two groups of first graders, both with kindergarten experience, but only one of which has had reading experience in kindergarten. Adding a control group, children who had no kindergarten experience at all, would permit evaluation of the possibility that organized activity alone is helpful preparation for grade-school performance.

1.2.4 Fixed and random variables

Implied in the discussion of this section has been the premise that we are dealing with *fixed* variables in our research, variables whose levels are arbitrarily chosen by the experimenter. A second, less frequently occurring, but equally important possibility is that the variable is *random*, i.e., that its levels were chosen from some larger population of levels on the principle that all members of the population have an equal opportunity to be chosen. The

---

* The word "levels" is actually not applicable to the qualitative variable inasmuch as all definitions of the word suggest an ordering or ranking. However, since it is a useful concept for later chapters, it has been employed for both the quantitative and qualitative variables.

experimenter chooses his levels in this way when his major consideration is to obtain a reliable estimate of the variability in the population. For example, in order to determine whether newly manufactured calculating machines perform similarly, a sample, representative of the entire population of such machines, would be tested. Another random variable which is of major concern in psychological research is the subject. Individual subjects are rarely chosen for unique personal attributes. Generally, subjects in psychological experimentation are a random sample from some population, perhaps all the students taking basic psychology at some college.

The distinction between fixed and random independent variables is important to our inferential processes. When the levels of the variable have been arbitrarily chosen, any inferences about differences among the effects of the levels are limited to the particular levels chosen. Having compared the effects of three arbitrarily chosen methods of teaching reading, it is possible to draw inferences about these three methods, not about any broader population of methods. On the other hand, the observed variability among performances on five calculators chosen randomly from a factory's output leads to conclusions about the variability in the population of machines (the factory's output). Our inferential statements extend beyond the actual levels sampled (the five machines in the experiment) to the broader population from which they were randomly sampled. This distinction also has important implications for the analysis of data, but this aspect will be considered at a later point in the text.

1.3 IRRELEVANT VARIABLES

Drawing conclusions about a certain behavior would present no problems if the only variables affecting the behavior were those selected for study by the experimenter. Unfortunately, behavior is seldom so simply caused: it may be a function of such variables as the intelligence, prior experience, attitude, and age of the subject, the time of day at which the data are collected, and even the tone of voice in which instructions are read. If one is not interested in the effects of these variables in some particular experiment, they are irrelevant in the limited sense that the experiment has not been performed to investigate them. However, since such "irrelevant" variables do influence behavior, care must be taken to ensure that their effects are minimized for the duration of the experiment in which they are not being studied. In this section, ways of accomplishing this will be considered.

It is difficult to ensure that different treatment groups will be perfectly matched with regard to all irrelevant variables which might influence the data. For example, the assignment of subjects to two problem-solving groups might, by chance, result in one treatment being applied to a group of subjects with a higher average intelligence than the second group. This bias is called a *random bias* if each subject had an equal chance of being assigned to either group.   In this case, our statistical techniques, which assume that biases are random, will take the bias into account.   However, if the assignment of the brighter subjects to one treatment occurred because of a lack of careful randomization, we have a *systematic bias*, which our statistical techniques cannot take into account.   Valid inferences could not then be properly drawn from the data.   If the brighter students, under treatment *A*, perform better, is intelligence or the treatment responsible?   If the two groups perform equally well, are the treatments equally effective, or is it possible that the more effective treatment was handicapped by being applied to the less able problem solvers?   Clearly, such systematic biases are one possible danger resulting from the presence of irrelevant variables.

Even when irrelevant variables do not result in systematic biases, their presence is reflected in error variance, that variability among scores which cannot be attributed to the effects of the independent variables.   There will always be some error variability, even among scores which have been obtained under the same experimental treatment, for these scores will either come from different individuals who differ in such variables as intelligence, attitudes, and age or from the same individuals at different points in time, who will show change in such variables as attentiveness, practice, and fatigue. The greater such error variability, the more difficult it is to determine the effects of independent variables.   The following example may illustrate why this is so.

Assume that the two sets of data below have been obtained under two treatments, *A* and *B*, each applied to three subjects.   The mean performance under treatment *B* is better, as reflected by a mean of 6 as against one of 5 for treatment *A*.   However, the individuals within a group differ by at least as much as do the group means, and we cannot be sure whether the difference between the *A* and *B* means is due to individual or treatment differences.

A	B
4	5
5	6
6	7

Now suppose that all the scores for *A* were 5 and all those for *B* were 6. The treatment means are the same as before, but if people treated alike do not differ and people treated differently do, it seems reasonable to conclude that the treatments do have different effects.

In the remainder of this section we will consider the control of irrelevant variables, that is, the elimination of systematic biases and the reduction of error variance.   The approaches to this control problem may be grouped in the following categories.

1.3.1 Uniform application of the irrelevant variable

If only one level of the irrelevant variable is present in the experiment, it contributes no variability at all and therefore cannot give advantage to any one level of the independent variable, nor can it contribute to error variance. A major aid in uniformly applying the irrelevant variable is automation. Thus, electronic timers allow us to keep inter-trial intervals constant over trials, subjects, and experimental conditions; tape-recorded instructions are presented in the same words and tone to every subject; and automated animal test cages (which also serve to house the animals) eliminate handling and provide a uniform environment for all animals. While automation is helpful, the careful experimenter can do much to minimize variability without it. Care can be taken to read the same instructions to all subjects or to provide similar living conditions and a minimal amount of handling for all animal subjects. There will also be some variables which cannot be uniformly applied through the use of automated equipment. For example, if the experimenter expects the age of his subjects to influence their behavior, and if he is not interested in this variable, he may choose subjects who fall within certain narrow age limits. Every experiment will have its own potential sources of irrelevant variation, but a careful analysis of the situation can result in the elimination or minimization of many of these.

1.3.2 Randomization

Randomization guards against the danger of systematic biases in the data. Suppose one is interested in comparing the effects of two sets of instructions upon problem-solving performance. One obvious potential source of bias is problem-solving ability; it is necessary to guard against a systematic bias due to the application of one set of instructions to the better problem solvers. One way to do this is to assign the subjects randomly to treatments, that is, by some method that ensures that each subject is equally likely to be assigned to either set of instructions. Each subject could draw a number from a hat, then the odd-numbered subjects could be assigned to one treatment and the even-numbered subjects to the second. Note that randomization does not ensure that the two experimental groups are perfectly matched on those variables which might influence problem solving. Randomization does ensure that over many replications of the experiment neither treatment will have an advantage. In any one experiment one group could have an advantage (the odd-numbered subjects might, by chance, have higher intelligence), but statistical procedures which assume randomization take these biases into account.

Randomization does not only apply to the assignment of subjects to the levels of independent variables. It can also be applied, for example, to the selection of orders of presentation of treatments when each subject is tested at a number of levels of the independent variable. In fact, there are a vast array of different schemes for collecting data. Some of these will be considered next, with particular emphasis on the ways in which error variance may be further reduced.

1.3.3 Experimental design and analysis

An experimental design is a plan for running the experiment. One such plan is complete randomization, in which each subject is randomly assigned to only one combination of levels of the independent variables. One might extend such a design by including irrelevant variables as independent variables. For example, in the experiment on instructions and problem solving, the subject pool might be divided into three levels of intelligence—low (I.Q. under 85), medium (86–115), and high (above 115). Low I.Q. subjects would then be randomly assigned to the two instructional sets, and similarly for medium and high subjects, giving six combinations of I.Q. and instructions with an equal number of subjects in each group. The advantage of this plan over the original completely random assignment of subjects to the two treatments is that it permits a more accurate assessment of the effects of instructions. One may now remove, through statistical analysis, variability in the data due to differences in problem-solving ability among the three levels of intelligence. This design, in which the levels of the independent variable are matched on some irrelevant variable, is said to be more *efficient*, i.e., to result in less error variability, than the completely randomized design first considered. A more extensive discussion of the matching design appears in Chapter 6.

Matching of treatments may be made on the basis of variables other than the subjects' personal attributes such as intelligence. For example, if it were necessary to divide the subject testing between two experimenters, subjects could be randomly assigned to experimenters regardless of treatment group, or one could ensure that half of each treatment group was run by each experimenter. The second method is similar to the matching of intelligence previously suggested and would be recommended if there were any reason to suspect that experimenter differences might be a source of variability in the data.

There are advantages to running each subject through all levels of the independent variable. For example, a subject might do one problem-solving task under one set of instructions and a second equivalent task under the second set of instructions. Since all subjects experience both treatments, there can be no systematic bias due to personal attributes such as intelligence. Furthermore, computations exist for removing variability due to individual differences, permitting evaluation of the effects of instructions against a smaller error variability. The major drawback of this design is the possibility of a systematic bias due to temporal effects. If one set of instructions is always given first, the second set might profit from practice or be handicapped because of fatigue. For this reason the order of presentation should be random; each treatment should have an equal chance of being assigned to each position in the sequence of treatment presentations. Repeated measurement designs of this sort are treated at length in Chapter 7.

The randomization just described might be restricted to ensure that each treatment appeared equally often in each position in the sequence of presentations. In the problem-solving experiment, each of 20 subjects could be assigned a number from 1 to 20; each number would be assigned exactly once. If the number is even, one instructional set is given first; otherwise the other set comes first. Such a design further reduces error variance by permitting removal of variability due to temporal effects in addition to that due to individual differences. This type of design is generally referred to as a Latin square design, and is more fully discussed in Chapter 10.

With any design, further control of the effects of irrelevant variables is possible if one can somehow analyze out that part of each score which is due to the irrelevant variable. For example, rather than matching subjects on intelligence test scores, one could use the design described earlier, in which subjects were randomly assigned to treatments regardless of intelligence level. Each subject's intelligence score could then be used as a basis for adjusting his problem-solving scores. The method of adjustment, called analysis of covariance, is discussed in Chapter 11.

If control of irrelevant variables were the only concern of the experimenter, there would be greater uniformity in the selection of experimental designs and possibly more extensive application of the analysis of covariance. However, there are at least three other factors to consider in selecting a design—the information desired, the model for the data analysis, and the practical requirements of the situation. These factors are considered next.

1.4 FACTORS IN SELECTING EXPERIMENTAL DESIGNS

1.4.1 Information

Different types of designs yield different sorts of information. If information about the effects of time is wanted, a repeated measurements design is required. If there is interest in the effects of the order of presentation of treatments, a Latin square design is indicated. If the experimenter hypothesizes that the effect of the independent variable will change as a function of certain characteristics of his subjects, some sort of matching on these characteristics might be undertaken. If certain single or joint effects of variables are of more interest than others, there are designs which permit a more efficient evaluation of these effects at the expense of a loss of information on others. These are but a few examples of the ways in which designs may differ with respect to the information they provide.

1.4.2 The model

The validity of any inference drawn from a statistical analysis rests upon the validity of an underlying model, a set of assumptions about the data. The violation of any one of the assumptions may result in an incorrect inference about the effects of the independent variable. Since the model is a function of the design employed, selection of the experimental design must involve consideration of which assumptions are implied, whether they are likely to be met, and how failure to meet them wi'l affect the validity of the inferences drawn from the statistical analysis. For example, the use of the Latin square design assumes that the size of the treatment effects does not change as a function of the order of presenting the treatments. This assumption will often be false, with the usual result being an increased probability of concluding that the treatment has no effect when in fact it has.

1.4.3 Practical requirements

The selection of designs must often be dictated, or at least narrowed, by such considerations as the number of available subjects or the time available per subject. For example, in animal research it may be more convenient, and certainly less expensive, to run a few subjects through many conditions than to run many groups of subjects each under a different treatment. On the other hand, in research with children, where teachers may object to any one child losing too much class time, it may be more reasonable to use a completely randomized design, with fewer measurements on more children.

1.5 THE DEPENDENT VARIABLE

1.5.1 Choice of the dependent variable

The choice of an appropriate dependent variable, or measure, may appear to be a trivial problem—after all, one is interested in leadership, or aggressive behavior, or learning, or visual acuity, and this is what will be measured. Unfortunately, there are always a number of measures which can be reasonably interpreted as indices of the behavioral process under investigation. For example, consider the learning of a list of words. Shall one measure the number of trials to attain some predetermined criterion? Shall the speed of each response be measured? Shall the basic datum be the number of errors in each block of five trials? ten trials? all trials? Should errors of commission (incorrect responses) and errors of omission (failures to respond) be analyzed separately? Certainly these alternatives are not mutually exclusive, but there are practical limits to the number of measures which can be considered in the analysis of any single experiment. In this section we will consider some of the factors involved in selecting the dependent variable or variables.

There are several characteristics of dependent variables upon which the accuracy of inferences depends. Ideally, the dependent variable should be reliable, sensitive, and distributed in a way which conforms to the assumptions of the data analysis model. Reliability will be a factor insofar as measures which are equivalent in all other respects differ in their variability. That measure which is least variable under constant experimental conditions is preferred.

Sensitivity refers to the fact that certain measures show greater differential effects than do other measures as a function of changes in the independent variable. For example, in a study of escape from conflict, animals under conflict might not differ from control subjects who were not under conflict in the number of escape responses (presses of a platform that result in removal of the conflictual stimuli). However, the two groups might differ in mean duration of the escape responses.

Statistical analysis is often complicated because the distribution of the measure does not conform to the assumptions of available statistical models. If all other considerations are equal, we want that measure whose distribution is consistent with the model associated with the statistical analysis to be applied. This implies a thorough knowledge of previous research and the type of results obtained with different measures, as well as a consideration, prior to data collection, of the statistical model.

As in every other phase of experimental planning, there are practical considerations involved in the choice of measures. All else being equal, we want measures which can be easily obtained. For example, in research on personality if a paper and pencil test and a projective test were equally reliable and sensitive and conformed similarly to the statistical model, the paper and pencil test is preferable; it is administered and scored much more rapidly. Of course all other things are rarely equal; the experimenter may consider the projective test to be more sensitive, while the paper and pencil test is probably more reliable and possibly more likely to result in a normal distribution of data. The moral is that in all phases of experimental planning the ideal is rarely attained; the experiment is a compromise among the factors that have been indicated.

Theory may also be an issue in the selection of measures. For example, consider an experiment in which the subject guesses which of two events will occur on each trial. The measure generally taken in such experiments is the per cent of each type of guess, partly because it is easily obtained and partly because pertinent theories of the behavior under investigation yield predictions of this measure. With the recent advent of theories which generate exact quantitative predictions of response latency for choice behavior, latency will probably be more frequently used as a measure in the future.

1.5.2 Choice of the measuring technique

In many instances the choice of a measure still leaves unanswered the question of how the measure is to be recorded. In deciding this point the experimenter should consider the ease of obtaining the data as well as the probable degree of reliability of the recording technique. Again, consider the situation in which the subject must guess which of two events will occur on each trial. There are at least these three methods of recording which response occurred on each trial: (a) the experimenter could manually record the subject's choice on each trial, (b) responses could be automatically recorded by some type of event-pen system, and (c) responses could be automatically punched out onto IBM cards. The manual technique is the least reliable, since it is subject to recording errors by the experimenter. However, the manually recorded data are generally easier to score and tabulate than ink records, and this nonautomated recording system is less subject to breakdowns. The event-pen method frees the experimenter's time during experimental sessions, involves an initial expenditure of several hundred dollars, is generally reliable in recording the data, but involves record-reading labor and possible error at that time. The data punch-out method is efficient in both the collection and analysis of data, is highly reliable, but may involve an initial expenditure of several thousands of dollars. The automatic system may also be less reliable from day to day in the sense that breakdowns may be more frequent than with the alternative procedures. Clearly, the choice of a system for recording the data is, like all other decisions made during the planning of an experiment, a compromise among numerous considerations.

1.6 SUBJECTS

There are basically two classes of decisions which the experimenter must make with regard to subjects: How many should be run? What population should they be drawn from? In this section we will consider the factors which should be involved in such decisions.

1.6.1 How many subjects?

A primary consideration in deciding upon the number of subjects is the *power* desired. Roughly, power is the probability of correctly concluding that differences among the effects of treatments exist. Power depends upon the direction and size of the effect to be detected, how large a risk of wrongly concluding that the treatments have different effects one is willing to take, and the error variance expected. The error variance, as noted earlier in this chapter, in turn depends upon the experimental design employed. For the time being, we merely note that decisions about the factors influencing power will influence the number of subjects required to attain a desired degree of power. In Chapters 2 and 4 we will consider the relationships among all these factors in much greater detail.

The second major determiner of the number of subjects selected is the number of subjects available. This depends largely on the subject population from which we draw—rats, college sophomores, first-grade children, and so forth. We will next present some of the factors which dictate choice of subject population.

1.6.2 The subject population

The major consideration in deciding which type of subject to employ in any experiment is *availability*. Since much psychological research is done by college professors and by graduate students in pursuit of a degree, the college sophomore is an extremely popular subject, perhaps the most popular subject in studies of human performance. The rat, small, easily housed and fed, is another convenient and therefore popular subject for research. However, there are other considerations, and some of these should influence the choice of subjects more than they usually do.

One can expect less *error variance* with some subjects than with others. Suppose an experiment on problem solving with children involved instructions which could be expected to be clear to all five-year-olds but which might prove too complex for some four-year-olds; one might then expect more error variability with the four-year-olds as subjects. In short, subjects should be drawn from a population which is as homogeneous as possible with regard to irrelevant variables that might influence scores.

Control of the subject's previous history is a factor in choosing the subject population and is an oft-stated reason for the abundance of data on animals. With such subjects, who are often born and reared in the laboratory, the experimenter can control eating habits, genetic history, and environmental influences. As Tolman has remarked,* ". . . rats live in cages; they do not go on binges the night before one has planned the experiment. . . ."

The *purpose of the research* is often a factor in selecting subjects. Certainly there are basic processes which can be studied in many different types of subjects. On the other hand, if the experimenter is specifically interested in human development, or schizophrenic performance, his choice of subject populations is immediately narrowed.

Theoretical considerations may also play a role in the choice of subjects. For example, adult human subjects, when asked to guess which of two events will occur, tend to guess one event if the other event has had a long run, that is, has come up several times in succession. This behavior conflicts with the predictions of some prominent theories of choice behavior. It has been hypothesized that the behavior results from the fact that the subject has experi-

---

* E. C. Tolman, "A Stimulus-Expectancy Need-Cathexis Psychology," *Science*, 101:160–166 (1945).

enced only short event runs in his pre-experimental history and therefore expects short runs in the laboratory. A test of this hypothesis might involve the use of subjects with a limited previous exposure to event sequences, for example, young children or rats.

1.7 CONCLUDING REMARKS

Several times in this chapter, it has been implied that experimental plans are in part related to the data analysis. We have noted that the choice of designs and of dependent variables is a function of the demands of the statistical model. This point is now made explicit: the statistical analysis should be planned *in detail* before a single subject is run. The alternative is a post-experiment search for an analysis that is consistent with the design and the distribution of the measure and that may not exist. One can only have reasonable assurance that an appropriate analysis exists if one considers design and analysis together, before the data are collected. It is worth noting that when alternative analyses exist, the choice depends upon factors similar to those which were previously cited in Section 1.4 in discussing the choice among experimental designs. Thus one should take into account the relative *efficiencies* of analyses, the resulting *information*, the *computational labor* involved, as well as *assumptions* and whether or not they are likely to be met.

In this chapter we have discussed those considerations involved in planning experiments. Sometimes these considerations will point to a single decision; more often they will be in conflict. Thus, the simplest measure to obtain may be the least reliable, and the most efficient design may imply a statistical model to which our data will not conform. Experimental planning is a weighing of such considerations, a compromise among them. It is impossible to state a single set of rules for weighing these considerations since one would need different rules for each experiment. However, we have attempted to state what the important factors influencing our decisions should be, and why they are important.

SUPPLEMENTARY READINGS

An excellent supplement to the discussion presented in this chapter may be found in the first two chapters of

COCHRAN, W. C. and G. M. COX, *Experimental Designs*, 2d ed. New York: Wiley, 1957.

A general and extensive discussion of topics merely touched on in this chapter appears in

UNDERWOOD, B. J., *Psychological Research*. New York: Appleton-Century-Crofts, 1957.

STATISTICAL INFERENCE

2

2.1 INTRODUCTION

Since it is often impractical to measure the behavior of all individuals in a population, the experimenter usually confines his investigation to a small sample of subjects. For example, an experimenter interested in the effects of amount of reward upon the running times of rats might randomly assign 40 rats to two groups of 20 subjects each; one group receives one food pellet at the end of a six-ft. runway and the other receives a reward of two food pellets. The experimenter is not usually concerned with whether these two groups of rats differ in their performances. However, he is interested in drawing conclusions about the relative performances of two populations of rats, systematically differing only in the amount of reward for running. If the subjects can be considered random samples from the populations in which the experimenter is interested, it is reasonable to use the sample data as a basis for conclusions about the populations. Conclusions from sample data about such things as the mean and variance of the running times of large populations of rats are statistical inferences. The primary purpose of this chapter is to examine briefly the processes by which such inferences are drawn. In large part, it should be a review, for much of the material that follows is adequately considered in several introductory statistics texts. Furthermore, it is a review of general concepts rather than of specific techniques. For example, we will not consider the mechanics of many different tests of statistical hypotheses. Instead some general aspects of hypothesis testing will be discussed; they will be illustrated through the example of one or two tests with which the reader should be familiar. This same approach will be followed throughout most of the chapter.

2.2 POINT ESTIMATION

A quantity which can be computed from the population data, such as the population mean or variance, is generally referred to as a *population parameter*. Throughout this book, Greek letters will be used to denote parameters. For example, the population mean will be indicated by μ and the population standard deviation by σ. Similar quantities computed from the sample data are referred to as sample *statistics*, and Latin letters will be used to denote these. Thus the sample mean and standard deviation are represented by $\bar{Y}$ and s, respectively. One purpose of experimentation is to obtain estimates of the magnitude of population parameters on the basis of sample statistics. This type of inference is often referred to as *point estimation* to distinguish it from the estimation of an interval containing the parameter.

2.2.1 Properties of estimators

There are an infinite number of possible estimators of any single population parameter. For example, the population mean might be estimated by the sample mean, the sample median, or even the first score drawn from the sample. The question of which quantity best estimates the parameter can be answered by establishing criteria for good estimators and then examining how closely various estimators meet these criteria. The criteria which are generally agreed upon are based on the knowledge that an estimate will fluctuate from sample to sample. For example, if the value of the sample mean is computed for each of 20 samples from the same population, the result will be a distribution of values. The same would be true of the median or mode or of any other sample statistic. It would seem desirable to choose an estimator such that the estimates obtained from different samples would be distributed about the estimated parameter with little variability. Then any one estimate will have high probability of being close to the parameter value. It also seems desirable that this requirement should have greater probability of being met as the size of the sample is increased; increased information should result in increased reliability. The following criteria embody the properties just described.

(a) *Lack of bias.* If the mean of the distribution of a statistic is equal to the parameter being estimated, the statistic is said to be an *unbiased estimator* of the parameter. A familiar example of such an estimator is the sample mean, $\bar{Y}$. If the distribution is plotted for the means of a large number of samples from the same population, the mean of this distribution of sample statistics will equal the population mean. The mean of a distribution is often referred to as the *expected value* of the statistic. Accordingly, the statement that the mean of the distribution of sample means equals the population mean may be more simply expressed by

(2.1)
$$E(\overline{Y}) = \mu$$

which is read as "the expected value of the sample mean equals μ." In general, the statement that $\hat{\theta}$, an estimator of some parameter, θ, is unbiased may be expressed by

(2.2)
$$E(\hat{\theta}) = \theta$$

The population variance, σ^2, is defined as $\sum (Y - \mu)^2/N$, the sum of the squared deviations of scores about the population mean divided by the number of scores in the population. A logical estimator of σ^2 would seem to be $\sum (Y - \overline{Y})^2/n$, the sum of the squared deviations about the sample mean divided by the number of scores in the sample. However, this estimate is biased since it can be proven that

(2.3) $$E\left[\frac{\sum (Y - \overline{Y})^2}{n}\right] = \left(\frac{n-1}{n}\right)\left[\frac{\sum (Y - \mu)^2}{N}\right] = \left(\frac{n-1}{n}\right)\sigma^2$$

Multiplying both sides of Equation (2.3) by $n/(n-1)$ yields an unbiased estimator, since

(2.4) $$E\left[\frac{\sum (Y - \overline{Y})^2}{n-1}\right] = \sigma^2$$

meeting the condition set forth in Equation (2.2). Because of the absence of bias, the estimator with $n - 1$ in the denominator is most frequently recommended.

(b) *Consistency.* An estimator is said to be consistent if

(2.5)
$$P(\hat{\theta} \rightarrow \theta) \rightarrow 1 \quad \text{as} \quad n \rightarrow \infty$$

The above expression is read as "the probability approaches one that the estimator approaches the parameter as the sample size approaches infinity." An alternative statement is that the probability of obtaining an estimate closer to the estimated parameter increases as the sample size increases. An example of a consistent estimator is the sample mean, $\overline{Y}$. However, it does not follow that an estimator must be unbiased in order to be consistent. If an estimator is to approach the population parameter as n increases, it need be unbiased only for very large values of n. The quantity $\sum (Y - \overline{Y})^2/n$ is an example of a biased estimator which is unbiased when the sample size is very large, and which is consistent. It follows from expression (2.3) that this estimator is unbiased for large n, since $(n - 1)/n \rightarrow 1$ as $n \rightarrow \infty$; for such values of n, the expression states that the expected value of the estimator equals the parameter. Nor does it follow that all unbiased estimators are consistent. Mood* points out that $E(Y_1) = \mu$ where Y_1 is the first score drawn from the sample. However, this estimator is not consistent. Note that it is not necessarily equal to μ even when the entire population is sampled.

* A. M. Mood, *Introduction to the Theory of Statistics* (New York: McGraw-Hill, 1950).

(c) *Efficiency.* In choosing between two estimators of a parameter, that estimator whose distribution exhibits less spread about the parameter is preferred. For example, assume that a large number of samples are obtained from a normally distributed population, a mean and a median is computed for each sample, and sums of squared deviations about μ are then computed, one for the sample means and one for the sample medians. The variability of the sample means about μ will be 64 per cent of the variability of the sample medians about μ. This is expressed by saying that the *relative efficiency* of the median to the mean (as estimators of μ) is 64 per cent. Conversely, the relative efficiency of the mean to the median is $1/.64$ or 157 per cent. The relative efficiency of $\hat{\theta}_1$ to $\hat{\theta}_2$ when these are two different estimators of θ is expressed by

$$\frac{E(\hat{\theta}_2 - \theta)^2}{E(\hat{\theta}_1 - \theta)^2}$$

Thus, relative efficiency is defined as the ratio of two averages of squared deviations of estimators about the same population parameter. Note that this is a measure of the efficiency of the estimator in the denominator relative to that in the numerator.

(d) *Asymptotic efficiency.* An estimator is said to be *asymptotically efficient*, or simply, *efficient*, if it fulfills the following requirements: (1) for very large n, the quantity $\sqrt{n}(\hat{\theta} - \theta)$ has a normal distribution with zero mean, and (2) no other estimator of the type defined in (1) has a smaller variance when n is very large.

The first requirement implies that the estimator is unbiased for large n (though not necessarily for finite samples) for if $E[\sqrt{n}(\hat{\theta} - \theta)] = 0$, $E(\hat{\theta}) = \theta$. The second requirement implies that the efficient estimator is a consistent one; otherwise some consistent estimator would have a smaller variance. If, for large n, an efficient estimator is unbiased and has a variance as small as, or smaller than, any other estimator, its efficiency relative to that of other estimators must always be equal to or greater than 100 per cent. The sample mean, $\overline{Y}$, is an example of this class of estimators. The quantity $\sqrt{n}(\overline{Y} - \mu)$ is normally distributed with zero mean and variance equal to σ^2. No other estimator of μ has a variance smaller than σ^2.

Since all the properties which have been described are not always present in one estimator, some conclusion regarding the relative importance of these properties is required. Although lack of bias is intuitively appealing, a biased estimator may be very satisfactory if its variability about the parameter is slight relative to that of other estimators and decreases with increasing sample size. The relative importance of efficiency and bias are illustrated in Figure 2-1; although the frequency distribution of $\hat{\theta}_1$ centers about θ, the probability of obtaining an estimate closer to θ is greater when θ_2 is the estimator, despite the fact that θ_2 is somewhat biased.

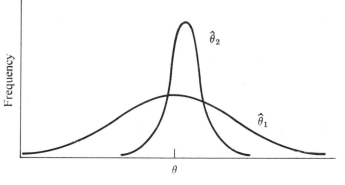

Estimates of θ

FIGURE 2-1   Sampling distributions of two estimators of θ

2.2.2 Principles of estimation

Once it is agreed that the properties just discussed are desirable, the problem
of deriving estimators which have such properties must be faced.   The following discussion deals with two principles which lead to such derivations.

(a) *Maximum likelihood estimation.*   Assume that we are concerned
with the problem of estimating the probability of obtaining a head on a toss
of a coin.   This is basically the problem of estimating the parameter π, the
proportion of heads in an infinite population of tosses.   Now suppose that
a sample of ten independent tosses has resulted in seven heads and three tails.
The maximum likelihood principle states that the best estimate is that which
gives the highest probability, the maximum likelihood, of obtaining the observed data.   Clearly $\hat{\pi} = 1$ or $\hat{\pi} = 0$ is an exceedingly poor estimate according to this principle, for if $\pi = 1$, the sample should have consisted of all
heads, and if $\pi = 0$, all tails would have resulted.   Somewhere between zero
and one is an estimate that makes the occurrence of the observed sequence of
results most likely.   The probability of the obtained sequence of outcomes,
P, is related to π by

$$(2.6) \qquad\qquad P = \pi^7(1 - \pi)^3$$

Table 2-1 is the result of substituting different estimates of π into Equation
(2.6).   When $\pi = .7$, the likelihood of obtaining the observed data is maxi-
mal, since P then takes on its largest value.   The maximum likelihood estimate is therefore .7.

It is not necessary to work with an actual set of data or to enumerate
likelihoods for various estimates.   Differential calculus is applied to the
equation describing the distribution of the data, and a general formula for
the maximum likelihood estimator is obtained.   In our example, Y/n would

TABLE 2-1

The probability, P, of obtaining seven heads and three tails in the observed sequence for various values of $\hat{\pi}$

$\hat{\pi}$	P
0	0
.1	.0000000729
.2	.0000065535
.3	.0000750133
.4	.00035390
.5	.00097656
.6	.0017886
.7	.0022236
.8	.0016778
.9	.0004783
1.0	0

be the general solution, where Y is the observed number of heads and n is the number of tosses.

Maximum likelihood estimators have the important property of being asymptotically efficient and consequently consistent as well. Although a maximum likelihood estimator is not necessarily unbiased, the center of its distribution is generally close to the value of the parameter being estimated.

(b) *Least-squares estimation.* Assume that any score in a sample is related to μ, the mean of the population, by

$$(2.7) \qquad Y_i = \mu + e_i$$

where Y_i is the score of subject i, and e_i is subject i's error component, the deviation of the score from μ. A measure of variability can be obtained by computing $\hat{e}_i$ ($= Y_i - \hat{\mu}$) for all individuals in the sample, squaring these quantities, and summing them. The least-squares principle states that the appropriate estimate of μ is that value which makes the sum of squared deviations as small as possible, i.e., which minimizes the variability about $\hat{\mu}$. For example, the least-squares estimate is $\bar{Y}$ and is arrived at by applying differential calculus to find the minimum point of the function relating the sum of the $\hat{e}_i^2$ to various values of $\hat{\mu}$. The same approach can be used to find estimators for other parameters. If the e_i are uncorrelated and their frequency distribution is normal, the method yields results essentially similar to those of maximum likelihood estimation. However, the least-squares computations are usually much simpler.

Figure 2-2 illustrates the two estimation procedures just discussed. On the top is plotted the probability of obtaining the observed set of data as a function of various estimates of the population parameter. The estimation problem reduces to finding the maxima of the function, the value of $\hat{\theta}$ for which P is greatest. On the bottom is plotted the error variance, the vari-

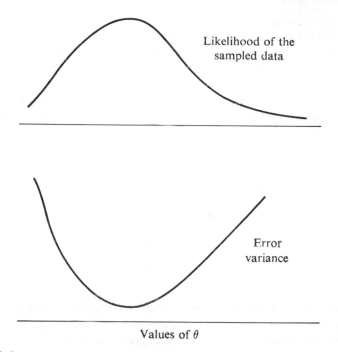

FIGURE 2-2   Two approaches to parameter estimation

ance of the data points about the estimated parameter, as a function of various estimates.   Now the estimation problem reduces to finding the minima of the function, the value of $\hat{\theta}$ for which the error variance is least.   The functions drawn are hypothetical and will of course vary depending on the parameter to be estimated and the distribution of the data.   However, the principles implied are general ones.

2.3 INTERVAL ESTIMATION

A point estimate will almost never be correct in the sense of equaling the parameter.   Nor can the extent of error of estimate be judged on the basis of the estimate itself, since this reflects no information about its sampling distribution.   In order to evaluate the adequacy of a point estimate it is desirable to have an estimate of certain limits within which the parameter falls and a quantitative statement of confidence that the parameter does fall within these limits.   Such confidence intervals can be established for many different parameters, but at present the process of establishing such limits will be exemplified by obtaining limits on μ.

The determination of a confidence interval for μ requires the following information:

(a) the value of the sample mean
(b) the value of the population standard deviation or some estimate of it
(c) the equation for the frequency distribution of scores in the population
(d) the size of the sample
(e) the degree of confidence required

This last item is decided upon by the experimenter and will always be a number between zero and one, generally .90 or above. For our example we will assume that

(a) $\bar{Y} = 25$
(b) $\sigma = 5$
(c) the distribution is known to be normal
(d) $n = 100$
(e) 95 per cent confidence is desirable

Since Y is normally distributed, the quantity

(2.8)
$$z = \frac{\bar{Y} - \mu}{\sigma / \sqrt{n}}$$

is also normally distributed, with mean equal to zero and standard deviation equal to one. The distribution of z-scores, with percentages lying between the mean and several selected values, is presented in Figure 2-3. The fact that 95 per cent of the z-scores lie between -1.96 and 1.96 may be interpreted as follows: if 100 samples of scores are collected from a normal distribution, and if the means of these samples are transformed into z-scores according to

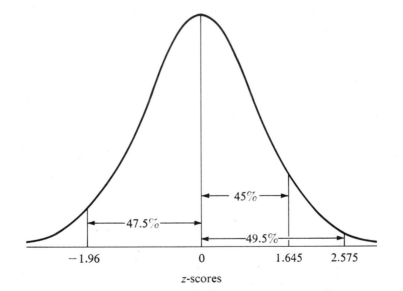

FIGURE 2-3 Normal distribution of z-scores

Equation (2.8), 95 of them would be expected to fall between −1.96 and 1.96. Equation (2.9) expresses this more succinctly.

$$(2.9) \qquad P\left(-1.96 < \frac{\overline{Y} - \mu}{\sigma/\sqrt{n}} < 1.96\right) = .95$$

which is read as "the probability that the z transform of the sample mean lies between −1.96 and 1.96 is .95." Algebraic manipulation of Equation (2.9) results in Equation (2.10), which states the probability that μ lies within the designated limits.

$$(2.10) \qquad P\left(\overline{Y} - \frac{1.96\sigma}{\sqrt{n}} < \mu < \overline{Y} + \frac{1.96\sigma}{\sqrt{n}}\right) = .95$$

Plugging in the appropriate values from our example results in the 95 per cent confidence interval, 24.02 < μ < 25.98. We have 95 per cent confidence in the sense that while 100 samples might give rise to 100 different sets of limits, 95 per cent of such intervals are expected to contain μ. We therefore have high confidence that the one interval actually derived does contain μ.

Three variables which affect the width of the confidence interval, and consequently the precision of the estimate, are σ, n, and the level of confidence. It can be seen in Equation (2.10) that as variability (σ) decreases, the upper limit of the interval is lowered and the lower limit is raised (becomes less negative). This reduced interval width reflects the increased precision which accompanies decreased variability. As a concrete illustration of the relationship between interval size and σ, suppose that σ is 2.5, rather than 5 as in the original example. The limits are now 25 ± (1.96)(.25) or 24.51 and 25.49.

The width of the interval containing μ also decreases as n increases. If n were 200 (σ, $\overline{Y}$, and the confidence level are again 5, 25, and .95, respectively), the limits would be 25 ± (1.96)(.354) or 24.31 and 25.69.

Increased confidence is paid for by wider interval widths. If the 99 per cent confidence interval were desired, 2.575 would be substituted for 1.96 in the previous calculations. (Note in Figure 2-3 that 99 per cent of the z-scores fall between 2.575 and −2.575.) Using the original values of σ, $\overline{Y}$, and n, the interval is now 25 ± 1.29 or 23.71 and 26.29. We have greater assurance than originally that μ falls within the specified interval, but the interval is wider than formerly and the interval estimate is therefore less precise.

2.4 HYPOTHESIS TESTING

Psychologists have generally been more concerned with the evaluation of specific hypotheses about the value of the parameter than with estimation (point or interval) of the parameter. Thus, they have usually asked questions of the form, Does μ equal 100? rather than, What does μ equal? or, Do these treatments differ in effect? rather than, What is the difference in effect among these treatments? This section presents an example of how a specific hypothesis would be tested. We are concerned with those steps common to various statistical tests (such as t, χ^2, or F), although we have had to confine ourselves to one particular test to exemplify the inferential process.

Twenty rats are trained to run to a box containing food; the food box is white for half the rats, black for the other half. On the day following the last training day all rats are tested for their preference between a white and a black box, neither of which contains food. The purpose is to determine whether a preference has been established for the box previously associated with food. In order to reach a conclusion, it is first necessary to state explicitly two hypotheses, the *null hypothesis*, H_0, and the *alternative hypothesis*, H_1. An appropriate null hypothesis is that in the population from which these subjects are a sample the percentage of correct responders (subjects who prefer the box which previously contained food) equals the percentage of incorrect responders. This might be expressed by

$$H_0: \pi = .5$$

where π is the proportion of correct responders in the population. The alternative hypothesis might be that in the population sampled, the proportion of correct responders exceeds the proportion of incorrect responders. This may be stated as

$$H_1: \pi > .5$$

This statement of H_1 ignores the possibility that there are a majority of incorrect responders in the population. Such a statement implies that the experimenter is willing to attribute the occurrence of more than 50 per cent incorrect responders in the sample to chance, that such an occurrence will be viewed as support for H_0. This situation is described as a test of H_0 against a one-tailed alternative, or simply as a one-tailed test.

Suppose the experimenter considered it possible that a majority of incorrect responders might exist in the population. Possibly, the box which did not contain food is reinforcing because it is a novel stimulus; the subject has not experienced it before. In this situation, H_0 should be tested against a two-tailed alternative, namely

$$H_1: \pi \neq .5$$

In discussing various aspects of hypothesis testing in relation to this example, a one-tailed procedure will first be assumed. Changes in the testing procedure which arise when H_1 is two-tailed will then be noted.

The choice between H_0 and H_1 requires that a test statistic be computed from the data. Such a statistic should have the following properties:

(a) the statistic should reflect the relative merits of the two hypotheses,
(b) its distribution should be obtainable under the assumption that H_0 is true,

(c) the assumptions which are necessary to derive the distribution should be reasonably valid for the data at hand.

Of the various statistics which meet these criteria for our example, the number of correct responders seems the least complicated and therefore the best for illustrative purposes. Let us consider how the number of correct responders meets our three requirements.

(a) If the null hypothesis is true, then the average number of correct responders (over many replications of the experiment) will be ten. If the true value of π is greater than .5, the average number of correct responders will be greater than ten. This monotone increasing relationship between π and the expected value of the test statistic meets requirement (a) above.

(b) If the performances of the 20 rats are independent, the probability that the number of correct responders equals x is

$$(2.11) \qquad P = \frac{n!}{x!(n-x)!}\, \pi^x (1-\pi)^{n-x}$$

where n is the number of subjects, x is the number of correct responders, and π is the proportion of correct responders in the population. In our example

TABLE 2-2

Probability of the number of correct responders when $n = 20$, assuming $\pi = .5$ and $\pi = .75$

Number Correct	$\pi = .5$	$\pi = .75$
0	.000	.000
1	.000	.000
2	.000	.000
3	.001	.000
4	.005	.000
5	.015	.000
6	.037	.000
7	.074	.000
8	.120	.001
9	.160	.003
10	.176	.010
11	.160	.027
12	.120	.061
13	.074	.112
14	.037	.169
15	.015	.202
16	.005	.190
17	.001	.134
18	.000	.067
19	.000	.021
20	.000	.003

$n = 20$, and under the null hypothesis $\pi = .5$.   The probability distribution may now be easily obtained by inserting these values of n and π into Equation (2.11) and letting x take on the values 0, 1, $\cdots$, 20.   The resulting probabilities of various values of x may be found in the column headed "$\pi = .5$" in Table 2-2 and in the solid-line histogram of Figure 2-4.

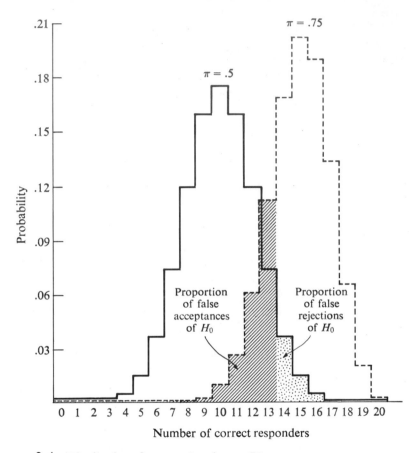

FIGURE 2-4   Distributions for $\pi = .5$ and $\pi = .75$

(c) Since each subject may be considered an independent replication of the same experiment, yielding only two classes of responses (correct, incorrect), the data seem appropriate to the assumptions underlying the application of Equation (2.11).

2.4.1   Type I errors

The null and alternative hypotheses have been stated, and a test statistic has been selected to provide a basis for choosing between them.   The next step is the determination of those values of the statistic which will result in rejection of H_0 in favor of H_1. Such values constitute a critical region, a set of possible values of the test statistic, consistent with H_1, which are so improbable if H_0 is assumed true, that their occurrence leads us to reject H_0. An arbitrarily chosen value, *alpha* (α), defines exactly how improbable "so improbable" is. More precisely, α, the *level of significance*, is the probability of obtaining a test statistic which falls within the critical region when H_0 is true. For example, if α equals .05, the test statistic can be expected to fall within the critical region in five of 100 replications of an experiment for which the null hypothesis is true, thus resulting in rejections of true null hypotheses in 5 per cent of the replications. The rejection of a true null hypothesis is generally referred to as a *Type I, or α, error*.

The size of the critical region will clearly depend upon the magnitude of α. We have also stated that this region is a set of values consistent with H_1. This means that the critical region is so chosen that its location is consistent with H_1. For example, if the alternative hypothesis is that π is greater than .5, the critical region should include only numbers of correct responders greater than half the sample size. If the alternative is two-tailed, the critical region should include numbers of responders both greater than and less than half the sample size.

In the example of the 20 rats faced with a black-white preference test, assume that α has been set equal to .06. Given the null hypothesis that the two choices are equally likely and the alternative that the correct side is preferred, the critical region can now be determined for the distribution of Table 2-2 and Figure 2-4 ($\pi = .5$). Since the probability of 14 or more responders is almost 6 per cent (.037 + .015 + .005 + .001 = .058) in the right-hand tail of the distribution, this is the critical region. If 14 or more subjects respond correctly, H_0 will be rejected. This region of rejection is indicated in Figure 2-4.

What if the alternative were two-tailed, i.e., that the proportion of correct responders in the population might be greater than or less than .5? If deviations in both directions are equally important to detect, and if it is still required that the proportion of cases in the critical region does not exceed 6 per cent, five or less or 15 or more correct responders would result in rejection of H_0.

To summarize briefly, tests of the null hypothesis require explicit statements of the null and alternative hypotheses, a choice of a statistic, and knowledge of the distribution of the statistic assuming H_0 to be true. These things, together with a stated significance level, result in the selection of a critical region. All these decisions must be made prior to the collection of data; the availability of experimental data could influence the statement of hypotheses or the selection of a critical region. Furthermore, if the test statistic and the assumptions underlying its distribution are not considered before the experiment is carried out, an experiment may be performed which results in data which are difficult to analyze properly. Once the critical region has been decided upon, the data may be collected, the appropriate statistic computed, and its value compared with those falling within the critical region.

2.4.2 Type II errors

Since α is the probability of rejecting true null hypotheses, why not set it extremely low? The answer is that decreases in α decrease the probability of rejection of both true and false null hypotheses. In the extreme case where α is zero, Type I errors would never be made. However, false null hypotheses would also never be rejected. Obviously, the failure to reject a false null hypothesis is also an error. This failure to establish a treatment effect when it actually exists is generally referred to as a *Type II, or beta* (β), *error*. The example of the 20 rats in the preference test will be used to illustrate the principles involved in computing β, the probability of a Type II error, as well as to examine the relationships between β and such variables as α and n.

Once again, assume that the null hypothesis that $\pi = .5$ is being tested against the alternative that $\pi > .5$. In addition, assume that unknown to the experimenter, H_0 is false and in fact the proportion of correct responders in the population is .75, i.e., $\pi = .75$. The probability distribution for $\pi = .75$ and $n = 20$ is presented in Table 2-2 and in Figure 2-4 (dashed-line histogram). If $\alpha = .06$, as previously stipulated, the experimenter will accept H_0 whenever 13 or fewer rats respond correctly. If π is really equal to .75, the probability of 13 or fewer rats responding correctly is $.001 + .003 + .010 + .027 + .061 + .112 = .214$. Thus β, the probability of accepting a false null hypothesis (false because $\pi = .75$ is the true state of affairs in the population), is .214. To summarize, the procedure for determining β against a specific alternative value of the parameter consists of dividing the baseline under the H_0 function into a region of acceptance and a region of rejection, and then determining the probability of the statistic falling in the acceptance region, given that the alternative is true.

An interpretation of β in terms of Figure 2-4 may also be helpful. Beta equals that proportion of the total area under the $\pi = .75$ function which is labeled "proportion of false acceptances of H_0." This region is that part of the $\pi = .75$ distribution which lies above abscissa values also underlying the $\pi = .5$ function, but which excludes the critical region of the $\pi = .5$ distribution.

Several sources contain tables or graphs for *operating characteristics* (*OC*) or *power* functions for some of the commonly used statistical tests.*

---

* R. R. Bush and F. Mosteller, "Selected Quantitative Techniques," in *Handbook of Social Psychology*, Vol. 1, ed. G. Lindzey (Reading, Mass.: Addison-Wesley, 1954), Chap. 8.

The OC function consists of values of β for the range of possible alternative values of the population parameter. The quantity $1 - \beta$ often appears rather than β. This is commonly referred to as the power of the test and is the probability of rejecting H_0 when it is false. Power or OC functions are important because several tests of the same H_0 may exist but have different power for the same critical region and sample size. If all other factors (e.g., validity of the model for the data, computational ease, availability of tables) are equal, the more powerful test is preferred. Furthermore, power and OC functions yield information on the relationship of power to α, H_1, and sample size, thus facilitating decisions about these variables.

Consider first the relationship between α and β. If the critical region of Figure 2-4 were reduced in size, the region of false acceptances of H_0 would consequently increase. Conversely, if α were increased, enlarging the critical region, there would be a corresponding decrease in the size of the region of false acceptances of H_0, and therefore in β. Because of this inverse relationship between α and β, the choice of α should always reflect a compromise between the relative importance of Type I and Type II errors. In some situations, Type I errors will be more undesirable. When the consequences of a significant finding (and such consequences may involve applications of the findings and/or future experiments) will be costly in time, effort, and money, the experimenter will want to be fairly certain that an effect really does exist before exploring it further. In such an instance, α may be set extremely low, guarding against Type I errors even at the increased risk of Type II errors. The relationship between one's experimental findings and those of previous studies is also a consideration. If a significant result will conflict with an established body of knowledge, more stringent significance levels (e.g., .01) might be required. On the other hand, in research areas in which the variables influencing behavior are less well understood, the experimenter might be willing to take a greater risk of a Type I error, reducing β in an attempt to avoid missing some promising lead.

The above comments are at best guides, rather than rules, for the setting of α. There are no nice, neat formulas for arriving at the appropriate level of α. As a consequence of this arbitrary quality of our inferential process it follows that statistical significance should not be the sole basis for judgments of experimental effects but merely one important piece of information. Inferences should not be ground out by a computer, but rather should be thought out by an experimenter. We will return to this problem in the last part of this chapter.

The choice between one- and two-tailed tests also has implications for β. If α is kept constant, the critical region of Figure 2-4 must be reduced to establish a similar region in the left-hand tail of the $\pi = .5$ distribution. The shift from a one-tailed to a two-tailed alternative permits the detection of π values less than .5, but only at the cost of reduced power to detect π values greater than .5.

Figure 2-5 presents distributions of correct responders for the null hypothesis $\pi = .5$ and for the alternative $\pi = .75$ with α equal to .06 and n equal to 15. Comparing these distributions with those of Figure 2-4, one notes that the decrease in n from 20 to 15 has resulted in an increase in the proportion of area under the $\pi = .75$ function which consists of false acceptances of H_0. Beta has shifted from 21.4 per cent to 31.4 per cent. A reduction in the amount of data increases the overlap between the two distributions, consequently reducing the ability to detect false null hypotheses. The converse is also true; increases in n result in decreases in β and increases in power.

Some concept of how β varies as a function of the true value of the parameter may be obtained by looking at Figure 2-6, which shows probability distributions for $\pi = .5$ and for $\pi = .9$. In both cases, α and n are again

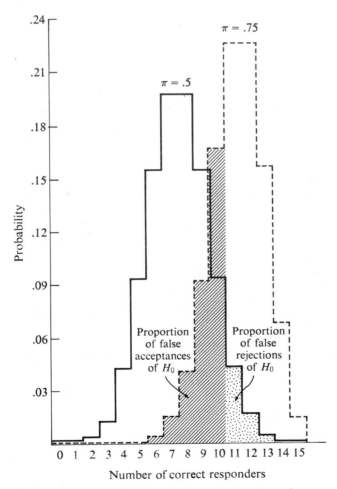

FIGURE 2-5 Probability distributions of correct responders when $n = 15$

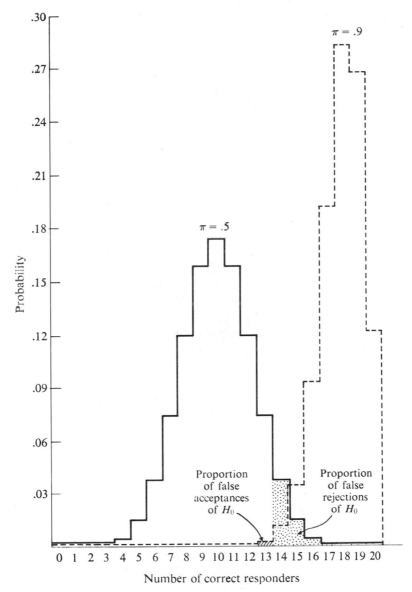

FIGURE 2-6   Distributions of correct responders for $\pi = .5$ and $\pi = .9$

equal to .06 and 20, respectively.   Note that the proportion of false acceptances of H_0 constitutes only .2 per cent of the area under the $\pi = .9$ function
as compared with 21.4 per cent for the $\pi = .75$ function in Figure 2-4.   This
result makes good sense; the further apart the null-hypothesized and true
parameter values are, the easier it should be to detect false null hypotheses.

To summarize, β is reduced (and power is consequently increased) as the difference between the value of the parameter under H_0 and the true value of the parameter increases, as α increases, and as n increases. These relationships are negatively accelerated, i.e., the reduction in β becomes less marked as the value of the parameter increases. Thus, for example, the reduction in β is much less when n is increased from 90 to 100 than when n is increased from 10 to 20. In addition to the effects just cited, a one-tailed test will always be more powerful than a two-tailed test against alternatives in that tail, but less powerful against alternatives in the second direction.

Beta differs from α in the sense that β can only be selected with reference to some minimal effect. To say that one will set β equal to .10 (as we might set α equal to .10) is meaningless; one can only require that β equal .10 for some stated minimal degree of falsity of the null hypothesis. It is not sufficient to select a level of β (or power); one must also decide what deviations from the parameter value assumed under H_0 are important to detect. In the example of the preference experiment with rats, it might be asked how much greater than .5 must π be before it becomes important to reject the null hypothesis. It may seem that any deviation from the value of the parameter assumed under H_0 is important to detect. However, it is rare that the null hypothesis is precisely true. This being the case, we wish to design the experiment so that the rejection of H_0 will not be a trivial result, merely reflecting the collection of a very large amount of data. Our interest lies not in whether H_0 is false (it usually is), but in whether it is so false that the fact is important. For example, suppose that one desires to compare the effect of traditional classroom procedures with the effect of using teaching machines on the rate of learning arithmetic. The null hypothesis might be that the two methods are equally effective, and the alternative hypothesis might be that the use of teaching machines is more effective. It might be considered important to reject H_0 only if the teaching machine was so much more effective that the added expense of developing teaching machine programs and of building machines was judged to be outweighed.

An important consequence of the preceding discussion of β is that there is now a rationale for deciding on the number of subjects to be run. We require an n sufficient to achieve a desired degree of power of rejecting H_0 against some specified alternative, given that the probability of a false rejection is α. The specific steps in deciding upon n are the following:

(a) State the null and alternative hypotheses. Continuing with our example of the rat experiment, we have

$$H_0: \pi = .5$$
$$H_1: \pi > .5$$

(b) Decide on the level of α. Assume that α is set equal to .06.

(c) Decide on the minimal degree of falsity of H_0 which it is important to detect. In our example, assume that if $\pi \geq .75$, it is important to reject H_0.

(d) Decide on the level of power, the probability of rejecting H_0 if the true parameter value deviates to the extent specified under (c). Assume that if $\pi \geq .75$, we wish at least an 80 per cent chance of rejecting H_0. Consequently, power $= .80$ and $\beta = .20$.

Given the outcomes of the above decisions, the required n can now be determined. Turning to Figure 2-4, we note that if $\alpha = .06$, $\pi = .5$ under H_0, $\pi = .75$ under H_1, and $n = 20$, then $\beta = .214$. To have $\beta = .20$, approximately 21 subjects would be required. The steps indicated above are essentially the same for all statistical tests. The major difference in the steps between the simple binomial test developed in this chapter and others such as the F and t tests is that the last two require some estimate of the population variance.*

2.5 CONFIDENCE INTERVALS AND SIGNIFICANCE TESTS

In the preceding two sections confidence intervals and significance tests have been separately considered. In this section, some similarities and differences in the two procedures will be briefly noted. Both techniques involve the same assumptions, manipulations of the same quantities, and the same definitions of probability, i.e., the probability of an event is the relative frequency of occurrence of the event. Despite these similarities, the two procedures do result in somewhat different presentations of the information obtained from the data. In this section, a more detailed comparison of the two procedures will be made, using the following example.

Twenty-five rats are run for 500 trials in a T-maze. One goal box contains food on 60 per cent of the trials, and the other goal box contains food on the remaining 40 per cent. One theory of maze behavior would lead the experimenter to predict that the rats will run to each goal box with the same relative frequency that the goal box contains reward: 60 per cent of the responses will be made to the more frequently rewarding goal box and 40 per cent to the less frequently rewarding box. In order to assess this "matching" hypothesis, the experimenter decides to test the null hypothesis that for the last block of 20 trials there are an average number of 12 runs (i.e., 60 per cent) to the more frequently rewarding goal box in a population of rats from which the 25 subjects have been sampled. The t test is the statistic chosen, the alternative hypothesis is that $\mu \neq 12$, and α is chosen as .05. The corresponding critical region consists of values of t less than -2.06 and greater than $+2.06$.

---

* In order to deal with a power function which could easily be computed by the reader, the foregoing discussion has omitted one factor, variability. Power for many tests (e.g., z, t, F) is plotted as a function of a ratio of the parameter value to the population variance. As might be expected, power varies inversely with variability. (A specific example is presented for the F test in Chap. 4.)

The mean number of runs to the more frequently rewarding goal box is 11, and the standard deviation is 3.   Inserting these values, together with the sample size, 25, into the following equation

(2.12)
$$t = \frac{\overline{X} - \mu}{s/\sqrt{n}}$$

results in $(11 - 12)/(3/5) = 1.57$, which does not fall within the critical region.   The experimenter concludes that the mean percentage of responses to a goal box does match the percentage of trials on which it contains food.

The experimenter could also approach this problem by establishing a confidence interval for μ.   Starting with Equation (2.13)

(2.13)
$$P\left(-2.06 < \frac{\overline{X} - \mu}{s/\sqrt{n}} < 2.06\right) = .95$$

algebraic manipulation and insertion of the values for $\overline{X}$, s, and n result in the 95 per cent confidence interval, $9.76 < \mu < 12.24$.   There is 95 per cent confidence that the population mean lies between these values, and again there is support for the belief that the true mean is 12.

With the two analyses completed, certain aspects may be compared. In both techniques the same information has been used: the values of the mean, standard deviation, and size of the sample.   Both techniques rest upon the properties of the t distribution and consequently upon the assumption that the scores constitute a random sample from a normally distributed population.   The t test of H_0: $\mu = 12$ provides evidence for the matching hypothesis.   The confidence interval does also, since the sample mean, 11, will not differ significantly (at the 5 per cent level if confidence is 95 per cent) from any value which falls in the obtained interval, $9.76 < \mu < 12.24$.   The confidence interval goes further in permitting the experimenter to note that certain other hypotheses are also tenable; e.g., the hypothesis that the rats develop no preference is consistent with the fact that the value 10 also falls within the interval.   In brief, the confidence interval approach permits the simultaneous consideration of all possible null hypotheses.

Suppose the confidence interval had been $4 < \mu < 18$.   While it is true that the value predicted by the matching hypothesis falls within this interval, the interval is so wide that it also contains support for numerous alternative theories.   Since no theory which predicts means from 5 through 12 can be rejected, this interval would result in a less firm statement that the matching hypothesis was correct.   The width of the confidence interval indicates how firmly an experimenter çan state an inference about any hypothesized population mean.

Tests of the null hypothesis can also provide the experimenter with an index of assurance when he accepts the null hypothesis.   If there is high power of detecting even small deviations from the value assumed under H_0, an experimenter can be quite firm in his support of the matching hypothesis when the statistical test does not yield significant results.· If he had little probability of detecting differences of the size observed, the experimenter might be more hesitant about drawing conclusions on the basis of the test. Thus the width of the confidence interval and the power of the statistical test provide similar types of information. However, there is a major difference which is to the advantage of the confidence interval approach. The computed confidence interval must of necessity provide information about its width, while null hypothesis tests can be, and usually are, made without reference to the appropriate power or OC functions.

To summarize, the confidence interval permits the experimenter to simultaneously consider the possible range of null hypotheses and immediately yields an index of the strength of an inference about any one null hypothesis. In addition, the confidence interval consists of a set of numbers on the same scale as the original data. In the case of the null hypothesis test, the experimenter is further removed from his original measures, since the test statistic is on a different scale. It may therefore be easier to digest the information provided by the confidence interval.

Tests of the null hypothesis are firmly entrenched in the statistical methodology of psychology. The intent of our comparison of null hypothesis tests and confidence intervals has not been to promote one at the expense of the other, but rather to make the reader aware of one useful approach to data analysis which has often been neglected by researchers. This book will generally reflect the overwhelming prevalence of hypothesis testing in the psychological literature. However, in subsequent chapters techniques will be presented for establishing confidence intervals for several parameters. Hopefully, the preceding discussion pointing to the availability of alternative techniques will at least facilitate an intelligent choice between estimation and hypothesis testing. Too often, psychologists have tested in ignorance of the alternative.

References to additional discussions of confidence intervals and null hypothesis tests may be found at the end of the chapter. There are also several references which present objections to both interval estimation and null hypothesis tests and in which alternative inferential procedures are proposed. Although a discussion of this material is beyond the scope of the present text, the reader should find the source material stimulating.

In concluding this chapter it is important to warn against a too literal translation of statistical results into scientific conclusions. Certainly the significance or nonsignificance of a test statistic should be a major factor in drawing conclusions about treatment effects, particularly when decisions about such things as α, β, and n have been made prior to the experiment. But, assuming nonsignificance, how sure can one be that an important effect does not exist when the probability of the test statistic falls .1 per cent above α, or when one finds that the observed variability is greater than the estimate used to decide n? What should be concluded about results which are barely significant or just fall short of significance when the assumptions underlying the test are not met by our data? Should one draw the same inference about two nonsignificant results when the qualitative trends in one set of data are consistent with expectations based on available data and theory, while no recognizable pattern exists in the second data set? How should published results of others be interpreted, when it is apparent that most experimenters give no thought to β in planning their experiment, that few even pre-select α? Under such circumstances the test statistic can be at best a rough indicator of population effects rather than a sharp inferential tool. There are no simple answers, but we reject any one-to-one relationship between the significance or nonsignificance of a test statistic and the existence or nonexistence of treatment effects or the tenability or nontenability of a theory under investigation. In drawing inferences the scientist has the responsibility of adding to the test statistic his a priori expectations, his knowledge of the literature, of the particular experimental conditions (e.g., Is there reason to suspect that some variable whose effects are not analyzable obscured the effects of independent variables?), and of the size and direction of effects, and to subjectively weight these factors. When the results of the data analysis (regardless of the type of analysis) conflict with those factors which are not built into the test, then the experimenter should reserve judgment. The ultimate criterion of the creditability of experimental conclusions is whether or not these conclusions are supported by subsequent replications of the experiment or by differently designed investigations of the hypotheses in question.

EXERCISES

2.1 Define the following terms:

(a) parameter
(b) consistent
(c) efficient
(d) unbiased
(e) expected value
(f) power
(g) Type I error

(h) Type II error
(i) alpha
(j) beta
(k) critical region
(l) one-tailed test
(m) confidence interval

2.2 One hundred random samples, each consisting of 225 scores, are drawn from a population of normally distributed scores, with $\mu = 0$, $\sigma = 1$. The 95 per cent confidence interval, $\overline{Y} - 1.96(1/15) < \mu < \overline{Y} + 1.96(1/15)$, is computed for each sample.

(a) Verify that the formula used is correct.
(b) Only 92 of the 100 computed confidence intervals contain the value of the true mean, 0. Does this fact conflict with the statement that these are 95 per cent confidence intervals? If a 95 per cent confidence interval does not mean that 95 per cent of the obtained intervals will include the parameter value, what does it mean?

2.3   I desire a 95 per cent confidence interval for μ, the mean of a normally distributed population whose standard deviation is 15.   I would like the interval to be no wider than ten units.   How large should my sample be to achieve this criterion?   (*Ans.: $n > 35$*)

2.4   In our discussion of hypothesis testing, the critical region was always selected to be in one or both tails of the distribution.   For example, against the alternative hypothesis, $\mu_1 > \mu_0$, using the z test with $\alpha = .05$, the critical region would consist of z values equal to or greater than 1.645.   Consider this rule for rejecting H_0: reject H_0 if the test statistic falls between $z = -.065$ and $z = .065$, this area also being approximately 5 per cent of the area under the normal curve.   What would happen to the power of the test?   Present diagrams similar to those in Figures 2-4 to 2-6 for the usual z test and for the suggested alternative to illustrate your argument.

SUPPLEMENTARY READINGS

For the student with a background in calculus, a more mathematical treatment of the material in Sections 2.1 through 2.3 may be found in

MOOD, A. M., *Introduction to the Theory of Statistics*, Chaps. 8, 11, 12.   New York: McGraw-Hill, 1950.

Some articles written by psychologists treating the problems of null hypothesis testing are

BINDER, A., "Further Considerations on Testing the Null Hypothesis and the Strategy and Tactics of Investigating Theoretical Models," *Psychological Review*, 70:107–115 (1963).

GRANT, D. A., "Testing the Null Hypothesis and the Strategy and Tactics of Investigating Theoretical Models," *Psychological Review*, 69:54–61 (1962).

NUNNALLY, J., "The Place of Statistics in Psychology," *Educational and Psychological Measurement*, 20:641–650 (1960).

ROZEBOOM, W. W., "The Fallacy of the Null Hypothesis Significance Test," *Psychological Bulletin*, 57:416–428 (1960).

All of the above include some discussion of significance tests and confidence intervals.   A more detailed comparison is presented in

NATRELLA, M. G., "The Relation Between Confidence Intervals and Tests of Significance—A Teaching Aid," *American Statistics*, 14:20–22, 38 (1960).

An excellent statement of the considerations involved in drawing inferences from data is to be found in

TUKEY, J. W., "Conclusions Versus Decisions," *Technometrics*, 2:423–433 (1960).

Sections 2.1 through 2.3 of the present chapter were designed to review briefly certain general principles of inference.   Students desiring a more extensive and basic presentation, with examples from a number of statistical distributions, may turn to

BLOMMERS, P. and E. F. LINDQUIST, *Elementary Statistical Methods in Psychology and Education*.   Boston: Houghton Mifflin, 1960.

NOTATION

3

If the reader is to be able to follow the derivations and computational formulas presented in this text, we must develop a common language which will be both explicit and relatively brief. Such a language, a notational system, is presented in this chapter. Whatever effort is required to attain a complete command of this material will be amply repaid in subsequent chapters. Our general approach will be to present a few simple rules and then to show their application to some elementary statistical quantities.

3.1 A SINGLE GROUP OF SCORES

Consider a group of scores: Y_1, Y_2, Y_3, Y_4, $\cdots$, Y_n. The subscript has no purpose other than to distinguish among the individual scores. The quantity n is the total number of scores in the group. Suppose $n = 5$, and we wish to indicate that all five scores are to be added together. We could write

$$Y_1 + Y_2 + Y_3 + Y_4 + Y_5$$

or, more briefly,

$$Y_1 + Y_2 + \cdots + Y_5$$

Still more briefly, we write

$$\sum_{i=1}^{5} Y_i$$

This expression is read as "sum the values of Y for all i from 1 to 5." In general, $i = 1, 2, \cdots, n$ (i.e., i takes on the values from 1 to n), and the summation of a group of n scores is indicated by

$$\sum_{i=1}^{n} Y_i$$

The quantity i is the *index*, and 1 and n are the *limits* of summation. Where the context of the presentation permits no confusion, the index and limits are often dropped. Thus we may often indicate that a group of scores are to be summed by $\sum Y$.

We will next consider three rules for summation and then some illustrative examples.

RULE 1. *The sum of a constant times a variable equals the constant times the sum of the variable.* That is,

(3.1) $$\sum CY = C \sum Y$$

C is a constant in the sense that its value does not change as a function of i; the value of Y depends upon i, and Y is therefore a variable with respect to i. Equation (3.1) is easily proven.

$$\sum CY = CY_1 + CY_2 + CY_3 + \cdots + CY_n$$
$$= C(Y_1 + Y_2 + Y_3 + \cdots + Y_n)$$
$$= C \sum Y$$

RULE 2. *The sum of a constant is equal to n times the constant, where n equals the number of quantities summed.* That is,

(3.2) $$\sum C = C + C + \cdots + C = nC$$

RULE 3. *The summation sign operates like a multiplier on quantities within parentheses.* Two examples follow:

EXAMPLE 1. $$\sum_{i}^{n} (X_i - Y_i) = \sum_{i}^{n} X_i - \sum_{i}^{n} Y_i$$

PROOF.

$$\sum (X - Y) = (X_1 - Y_1) + (X_2 - Y_2) + \cdots + (X_n - Y_n)$$
$$= (X_1 + X_2 + \cdots + X_n) - (Y_1 + Y_2 + \cdots + Y_n)$$
$$= \sum X - \sum Y$$

EXAMPLE 2. $$\sum (X - Y)^2 = \sum X^2 + \sum Y^2 - 2 \sum XY$$

PROOF.

$$\sum (X - Y)^2 = (X_1 - Y_1)^2 + \cdots + (X_n - Y_n)^2$$
$$= (X_1^2 + Y_1^2 - 2X_1Y_1) + (X_2^2 + Y_2^2 - 2X_2Y_2) + \cdots$$
$$+ (X_n^2 + Y_n^2 - 2X_nY_n)$$
$$= (X_1^2 + X_2^2 + \cdots + X_n^2) + (Y_1^2 + Y_2^2 + \cdots + Y_n^2)$$
$$- 2(X_1Y_1 + X_2Y_2 + \cdots + X_nY_n)$$
$$= \sum X^2 + \sum Y^2 - 2 \sum XY$$

Next, consider the application of these three rules to some commonly computed statistics. The mean of a group of n scores is given by

(3.3)
$$\bar{Y} = \frac{\sum Y}{n}$$

The operation of subtracting each score from the mean and adding the deviations may be represented by $\sum (Y - \bar{Y})$. Applying Rule 3, we have

(3.4)
$$\sum (Y - \bar{Y}) = \sum Y - \sum \bar{Y}$$

However, $\bar{Y}$ is a constant; its value remains the same regardless of the value of the index, i. It should be clear that we are summing over i from 1 to n throughout this presentation, even though the index and limits are not explicitly presented in each expression. Applying Rule 2, we rewrite Equation (3.4) as

(3.5)
$$\sum (Y - \bar{Y}) = \sum Y - n\bar{Y}$$

At this point, we substitute Equation (3.3) into Equation (3.5), giving

(3.6)
$$\sum (Y - \bar{Y}) = \sum Y - n\left(\frac{\sum Y}{n}\right) = \sum Y - \sum Y = 0$$

It has been proven that the sum of deviations of scores about their mean is zero, rather an elementary, but nevertheless important, result. Of course, our purpose has been primarily to illustrate how the application of the summation rules may result in proofs of basic statistical properties.

Next we will show how the summation rules may be applied to simplify computations. Two examples will be used, the sample variance and the sample correlation. The sample variance, when used as an estimator (as it will be throughout this book) is defined as follows:

(3.7)
$$s^2 = \frac{\sum (Y - \bar{Y})^2}{n - 1}$$

Computations, particularly with a desk calculator, are greatly simplified by obtaining a *raw score formula* for s^2, so called because the mean is eliminated and only individual, or raw, scores are manipulated. To obtain such a formula only the numerator of the right side of Equation (3.7) will be manipulated. First expand the quantity within the summation sign. Thus,

(3.8)
$$\sum (Y - \bar{Y})^2 = \sum (Y^2 + \bar{Y}^2 - 2Y\bar{Y})$$

Rule 3 is applied, permitting elimination of the parentheses:

(3.9)
$$\sum (Y - \bar{Y})^2 = \sum Y^2 + \sum \bar{Y}^2 - \sum 2Y\bar{Y}$$

Application of Rule 2 leads to a further change, when it is noted that $\bar{Y}^2$ is a constant:

(3.10)
$$\sum (Y - \bar{Y})^2 = \sum Y^2 + n\bar{Y}^2 - \sum 2Y\bar{Y}$$

The quantity $2\bar{Y}$ is a constant and can, by Rule 1, be placed in front of the summation sign. Thus,

(3.11)
$$\sum (Y - \bar{Y})^2 = \sum Y^2 + n\bar{Y}^2 - 2\bar{Y}\sum Y$$

Now substitute for $\bar{Y}$, using Equation (3.3).

(3.12)
$$\sum (Y - \bar{Y})^2 = \sum Y^2 + n\frac{(\sum Y)^2}{n^2} - 2\left(\frac{\sum Y}{n}\right)\sum Y$$

The final step is to obtain the simplest possible form of the above expression, which is

(3.13)
$$\sum (Y - \bar{Y})^2 = \sum Y^2 - \frac{(\sum Y)^2}{n}$$

Dividing the right-hand side of Equation (3.13) by $n - 1$ gives the raw score formula for s^2 which was sought.

A similar approach to that just illustrated may be used to obtain a raw score formula for the Pearson product-moment correlation coefficient. The equation is generally given as

(3.14)
$$r = \frac{\sum (X - \bar{X})(Y - \bar{Y})}{\sqrt{\sum (X - \bar{X})^2}\sqrt{\sum (Y - \bar{Y})^2}}$$

The raw score formula for the denominator is already known from Equation (3.13). We will therefore concern ourselves with the transformation of the numerator. First expand, obtaining

(3.15)
$$\sum (X - \bar{X})(Y - \bar{Y}) = \sum (XY - X\bar{Y} - \bar{X}Y + \bar{X}\bar{Y})$$

Parentheses are then removed according to Rule 3, yielding

(3.16)
$$\sum (X - \bar{X})(Y - \bar{Y}) = \sum XY - \sum X\bar{Y} - \sum \bar{X}Y + \sum \bar{X}\bar{Y}$$

Application of Rule 2 permits removal of one of the summation signs, and

(3.17)
$$\sum (X - \bar{X})(Y - \bar{Y}) = \sum XY - \sum X\bar{Y} - \sum \bar{X}Y + n\bar{X}\bar{Y}$$

Application of Rule 1 results in a further change:

(3.18)
$$\sum (X - \bar{X})(Y - \bar{Y}) = \sum XY - \bar{Y}\sum X - \bar{X}\sum Y + n\bar{X}\bar{Y}$$

Substituting for the means results in

(3.19)
$$\sum (X - \bar{X})(Y - \bar{Y}) = \sum XY - \left(\frac{\sum Y}{n}\right)(\sum X) - \left(\frac{\sum X}{n}\right)(\sum Y) + n\left(\frac{\sum X}{n}\right)\left(\frac{\sum Y}{n}\right)$$

and algebraic simplification gives the final result,

(3.20)
$$\sum (X - \bar{X})(Y - \bar{Y}) = \sum XY - \frac{(\sum X)(\sum Y)}{n}$$

Thus the raw score formula for the correlation coefficient is

(3.21)
$$r = \frac{n\sum XY - (\sum X)(\sum Y)}{\sqrt{n\sum X^2 - (\sum X)^2}\sqrt{n\sum Y^2 - (\sum Y)^2}}$$

Note that a little insight provides a short cut.   Equation (3.13) could be rewritten as

$$(3.13') \quad \sum (Y - \bar{Y})^2 = \sum (Y - \bar{Y})(Y - \bar{Y}) = \sum YY - \frac{(\sum Y)(\sum Y)}{n}$$

By analogy, Equation (3.20) follows.

Obtaining raw score formulas from those formulas originally used to define a statistic is a common enough problem to warrant a brief summary of the steps involved in the preceding two examples.   They are expansion, application of Rule 3 (removal of parentheses), application of Rule 2 (replacing summation signs which precede constants by appropriate multipliers), application of Rule 1 (placing constants before summation signs), substitution for quantities not presently in raw score form, and algebraic simplification.

3.2 SEVERAL GROUPS OF SCORES

The simplest possible experimental design is one involving several groups of scores.   Thus one might have a groups of n subjects each, which differ in the amount of reward they receive for their performance on some learning task. In setting the data down on paper, there would be a column for each level of amount of reward, i.e., for each experimental group.   The scores for a group could be written in any order within the appropriate column.   In referring to a score we would designate it by its position in the column (or experimental group) and by the position of the column.   Table 3-1 illustrates this pro-

TABLE 3-1

A two-dimensional matrix

			Groups		
	Y_{11}	Y_{12}	$\cdots$ Y_{1j}	$\cdots$	Y_{1a}
	Y_{21}	Y_{22}	$\cdots$ Y_{2j}	$\cdots$	Y_{2a}
Subjects	$\vdots$	$\vdots$	$\vdots$		$\vdots$
	Y_{i1}	Y_{i2}	$\cdots$ Y_{ij}	$\cdots$	Y_{ia}
	$\vdots$	$\vdots$	$\vdots$		$\vdots$
	Y_{n1}	Y_{n2}	$\cdots$ Y_{nj}	$\cdots$	Y_{na}

cedure.   Note that the first subscript refers to the position in the group (row), the second to the position of the group (column).   Thus Y_{22} is the second score in group 2 and, in general, Y_{ij} is the ith score in the jth group.

Suppose we wish to refer to the mean of a single column.   The term used previously, $\bar{Y}$, is obviously misleading since it does not designate the row or column which we want.   Even $\bar{Y}_1$ is not sufficient since it might as easily refer to the mean of the first row as of the first column.* The appropriate designation is $\overline{Y}_{.1} = [(1/n) \sum_{i=1}^{n} Y_{i1}]$; the dot represents summation over i, the index which ordinarily appears in that position. Similarly, the mean of row i would be designated by $\overline{Y}_{i.} = [(1/a) \sum_{j=1}^{a} Y_{ij}]$; summation is over the index j. The mean of all an scores would be designated by $\overline{Y}_{..} = [(1/an) \sum \sum Y_{ij}]$, or merely $\overline{Y}$.

Some examples of the application of the double summation $(\sum_i \sum_j)$ may be helpful. Suppose we have

$$\sum_{j=1}^{a} \sum_{i=1}^{n} Y_{ij}^2$$

This indicates

$$(Y_{11}^2 + Y_{21}^2 + \cdots + Y_{n1}^2) + (Y_{12}^2 + Y_{22}^2 + \cdots + Y_{n2}^2) + \cdots$$
$$+ (Y_{1a}^2 + Y_{2a}^2 + \cdots + Y_{na}^2)$$

If we have

$$\sum_{j=1}^{a} \left(\sum_{i=1}^{n} Y_{ij} \right)^2$$

the appropriate operation is

$$(Y_{11} + Y_{21} + \cdots + Y_{n1})^2 + (Y_{12} + Y_{22} + \cdots + Y_{n2})^2 + \cdots$$
$$+ (Y_{1a} + Y_{2a} + \cdots + Y_{na})^2$$

A third possibility is

$$\left(\sum_{j=1}^{a} \sum_{i=1}^{n} Y_{ij} \right)^2$$

which indicates

$$[(Y_{11} + Y_{21} + \cdots + Y_{n1}) + (Y_{12} + Y_{22} + \cdots + Y_{n2}) + \cdots$$
$$+ (Y_{1a} + Y_{2a} + \cdots + Y_{na})]^2$$

The examples may be clearer if we use some numbers. Let us use the three groups of four scores each shown in Table 3-2.

Now,

$$\sum_j \sum_i Y_{ij}^2 = 30 + 70 + 93 = 193$$

and

$$\sum_j \left(\sum_i Y_{ij} \right)^2 = (10)^2 + (14)^2 + (19)^2 = 657$$

and

$$\left(\sum_j \sum_i Y_{ij} \right)^2 = (10 + 14 + 19)^2 = 1,849$$

* In the design we used for an example, the mean of the first row would not be a quantity of interest, since we stipulated that the order within each column was arbitrary. However, there are designs giving rise to tables similar to Table 3-1 for which it is as interesting to obtain row means as it is to obtain column means.

TABLE 3-2

Some sample data

	Group 1	Group 2	Group 3
	4	1	6
	1	7	4
	3	2	5
	2	4	4
$\sum_i Y_{ij} = 10$		14	19
$\sum_i Y_{ij}^2 = 30$		70	93

As another example of the use of the double summation, we might derive a raw score formula for the average group variance, often referred to as the *within-groups mean square*. This is the sum of the group variance divided by a, the number of groups, or

$$\frac{1}{a}\left[\frac{\sum_{i=1}^{n}(Y_{i1} - \bar{Y}_{.1})^2}{n-1} + \cdots + \frac{\sum_{i=1}^{n}(Y_{ia} - \bar{Y}_{.a})^2}{n-1}\right]$$

More briefly, this average is indicated by

$$\frac{1}{a(n-1)}\sum_j^a \sum_i^n (Y_{ij} - \bar{Y}_{.j})^2$$

Now, expanding the numerator (or "sums of squares") of the above quantity, we obtain

(3.22) $$\sum_{j=1}^{a}\sum_{i=1}^{n}(Y_{ij} - \bar{Y}_{.j})^2 = \sum_{j=1}^{a}\sum_{i=1}^{n}(Y_{ij}^2 + \bar{Y}_{.j}^2 - 2Y_{ij}\bar{Y}_{.j})$$

We "multiply through" by $\sum_i$, noting that $\bar{Y}_{.j}$ varies only with j; it is constant when i is the index of summation. Terms are also rearranged so that sums are premultiplied by constants.

(3.23) $$\sum_j \sum_i (Y_{ij} - \bar{Y}_{.j})^2 = \sum_j \left(\sum_i Y_{ij}^2 + n\bar{Y}_{.j}^2 - 2\bar{Y}_{.j}\sum_i Y_{ij}\right)$$

Substituting raw score formulas for the group means gives

(3.24) $$\sum_j \sum_i (Y_{ij} - \bar{Y}_{.j})^2 = \sum_j \left[\sum_i Y_{ij}^2 + n\frac{\left(\sum_i Y_{ij}\right)^2}{n^2} - 2\left(\frac{\sum_i Y_{ij}}{n}\right)\sum_i Y_{ij}\right]$$

Simplifying results in

(3.25) $$\sum_j \sum_i (Y_{ij} - \bar{Y}_{.j})^2 = \sum_j \left[\sum_i Y_{ij}^2 - \frac{\left(\sum_i Y_{ij}\right)^2}{n}\right]$$

which may also be written as

$$\sum_j \sum_i Y_{ij}^2 - \frac{\sum_j \left(\sum_i Y_{ij} \right)^2}{n}$$

The principles developed in this chapter extend to any number of summations and variables. While some expressions in subsequent chapters may at first appear forbidding, they are invariably only extensions of what has already been done thus far.

EXERCISES

Answers are provided after the exercises. It is extremely important to try to do each problem before turning to the answers for corroboration or help.

3.1   Write the summation of the Y's encircled below, indicating the limits.

$$Y_1 + Y_2 + \boxed{Y_3 + Y_4 + Y_5 + Y_6} + Y_7 + Y_8$$

3.2   Simplify the following expressions (k is a constant):

(a) $\sum_{i=1}^{n} (Y_i - \overline{Y})$

(b) $\sum_{i=1}^{n} (Y_i + k - n)$

3.3   Show that

$$\frac{1}{k} \sum_{i=1}^{k} (k + kY_i) = k + \sum_{i=1}^{k} Y_i$$

indicating which summation rules have been applied.

3.4   Prove that $S_{y+c}^2 = S_y^2$ (c is a constant).

3.5   Prove that $S_{cy}^2 = C^2 S_y^2$.

3.6   Let $Z_i = (Y_i - \overline{Y})/S_y$.   Prove that

(a) $E(Z) = 0$
(b) $S_z^2 = 1$

3.7   Let $D_i = X_i - Y_i$.   Express

(a) $\overline{D}$ in terms of $\overline{X}$ and $\overline{Y}$
(b) S_d^2 in terms of S_x^2 and S_y^2

3.8   In an experiment on the effects of several variables upon the running times of rats, there are a levels of amount of reward (A), d levels of delay of reward (D), and t levels of inter-trial interval (T). There are n subjects in each of the adt combinations of treatments, yielding a total of $nadt$ subjects. Write the following verbal instructions in a complete and specific notational form, first clearly specifying your indices and limits of summation:

(a) Sum all scores obtained under A_1. Square the sum. Do the same for all other levels of A. Add the squared quantities together.
(b) Add all the scores obtained under D_1T_1. Square this sum. Do the same for each DT combination. Add the squared quantities.

3.9 Assume that each of n subjects is tested under each of a conditions. Prove that

$$\sum_{j=1}^{a} \sum_{i=1}^{n} (\bar{Y}_{i.} - \bar{Y}_{..})^2 = \frac{\sum_{i=1}^{n} \left(\sum_{j=1}^{a} Y_{ij} \right)^2}{a} - \frac{\left(\sum_{i=1}^{n} \sum_{j=1}^{a} Y_{ij} \right)^2}{an}$$

3.10 There are a levels of A, b levels of B, and n subjects in each of the ab combinations.

Let $i = 1, 2, \cdots, n$
$j = 1, 2, \cdots, a$
$k = 1, 2, \cdots, b$

Prove that

$$na \sum_{k=1}^{b} (\bar{Y}_{.k.} - \bar{Y}_{...})^2 = \frac{\sum_{k} \left(\sum_{i} \sum_{j} Y_{ijk} \right)^2}{na} - \frac{\left(\sum_{i} \sum_{j} \sum_{k} Y_{ijk} \right)^2}{nab}$$

3.11

		C_1			C_2	
	A_1	A_2	A_3	A_1	A_2	A_3
B_1	14	3	4	2	1	12
	12	8	11	8	9	5
B_2	3	4	5	4	1	7
	6	7	3	2	8	6
B_3	4	⑦	2	1	2	6
	5	1↖	3	④	7	3

Y_{1231}

Y_{2132}

Let $i = 1, 2$ (scores in cells)
$j = 1, 2, 3$ (levels of A)
$k = 1, 2, 3$ (levels of B)
$m = 1, 2$ (levels of C)

Thus $Y_{2132} = 4$ and $Y_{1231} = 7$. Find

(a) $\displaystyle\sum_{j} \sum_{k} \left(\sum_{m} \sum_{i} Y_{ijkm} \right)^2$

(b) $\displaystyle\sum_{j} \sum_{k} \sum_{i} \left(\sum_{m} Y_{ijkm} \right)^2$

(c) $\bar{Y}_{...2}$
(d) $\bar{Y}_{..2.}$

ANSWERS TO EXERCISES

3.1 $\displaystyle\sum_{i=3}^{6} Y_i$

3.2 (a) $\displaystyle\sum_{i=1}^{n} (Y_i - \bar{Y}) = \sum_{i=1}^{n} Y_i - \sum_{i=1}^{n} \bar{Y}$ (Rule 3)

$\displaystyle = \sum Y_i - n\bar{Y}$ (Rule 2)

$\displaystyle = \sum Y_i - n\frac{\sum Y_i}{n}$ (Substitution)

$= 0$

(b) $\displaystyle\sum_{i=1}^{n} (Y_i + k - n) = \sum_{i=1}^{n} Y_i + nk - n^2$

3.3 $\displaystyle\frac{1}{k}\sum_{i=1}^{k} (k + kY_i) = \frac{1}{k}\left(\sum_{i=1}^{k} k + \sum_{i=1}^{k} kY_i\right)$ (Rule 3)

$\displaystyle = \frac{1}{k}\left(k^2 + k\sum_{i=1}^{k} Y_i\right)$ (Rules 1 and 2)

$\displaystyle = k + \sum_{i=1}^{k} Y_i$

3.4 $\displaystyle S_{y+c}^2 = \frac{\sum_{i=1}^{n} [(Y_i + C) - E(Y_i \mid C)]^2}{n - 1}$ (by definition of a variance)

$\displaystyle E(Y_i + C) = \frac{\sum_{i=1}^{n} (Y_i + C)}{n}$

$\displaystyle = \frac{\sum Y_i}{n} + \frac{\sum C}{n}$

$= \bar{Y} + C$

Then, $\displaystyle S_{y+c}^2 = \frac{\sum_{i=1}^{n} [(Y_i + C) - (\bar{Y} + C)]^2}{n - 1}$

$\displaystyle = \frac{\sum (Y_i - \bar{Y})^2}{n - 1} = S_y^2$

3.5 $\displaystyle S_{cy}^2 = \frac{\sum_{i=1}^{n} [CY_i - E(CY)]^2}{n - 1}$

$$E(CY) = \frac{\sum\limits_{i=1}^{n} CY_i}{n}$$

$$= \frac{C \sum Y_i}{n}$$

$$= C\bar{Y}$$

Then, $S_{cy}^2 = \sum\limits_{i=1}^{n} \frac{(CY_i - C\bar{Y})^2}{n-1}$

$$= \frac{\sum [C(Y_i - \bar{Y})]^2}{n-1}$$

$$= C^2 \frac{\sum (Y_i - \bar{Y})^2}{n-1} = C^2 S_y^2$$

3.6 (a) $E(Z) = \sum\limits_{i=1}^{n} \frac{(Y_i - \bar{Y})}{S_y}$

$$= \frac{1}{S_y} \sum (Y_i - \bar{Y}) \qquad \text{(since } S_y \text{ is a constant)}$$

$$= \frac{1}{S_y} \cdot 0 \qquad\qquad \text{(see Exercise 3.2)}$$

(b) $S_z^2 = \dfrac{\sum\limits_{i=1}^{n} (Z_i - \bar{Z})^2}{n-1} \qquad \text{(by definition)}$

$$\bar{Z} = 0$$

Therefore, $S_z^2 = \dfrac{\sum\limits_{i=1}^{n} Z_i^2}{n-1}$

$$Z_i^2 = \frac{(Y_i - \bar{Y})^2}{S_y^2}$$

Then, $\sum\limits_{i=1}^{n} Z_i^2 = \dfrac{\sum\limits_{i=1}^{n} (Y_i - \bar{Y})^2}{S_y^2}$

Dividing by $n-1$, $S_z^2 = \dfrac{\sum (Y_i - \bar{Y})^2/(n-1)}{S_y^2}$

$$= \frac{S_y^2}{S_y^2}$$

$$= 1$$

3.7 (a) $\bar{D} = \dfrac{\sum\limits_{i=1}^{n} (X_i - Y_i)}{n}$

$= \dfrac{\sum X_i - \sum Y_i}{n}$

$= \bar{X} - \bar{Y}$

(b) $S_d^2 = \dfrac{\sum\limits_{i=1}^{n} (D_i - \bar{D})^2}{n-1}$

$= \dfrac{\sum [(X_i - Y_i) - (\bar{X} - \bar{Y})]^2}{n-1}$

Rearrange terms inside the brackets. Then,

$S_d^2 = \dfrac{\sum [(X_i - X) - (Y_i - \bar{Y})]^2}{n-1}$

$= \dfrac{\sum [(X_i - \bar{X})^2 + (Y_i - \bar{Y})^2 - 2(X_i - \bar{X})(Y_i - \bar{Y})]}{n-1}$

$= \dfrac{\sum (X_i - \bar{X})^2}{n-1} + \dfrac{\sum (Y_i - \bar{Y})^2}{n-1} - \dfrac{2\sum (X_i - \bar{X})(Y_i - \bar{Y})}{n-1}$

$= S_x^2 + S_y^2 - \dfrac{2\sum (X_i - \bar{X})(Y_i - \bar{Y})}{n-1}$

Note: $r_{xy} = \dfrac{\sum\limits_{i=1}^{n} (X_i - \bar{X})(Y_i - \bar{Y})/(n-1)}{S_x S_y}$

Then $\dfrac{\sum (X_i - \bar{X})(Y_i - \bar{Y})}{n-1} = r_{xy} S_x S_y$

Therefore, $S_d^2 = S_x^2 + S_y^2 - 2r_{xy} S_x S_y$

3.8 $i = 1, 2, \cdots, n$ (subjects)
$j = 1, 2, \cdots, a$ (A)
$k = 1, 2, \cdots, d$ (D)
$m = 1, 2, \cdots, t$ (T)

(a) $\sum\limits_{j=1}^{a} \left[\sum\limits_{i=1}^{n} \sum\limits_{k=1}^{d} \sum\limits_{m=1}^{t} Y_{ijkm} \right]^2$

(b) $\sum\limits_{k=1}^{d} \sum\limits_{m=1}^{t} \left[\sum\limits_{i=1}^{n} \sum\limits_{j=1}^{a} Y_{ijkm} \right]^2$

3.9 $\displaystyle\sum_{j=1}^{a}\sum_{i=1}^{n}(\bar{Y}_{i.}-\bar{Y}_{..})^2 = \sum_{j}^{a}\sum_{i}^{n}(\bar{Y}_{i.}^2+\bar{Y}_{..}^2-2Y_{i.}\bar{Y}_{..})$

$$= \sum_i (a\bar{Y}_{i.}^2+a\bar{Y}_{..}^2-2a\bar{Y}_{i.}\bar{Y}_{..})$$

$$= a\sum_i \bar{Y}_{i.}^2+an\bar{Y}_{..}^2-2a\bar{Y}_{..}\sum_i\bar{Y}_{i.}$$

$$= a\sum_i\frac{\left(\sum_j Y_{ij}\right)^2}{a^2}+an\frac{\left(\sum_i\sum_j Y_{ij}\right)^2}{a^2n^2}$$

$$-2a\left(\frac{\sum_i\sum_j Y_{ij}}{an}\right)\sum_i\left(\frac{\sum_j Y_{ij}}{a}\right)$$

$$= \frac{\sum_i\left(\sum_j Y_{ij}\right)^2}{a}+\frac{\left(\sum_i\sum_j Y_{ij}\right)^2}{an}-\frac{2\left(\sum_i\sum_j Y_{ij}\right)^2}{an}$$

$$= \frac{\sum_i\left(\sum_j Y_{ij}\right)^2}{a}-\frac{\left(\sum_i\sum_j Y_{ij}\right)}{an}$$

3.10 $\displaystyle na\sum_{k=1}^{b}(\bar{Y}_{.k.}-\bar{Y}_{...})^2$

$$= na\sum_k(\bar{Y}_{.k.}^2+\bar{Y}_{...}^2-2\bar{Y}_{.k.}\bar{Y}_{...})$$

$$= na\sum_k\bar{Y}_{.k.}^2+nab\bar{Y}_{...}^2-2na\bar{Y}_{...}\sum_k\bar{Y}_{.k.}$$

$$= na\sum_k\frac{\left(\sum_i\sum_j Y_{ijk}\right)^2}{n^2a^2}+nab\frac{\left(\sum_i\sum_j\sum_k Y_{ijk}\right)^2}{n^2a^2b^2}$$

$$-2na\frac{\left(\sum_i\sum_j\sum_k Y_{ijk}\right)}{nab}\sum_k\frac{\left(\sum_i\sum_j Y_{ijk}\right)}{na}$$

$$= \sum_k\frac{\left(\sum_i\sum_j Y_{ijk}\right)^2}{na}-\frac{\left(\sum_i\sum_j\sum_k Y_{ijk}\right)^2}{nab}$$

3.11 (a) $(14+12+2+8)^2+(3+8+1+9)^2+\cdots+(2+3+6+3)^2$

(b) $(14+2)^2+(12+8)^2+\cdots+(3+3)^2$

(c) $\displaystyle\bar{Y}_{...2}=\frac{\displaystyle\sum_i^2\sum_j^3\sum_k^3 Y_{ijk2}}{18}=\frac{2+8+1+9+\cdots+7+6+3}{18}$

(d) $\displaystyle\bar{Y}_{..2.}=\frac{\displaystyle\sum_i^2\sum_j^3\sum_m^2 Y_{ij2m}}{12}=\frac{3+6+4+7+\cdots+7+6}{12}$

COMPLETELY RANDOMIZED

ONE-FACTOR DESIGNS

4

4.1 INTRODUCTION

In this and the following chapter we will consider *completely random-ized designs*. These designs are characterized by the random assignment of each subject to only one level of the independent variable or to only one combination of levels if more than one independent variable is under investigation. The term "random" represents the requirement that each subject has an equal probability of assignment to any level or combination of levels. As an example of a completely randomized design involving one independent variable, consider the following experiment. Each subject is required to learn the appropriate response to each of 12 stimulus words; the dependent variable is the number of trials (times through the list of 12 stimulus-response pairs) required to attain a criterion of two errorless trials. The independent variable is level of intensity of noise, and it is planned to have 40 subjects, ten tested at each of four levels of noise. Subjects are college students, volunteers from a basic psychology course, who indicate on a sign-up sheet their willingness to participate. One way to assign these subjects randomly to noise levels would be to write the numbers from 1 to 40 on separate slips of paper, place these in a hat, mix well, and then note the order in which the slips are selected out of the hat. If the slip of paper numbered 17 were selected first, then the 17th subject to volunteer would be placed in the first treatment group, for example, the one corresponding to the lowest level of noise. The first ten selected pieces of paper designate the subjects who go into the first group, the second ten, those who are placed in the second treatment group, and so on. A simpler way to accomplish this would be to employ a table of random numbers such as Table A-1 in the Appendix.

Two adjacent columns of digits are chosen at random within a five-column set, and a row within the columns is then selected randomly. Beginning with this row, one proceeds down the columns, noting the order of appearance of the numbers from 01 to 40 and ignoring all other numbers. This order provides the basis for assignment to groups in the same way as did the order of drawing numbered slips. Numbers other than 01 to 40 might be used by making 41 equivalent to 01, 42 equivalent to 02, and so on. The numbers 81 to 00 would still be omitted in order to give all numbers an equal chance of being selected.

The procedures described for assigning subjects to experimental treatments ensure that all subjects have an equal probability of assignment to each treatment and, consequently, that there exists no systematic source of error. In contrast with such procedures, note the possible consequences when the first ten subjects to volunteer are assigned to one treatment, the second ten volunteers to a second treatment, and so on. Under this procedure it is difficult to defend any inference based upon the data analysis. For example, if the low noise group learns most quickly, is this a function of differences in the effects of noise upon performance, or were the earlier volunteers more interested in the experiment, more motivated to do well?

The completely randomized design has one major advantage over other designs—simplicity. This characteristic of such designs extends to the experimental layout, the model underlying the data analysis, and the computations involved in the data analysis. Let us briefly consider these advantages.

(a) *The experimental layout.* The experimental layout is a statement of who is tested under what conditions. If the design requires that each subject be tested under a number of experimental conditions, the order of presentation of conditions for each subject is part of the layout. For the completely randomized design, only the random assignment described previously is required to lay out the experiment. In contrast, stratified designs (see Chap. 6) require the division of subjects into strata or levels on the basis of some additional measure; then random assignment to the levels of the independent variable is carried out within these strata. Other designs involve still other complications in obtaining the experimental layout.

(b) *The model.* The model underlying the completely randomized design will shortly be considered in some detail. Its important feature is that it involves fewer assumptions than that for any other experimental design. Consequently, the derivations of parameter estimates are simpler than in any other instance. An even more important consequence of the parsimony of assumptions is that there is less that can go wrong with the inferential machinery than in the case of other, more complex, models. Each additional assumption underlying the derivation of the test statistic is one more assumption which may be violated, undermining the validity of the statistical inference.

(c) *The computations.* The analysis of variance for the completely randomized design involves fewer terms than that for other designs, and the terms are often easier to compute. Furthermore, related analyses such as the analysis of covariance and the estimation of missing data will also generally be simpler for the completely randomized design.

The major disadvantage of the completely randomized design is its relative inefficiency. The error variance will usually be large compared to that resulting from the use of other designs. This is in part offset by the fact that no design yields as many degrees of freedom for the error variance as does the completely randomized design, assuming some fixed amount of data. The degrees of freedom will be discussed at greater length later in this chapter; for now it is enough to note only that the power of a test increases monotonically with degrees of freedom.

In order to facilitate the learning of the subject matter of this book, we shall first consider only limited aspects of a topic, and then gradually develop additional concepts and computations in later chapters. Thus, in the present chapter, the following limitations have been placed on the presentation:

(a) We consider only that subset of completely randomized designs which involve only one independent variable; we refer to these as one-factor designs.

(b) We consider only independent variables whose levels are fixed; i.e., we define the population of levels as consisting only of those which have been selected for the experiment.

(c) We consider only the test of the general null hypothesis that $\mu_1 = \mu_2 = \cdots = \mu_j = \cdots = \mu_a$, where μ_j is the mean of a population of individuals tested under A_j, the jth level of the independent variable A.

The above restrictions are loosened in subsequent chapters. In Chapter 5, designs involving several independent variables are discussed; in Chapter 7, the implications of randomly sampling a subset of the possible levels of an independent variable are examined; and in Chapters 13 and 14 the rationale and computations for several additional tests on the data are discussed.

4.2 A MODEL FOR THE COMPLETELY RANDOMIZED ONE-FACTOR DESIGN

Consider an infinitely large population of individuals. Assume that each individual in this parent population is randomly assigned to exactly one of a possible treatments (levels of the independent variable). There are now a very large *treatment populations*, systematically differing from each other only with respect to the levels of the independent variable A. Next consider a completely randomized one-factor experiment, in which an subjects are randomly distributed among a treatments in the manner described earlier or by some other procedure which equally assures randomness of assignment. The a experimental groups of n subjects may be considered as a random samples, one from each of the treatment populations hypothesized previously. In general, we are interested in drawing inferences about μ_1, μ_2, $\cdots$, μ_j, $\cdots$, μ_a, the means of the treatment populations. At present, our specific concern is with developing a test of the null hypothesis that the μ_j are equal. To develop such a test and to answer other questions about the population parameters we require some statement about the relationship between the data and the parameters of the population. A simple possibility is the following:

(4.1) $$Y_{ij} = \mu + \alpha_j + \epsilon_{ij}$$

where Y_{ij} is the score of subject i of treatment group j; μ is the mean of the μ_j, or equivalently, the mean of the parent population prior to the establishment of treatment populations; $\alpha_j = \mu_j - \mu$, the *effect* of treatment A_j; and $\epsilon_{ij} = Y_{ij} - \mu - \alpha_j = Y_{ij} - \mu_j$.

The quantity ϵ_{ij} is the error associated with the ith score in the jth group and is a unique contribution of the individual, a deviation of the total score from μ which cannot be accounted for by the treatment effect. The variability in ϵ_{ij} may be due to differences among subjects in such factors as ability, set, motivation, the tone in which instructions are read, or the temperature of the room.

Before developing the consequences of Equation (4.1) it may be helpful to consider the rationale underlying the equation. If our subjects were identical individuals, identically treated, we would have

$$Y_{11} = Y_{21} = \cdots = Y_{ij} = \cdots = Y_{na} = \mu$$

But each group of n individuals has been treated differently. Assuming n identical individuals in each treatment population, but now allowing for the possibility that the treatments do not have identical effects, we obtain

$$Y_{11} = Y_{21} = \cdots = Y_{i1} = \cdots = Y_{n1} = \mu_{.1}$$
$$\vdots$$
$$Y_{1j} = Y_{2j} = \cdots = Y_{ij} = \cdots = Y_{nj} = \mu_{.j}$$
$$\vdots$$
$$Y_{1a} = Y_{2a} = \cdots = Y_{ia} = \cdots = Y_{na} = \mu_{.a}$$

Finally, we take into account the fact that even individuals treated alike with respect to the independent variable will rarely perform in an identical manner. Due to individual differences the score of subject i in group j will deviate from μ_j by an amount, ϵ_{ij}. Consequently,

$$Y_{11} = \mu_{.1} + \epsilon_{11}$$
$$\vdots$$
(4.2) $$Y_{ij} = \mu_{.j} + \epsilon_{ij}$$
$$\vdots$$
$$Y_{na} = \mu_{.a} + \epsilon_{na}$$

Equation (4.2) is unchanged if we add and subtract the constant μ, resulting in

$$Y_{ij} = \mu + \mu_{.j} - \mu + \epsilon_{ij}$$

Since $\mu_{.j} - \mu = \alpha_j$ by definition, Equations (4.2) and (4.1) are equivalent. Thus the model underlying the data analysis asserts that the score of the ith individual in the jth group is the sum of the following three components:

(a) μ, *the parent population mean.* This quantity is a constant component of all scores in the data matrix.

(b) α_j, *the effect of treatment A_j.* This effect is a constant component of all scores obtained under A_j, but may vary over treatments (levels of j). If the a levels of A are arbitrarily selected, as assumed, they exhaust the population of levels of A, and therefore $\sum_j \alpha_j = 0$, since the sum of all deviations of scores (μ_j) about their mean (μ) is zero. The null hypothesis asserts that $\alpha_1 = \alpha_2 = \cdots = \alpha_j = \cdots = \alpha_a = 0$.

(c) ϵ_{ij}, *the deviation, due to uncontrolled variability, of the ith score in group j from the jth treatment population mean.* This component of Y_{ij} is the only source of variance among scores in the jth group and, if the null hypothesis is true, the only source of variance in the data matrix.

Equation (4.1) is not a sufficient basis for the derivation of parameter estimates and statistical tests. In addition, the following assumptions about the distribution of the ϵ_{ij} are required:

(a) The ϵ_{ij} are independently distributed. This means that the probability of sampling some value of ϵ_{ij} does not depend on any other values of ϵ_{ij} in the sample. An important consequence of this is that the ϵ_{ij} are uncorrelated.

(b) The distribution of the ϵ_{ij} is normal, with zero mean, in each of the a treatment populations.

(c) The distribution of the ϵ_{ij} has variance of σ_e^2 in each of the a treatment populations, i.e., $\sigma_1^2 = \sigma_2^2 = \cdots = \sigma_j^2 = \cdots = \sigma_a^2 = \sigma_e^2$.

Since the ϵ_{ij} are solely responsible for the variability in the jth treatment population, it follows that the Y_{ij} should also be normally and independently distributed with mean μ_j and variance equal to σ_e^2. This fact provides a basis for testing the above assumptions. A more detailed analysis of the assumptions will be presented later; for the present some consequences of the model are shown.

4.2.1 Estimates of the population parameters

Under the normal distribution assumption, the least-squares and maximum likelihood procedures described in Chapter 2 result in identical values of $\hat{\mu}$ and $\hat{\alpha}$, the estimates of μ and α. Both procedures ordinarily require the application of differential calculus to obtain the estimates; we will therefore omit the derivation but will offer an algebraic proof that the least-squares estimates of μ and α are $\bar{Y}$ and $\bar{Y}_j - \bar{Y}$, respectively.

We desire values of $\hat{\mu}$ and $\hat{\alpha}$ which minimize the quantity

(4.3) $$S = \sum_i \sum_j \hat{\epsilon}_{ij}^2 = \sum_i \sum_j (Y_{ij} - \hat{\mu} - \hat{\alpha}_j)^2$$

Let us assume that $\hat{\mu} = \bar{Y}_{..} + C$ where $\bar{Y}_{..}$ is the grand mean (the mean of all an scores) and C is any real number. Substituting in Equation (4.3), we obtain

(4.4) $$S = \sum_i \sum_j (Y_{ij} - \bar{Y}_{..} - C - \hat{\alpha}_j)^2$$

Applying the techniques of Chapter 3 (and noting that $an\bar{Y}_{..} = \sum_i \sum_j Y_{ij}$ and $n\bar{Y}_{.j} = \sum_i Y_{ij}$),

(4.5) $$S = \sum_i \sum_j Y_{ij}^2 + n \sum_j \hat{\alpha}_j^2 - an\bar{Y}_{..}^2 - 2n \sum_j \hat{\alpha}_j \bar{Y}_{.j} + 2n\bar{Y}_{..} \sum_j \hat{\alpha}_j$$
$$+ anC^2 + anC \sum_j \hat{\alpha}_j$$

To complete the proof we require that $\sum_j \hat{\alpha}_j = 0$, which follows from the fact that the average value of α_j is zero. Now we have

(4.6) $$S = \sum_i \sum_j Y_{ij}^2 + n \sum_j \hat{\alpha}_j^2 - an\bar{Y}_{..}^2 - 2n \sum_j \hat{\alpha}_j \bar{Y}_{.j} + anC^2$$

Clearly, S is minimal when $C = 0$, i.e., when $\hat{\mu} = \bar{Y}_{..}$.

Next consider

(4.7) $$S_j = \sum_i (Y_{ij} - \hat{\mu}_j)^2$$

Let $\hat{\mu}_j = \bar{Y}_{.j} + C_{.j}$, where $\bar{Y}_{.j}$ is the mean of the jth treatment group and $C_{.j}$ is a real number which is constant for that group. Then

(4.8) $$S_j = \sum_i (Y_{ij} - \bar{Y}_{.j} - C_{.j})^2$$
$$= \sum_i Y_{ij}^2 - n\bar{Y}_{.j}^2 + nC_{.j}^2$$

S_j is minimal when $C_{.j} = 0$, i.e., when $\hat{\mu}_j = \bar{Y}_{.j}$. Since the least-squares estimates of μ and μ_j are $\bar{Y}_{..}$ and $\bar{Y}_{.j}$, $\bar{Y}_{..} - \bar{Y}_{.j}$ is the appropriate estimate of α_j. An additional consequence of the preceding developments is that we have established $Y_{ij} - \bar{Y}_{.j}$ as the least-squares estimate of ϵ_{ij}, since $\epsilon_{ij} = Y_{ij} - \mu_j$.

To summarize, we have the following least-squares estimators of the population parameters:

(4.9) $$\hat{\mu}_j = \bar{Y}_{.j}$$
$$\hat{\mu} = \bar{Y}_{..}$$
$$\hat{\alpha}_j = \bar{Y}_{.j} - \bar{Y}_{..}$$
$$\hat{\epsilon}_{ij} = Y_{ij} - \bar{Y}_{.j}$$

If the ϵ_{ij} are, as assumed, normally distributed, then the above estimates are efficient and consistent.

4.2.2 The F ratio

If the assumptions of the model are met, an appropriate test of the null hypothesis that the μ_j are equal is provided by

$$(4.10) \qquad F = \frac{n \sum_j \hat{\alpha}_j^2/(a-1)}{\sum_i \sum_j \hat{\epsilon}_{ij}^2/a(n-1)} = \frac{n \sum_j (\overline{Y}_{\cdot j} - \overline{Y}_{\cdot\cdot})^2/(a-1)}{\sum_i \sum_j (Y_{ij} - \overline{Y}_{\cdot j})^2/a(n-1)}$$

The numerator of F is generally referred to as the *between-groups mean square* and we will use the notation MS_A, where the subscript designates the independent variable. The denominator of the F ratio is generally referred to as the *within-groups mean square* and we will use the notation $MS_{S/A}$, where the subscript is read as "subjects within levels of A." Thus $F = MS_A/MS_{S/A}$. Each MS is a ratio of a *sum of squares* (SS) to its *degrees of freedom* (df). Thus, $MS_A = SS_A/df_A$ and $MS_{S/A} = SS_{S/A}/df_{S/A}$. The origins of these components of the F ratio will be discussed later.

Let us now consider why the ratio of mean squares should be sensitive to violations of the null hypothesis. The numerator of the F ratio is n times the variance of the treatment group means. These means will differ simply because each is based on a different set of n individuals; error variance is contributing to the variance of group means. There is another *possible* source of the variance of group means. If the treatments really differ in their effects and the μ_j are therefore not all equal, one would expect this to be reflected in the spread among the group means. Thus there are two possible sources of the variability among the group means and therefore of the magnitude of the MS_A—individual differences and treatment effects. Next consider the denominator of the F ratio, $MS_{S/A}$. The variance among individuals in the jth treatment group is $\sum_{i=1}^{n}(Y_{ij} - \overline{Y}_{\cdot j})^2/(n-1)$. Summing over groups and dividing by a yields the variance of individuals averaged over groups. Treatment effects do not contribute to this mean square, for if a constant (e.g., $\hat{\alpha}_j$) is added to all the scores in a group, the variance of the scores is unchanged. The $MS_{S/A}$ is a function only of σ_e^2, the error variance. In view of the preceding line of reasoning, one would expect the F ratio to be close to 1 if the μ_j were equal, for in that case both numerator and denominator would reflect only the error variance in the population. The ratio would not necessarily be exactly 1 since by chance there might be greater (or smaller) differences among individuals in different groups than among individuals in the same group. However, the average value of F over many experiments should be 1. If an F ratio were very large, there would be grounds for suspecting that treatment effects were being added to error variance in the numerator. If these intuitive arguments can be proved, we will have met one important criterion for a test statistic: it should reflect the relative merits of the null and alternative (that the μ_j are not equal) hypotheses. Such a proof follows. Specifically, it will be proved that if H_0

is true, the value of F, averaged over many replications of the experiment, is 1; if H_0 is false, the average F value is greater than 1. This average value is denoted by $E(F)$, representing the expected value of F.

Our approach is to derive separately the expectations of $n \sum_j (\bar{Y}_{.j} - \bar{Y}_{..})^2$ and $\sum_i \sum_j (Y_{ij} - \bar{Y}_{.j})^2$. These quantities are the numerators of the mean squares and are respectively referred to as the *sum of squares for A (SS_A)* and the *sum of squares within groups ($SS_{S/A}$)*. First the SS_A is redefined in terms of the analysis of variance model. From Equation (4.1),

(4.11)
$$\bar{Y}_{.j} = \frac{\sum_i (\mu + \alpha_j + \epsilon_{ij})}{n}$$

$$= \frac{n\mu + n\alpha_j + \sum_i \epsilon_{ij}}{n}$$

$$= \mu + \alpha_j + \frac{\sum_i \epsilon_{ij}}{n}$$

and

(4.12)
$$\bar{Y}_{..} = \frac{\sum_i \sum_j (\mu + \alpha_j + \epsilon_{ij})}{an}$$

$$= \frac{an\mu + n\sum_j \alpha_j + \sum_i \sum_j \epsilon_{ij}}{an}$$

$$= \mu + \frac{\sum_i \sum_j \epsilon_{ij}}{an}$$

since $\sum_j \alpha_j = 0$. Then

(4.13)
$$E(SS_A) = E\left[n \sum_j \left(\alpha_j + \frac{\sum_i \epsilon_{ij}}{n} - \frac{\sum_i \sum_j \epsilon_{ij}}{an} \right)^2 \right]$$

Expanding Equation (4.13), we obtain

(4.14)
$$E\left(SS_A \right) = nE\left[\sum_j \alpha_j^2 + \frac{\sum_j \left(\sum_i \epsilon_{ij} \right)^2}{n^2} + \frac{\sum_j \left(\sum_i \sum_j \epsilon_{ij} \right)^2}{a^2 n^2} \right.$$

$$\left. + \frac{2 \sum_i \sum_j \alpha_j \epsilon_{ij}}{n} - \frac{2 \sum_j \alpha_j \sum_i \sum_j \epsilon_{ij}}{an} - 2\left(\frac{\sum_i \sum_j \epsilon_{ij}}{an} \right)\left(\frac{\sum_i \sum_j \epsilon_{ij}}{n} \right) \right]$$

Since the expectation of a sum equals the sum of the expectations, the expectation of each term on the right side of Equation (4.14) may be evaluated separately.

(4.14a)
$$E\left(n \sum_j \alpha_j^2 \right) = n \sum_j \alpha_j^2$$

since α_j is assumed to be constant over replications of the experiment, and the expectation of a constant is the constant.

(4.14b)
$$E\left[\frac{n\sum\limits_{j}\left(\sum\limits_{i}\epsilon_{ij}\right)^2}{n^2}\right] = \sum_{j} E\left(\frac{\sum\limits_{i}\epsilon_{ij}^2}{n}\right)$$
$$= a\sigma_e^2$$

where σ_e^2 is the variance of ϵ_{ij} in the jth treatment population. We might do well to consider Equation (4.14b) in more detail. Note that

$$\left(\sum_{i}\epsilon_{ij}\right)^2 = \epsilon_{1j}^2 + \cdots + \epsilon_{nj}^2 + 2\epsilon_{1j}\epsilon_{2j} + \cdots + 2\epsilon_{ij}\epsilon_{i'j} + \cdots$$
$$+ 2\epsilon_{n-1,j}\epsilon_{nj} \qquad (i \neq i')$$

But $E(\epsilon_{ij}\epsilon_{i'j})$ is the numerator of a correlation of ϵ's and must be zero, since the ϵ's are independently distributed. Hence,

$$E\left[\frac{\left(\sum\limits_{i}\epsilon_{ij}\right)^2}{n}\right] = E\left(\frac{\sum\limits_{i}\epsilon_{ij}^2}{n}\right)$$

By definition,

$$\text{var}\,(\epsilon_{ij}) = \sigma_{\epsilon_{ij}}^2 = E(\epsilon_{ij}^2) - [E(\epsilon_{ij})]^2$$
$$= E(\epsilon_{ij}^2)$$

since $E(\epsilon_{ij}) = 0$.

Since the ϵ_{ij} are assumed to be identically distributed (in particular, since the variances are assumed to be the same),

$$\frac{\sum\limits_{j}\sum\limits_{i}\sigma_{\epsilon_{ij}}^2}{n} = \frac{\sum\limits_{j}\sum\limits_{i}\sigma_e^2}{n} = a\sigma_e^2$$

Moving to the next component of Equation (4.14),

(4.14c)
$$E\left[\frac{n\sum\limits_{j}\left(\sum\limits_{i}\sum\limits_{j}\epsilon_{ij}\right)^2}{a^2n^2}\right] = \sigma_e^2$$

The proof follows that for Equation (4.14b).

The next two terms vanish. Since α_j is a constant independent of ϵ_{ij},

(4.14d)
$$E\left(\frac{\sum\limits_{i}\sum\limits_{j}\alpha_j\epsilon_{ij}}{n}\right) = 0$$

Since $\sum_j \alpha_j = 0$,

(4.14e)
$$E\left(\frac{\sum\limits_{j}\alpha_j\sum\limits_{i}\sum\limits_{j}\epsilon_{ij}}{an}\right) = 0$$

Finally,

(4.14f)
$$E\left[-2n\left(\frac{\sum\limits_{i}\sum\limits_{j}\epsilon_{ij}}{an}\right)\left(\frac{\sum\limits_{i}\sum\limits_{j}\epsilon_{ij}}{n}\right)\right] = -2\sigma_e^2$$

The proof is similar to those for Equations (4.14b) and (4.14c).

Combining terms, we obtain

$$(4.15) \qquad E(SS_A) = (a - 1)\sigma_e^2 + n \sum_j \alpha_j^2$$

and for the expected mean square of A, $E(MS_A)$, we have

$$(4.16) \qquad E(MS_A) = E\left(\frac{SS_A}{a - 1}\right) = \sigma_e^2 + n\theta_A^2$$

θ_A^2 rather than σ_A^2 is used to represent the variability among the μ_j for two reasons: (a) in a strict sense $\sum (\mu_j - \mu)^2/(a - 1)$ is not a population variance because of the divisor, and (b) the use of θ^2 is a reminder that the effects of A are fixed rather than random.

The derivation of $E(MS_{S/A})$ is similar to that for $E(MS_A)$. Applying Equation (4.2),

$$(4.17) \qquad E\left[\sum_i \sum_j (Y_{ij} - \bar{Y}_{.j})^2\right] = E\left[\sum_i \sum_j \left(\epsilon_{ij} - \frac{\sum_i \epsilon_{ij}}{n}\right)^2\right]$$

Expansion yields

$$(4.18) \qquad E\left[\sum_i \sum_j (Y_{ij} - \bar{Y}_{.j})^2\right] = E\left[\sum_i \sum_j \epsilon_{ij}^2 - \frac{\sum_j \left(\sum_i \epsilon_{ij}\right)^2}{n}\right]$$
$$= a(n - 1)\sigma_e^2$$

Dividing both sides of Equation (4.18) by $a(n - 1)$ yields

$$(4.19) \qquad E(MS_{S/A}) = \sigma_e^2$$

The expected value of a ratio of two quantities equals the ratio of the expectations of the two quantities, i.e., $E(A/B) = [E(A)]/[E(B)]$, if the quantities are independently distributed. It can be proven that the mean squares are independent of each other in the model under investigation. Therefore,

$$(4.20) \qquad E(F) = \frac{E(MS_A)}{E(MS_{S/A})} = \frac{\sigma_e^2 + n\theta_A^2}{\sigma_e^2}$$

If H_0 is true, $\theta_A^2 = 0$ and $E(F) = 1$. If H_0 is false, $\theta_A^2 > 0$ and $E(F) > 1$. Thus the ratio of mean squares satisfies one requirement of a test statistic; its magnitude can be expected to reflect the validity of H_0.

The second requirement of the test statistic is that its distribution under H_0 be known. The distribution of F must be known in order to determine the critical region, those values whose probability of occurrence is less than α, given that H_0 is true. If the F obtained from an experiment is so large that it falls within the critical region, one may conclude that the observed ratio has been sampled from some distribution whose mean is greater than 1. We reject H_0 in favor of the alternative hypothesis that $\theta_A^2 > 0$.

The distribution of F is known to be the distribution of the ratio of two independently distributed chi-squares (χ^2) divided by their df, i.e.,

$$(4.21) \qquad F = \frac{\chi_1^2/df_1}{\chi_2^2/df_2}$$

If the conditions of normality, independence, and homogeneity of variance hold, and if H_0 is true, the ratio of mean squares meets the condition described by Equation (4.21). (Note that the normality assumption was not invoked in deriving the $E(MS)$; however, it is necessary if the sums of squares are to have the χ^2 distribution.) Consequently, the probability of obtaining various F values can be computed. Values of F required for significance are presented for several combinations of df's and α levels in Table A-5 in the Appendix. As an example of the use of Table A-5, assume an experiment with five levels of the independent variable A and six subjects at each level. Then the df of the numerator (df_1) are 4 and the df of the denominator (df_2) are 25. If α equals .05, then values of F greater than 2.76 will result in the rejection of H_0. If the selected α equaled .01, then F's greater than 4.18 would be required for significance.

4.2.3 Assumptions underlying the F test

The third requirement for a statistic to be an appropriate test of H_0 is that the data conform to the assumptions underlying the test. The ratio of mean squares will be distributed as F if:

(a) the ϵ_{ij} are independently distributed,
(b) the ϵ_{ij} are normally distributed,
(c) the variance of the ϵ_{ij} is the same for all treatment populations,
(d) the null hypothesis is true.

If the first three assumptions are valid, then significant F's may be attributed to the falsity of assumption (d). However, if any of the first three assumptions are false, the distribution of mean squares may be such that the true probability of obtaining a result in the critical region is actually not α; whether the true probability of a Type I error is greater or less than α will depend on the form of the violation, although an excess of Type I errors is the more usual occurrence. Figure 4-1 exemplifies the potential problem.

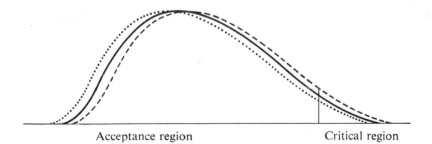

Acceptance region   Critical region

FIGURE 4-1 An example of the distribution of the ratio of mean squares when assumptions are valid (solid line), when violations result in loss of power (dotted line), and when violations result in increased risk of Type I errors (dashed line)

The solid line represents the F distribution, the distribution of the ratio of mean squares, when all four assumptions are valid. Under some departures from assumptions (a) through (c), the distribution of the ratio of mean squares might resemble that described by the dotted line. In this case, the probability of obtaining an F in the critical region is less than α and consequently the power of the F test has been reduced. A more common result of violations of any of the first three assumptions is represented by the dashed line in Figure 4-1. The distribution of the ratio of mean squares is now such that the probability of obtaining an F in the critical region is greater than α, and the risk of a Type I error is therefore greater than that which the experimenter wishes to assume.

The validity of the independence assumption, (a), depends upon the experimenter's manipulations, upon the care he takes to ensure the random assignment of treatments to subjects. For example, suppose that the scores of subjects tested on the same day are positively correlated while those of subjects tested on different days are negatively correlated. This might be so because of slight day-to-day changes in the wording of instructions. If treatment A_1 is given on day 1, treatment A_2 on day 2, etc., differences among treatment means may merely reflect day-to-day differences, which in turn are a function of the correlation among scores referred to above. Under such circumstances, inferences based on the statistical test are invalid. Randomization will not eliminate the correlations among measures, but it provides for an equal opportunity for any two treatments to appear in adjacent and in nonadjacent points in time. Randomization provides a mechanism by which the expected correlations (as n increases) tend to cancel, leaving treatment effects independent of day-to-day effects.

The validity of the normality assumption, (b), will depend upon the measure chosen. For example, projective test scores tend to exhibit a skewed distribution, and percentage scores will be binomially distributed. The χ^2 test can be used to evaluate the significance of departures of the obtained distribution from the assumed normal distribution; the test would be applied to each of the a sets of n scores in turn. Generally, such a procedure will be unnecessary, since the distribution of the ratio of mean squares seems little affected by departures from normality. A number of empirical studies attest to this conclusion. In the most extensive of these, Norton* obtained a number of samples from the same population or from populations having the same mean, computed an F ratio for these samples, repeated this sampling and computational process a large number of times, and then enumerated the percentage of F ratios which exceeded various probability levels. Sampling from non-normal distributions, Norton found that the F expected in 1 per cent of the cases (under the assumptions of the distribution) was ex-

---

* The Norton study is described in E. F. Lindquist, *Design and Analysis of Experiments in Psychology and Education* (Boston: Houghton Mifflin, 1953), pp. 78–90.

ceeded in .8 per cent to 2.76 per cent of his "experiments"; the 5 per cent level was exceeded from 4.76 per cent to 7.83 per cent of the time. However, sampling from a normal distribution, F's which were significant at the 1 per cent and 5 per cent levels were obtained 1.44 per cent and 5.61 per cent of the time, respectively. Considering this random variation which occurred with a normal distribution, the distortion of tabled probability that occurs with non-normal distribution is not overly marked. The worst distortions occurred with a leptokurtic distribution, in which the samples taken involved very small numbers of degrees of freedom for the F ratio. This optimistic picture of the role of the normality assumption might be qualified by noting that substantial errors can occur in the estimation of intervals for variance components (e.g., confidence intervals for θ_A^2) if normality is incorrectly assumed.

The validity of the homogeneity of variance assumption, (c), will depend upon how careful the experimenter is to administer the experimental treatments in a consistent manner to all subjects; upon the type of measure taken; and upon the treatment levels employed. Certainly, the uniform application of treatments to subjects will tend to stabilize variances from group to group. However, despite proper experimental methodology, heterogeneity of variance can occur. For example, some measures (response frequency is a common instance) are Poisson-distributed, in which case the mean and variance are equal, and either both are homogeneous or both are heterogeneous over treatments. Several methods exist for detecting departures from homogeneity of variance. Hartley* has proposed a test based on the ratio of the largest to the smallest within-groups variance. Cochran† has proposed a more sensitive measure, which takes account of all the data collected. The application of these two procedures, which generally give similar results, is illustrated in Section 4.3, and the 1 per cent and 5 per cent significance points are in Tables A-6 and A-7 in the Appendix. A third test, derived by Bartlett,‡ has the advantage of using the χ^2 tables, which are more generally available. However, it is computationally laborious and, more important, extremely sensitive to departures from normality. In view of our earlier discussion of the relative insensitivity of F to violations of the normality assumption, we feel justified in not further pursuing the Bartlett test.

Data on the consequences of heterogeneity of variance are provided by the second phase of Norton's study. Samples were randomly selected from normal populations with variances of 25, 100, and 225, respectively; the means of these populations were equal. Significant F's at the 1 per cent and

---

* H. O. Hartley, "The Maximum F-Ratio as a Short-cut Test for Heterogeneity of Variance," *Biometrika*, 37:308–312 (December 1950).

† W. G. Cochran, "The Distribution of the Largest of a Set of Estimated Variances as a Fraction of Their Total," *Annals of Eugenics*, 11:47–52 (1941).

‡ M. S. Bartlett, "Properties of Sufficiency and Statistical Tests," *Proceedings of the Royal Society of London*, A, 160:238 (1937).

5 per cent levels were obtained approximately 2 per cent and 7 per cent of the time, with some variation as a function of degrees of freedom. When the populations from which the samples were drawn differed in their shapes, the results were about the same as when they differed in their variances. In the case where the populations differed in both shape and variance, a significant F at the 1 per cent level was obtained about 3 to 3.5 per cent of the time, and at the 5 per cent level, about 8 to 10 per cent of the time, again depending on the degrees of freedom. Except for the case of heterogeneity of shape and variance, the deviation from assumption (c) has relatively small effect.

If an experiment results in extreme heterogeneity of variance, the F test may still be applicable if an appropriate transformation of the data can be found. Bartlett* has presented a formula which yields a transformation resulting in homogeneity of the group variances, provided that the relationship between the treatment population mean and variance is continuous and is known. In many instances where there is no recognizable relationship between mean and variance, the experimenter can through trial and error find a transformation which will stabilize the within-groups variances. Three of the more useful transformations are noted below.

(a) *The square-root transformation.* This transformation is applicable when $\sigma_j^2 = k\mu_j$, i.e., when the means and variances are proportional for each treatment. This situation is not unusual when the data are in the form of frequency counts, for example, when the dependent variable is number correct or number of "yes" responses. In such cases, the analysis of variance is carried out on Y' rather than on Y, where

(4.22) $$Y'_{ij} = \sqrt{Y_{ij}}$$

and Y_{ij} is the score originally obtained from the ith subject in the jth group. If some of the values of Y_{ij} are less than 10, homogeneity of variance is more likely to be produced by the transformation,

(4.23) $$Y'_{ij} = \sqrt{Y_{ij} + .5}$$

(b) *The arc sine transformation.* This transformation is applicable when $\sigma_j^2 = \mu_j(1 - \mu_j)$, i.e., when the scores are proportions, for example, percentage correct or percentage predictions of some event. In such cases, the appropriate transformation is

(4.24) $$Y'_{ij} = \text{arc sin } \sqrt{Y_{ij}}$$

The transformed score is the angle whose sine is equal to the square root of the original score. If the original score is .50, its square root is approximately .707. Turning to a table of natural trigonometric functions (available in most books of mathematical and/or statistical tables), we find that the sine

---

* M. S. Bartlett, "Some Examples of Statistical Methods of Research in Agriculture and Applied Biology," *Supplement to the Journal of the Royal Statistical Society,* 4:137–183 (1937).

of 45° is .707; Y'_{ij} is 45.   The transformation may be made directly, without computation of the square root, if tables of arc sin $\sqrt{Y}$ are available.   Such a table may be found in Snedecor.*

(c) *The logarithmic transformation.*   This transformation is applicable when $\sigma_j^2 = k\mu_j^2$, i.e., when the treatment standard deviation is proportional (k is a constant of proportionality) to the treatment mean.   This situation will sometimes arise when the distribution of scores is markedly skewed; thus, reaction time scores may be amenable to this transformation.   Equation (4.25) characterizes the transformation.

$$(4.25) \qquad\qquad Y'_{ij} = \log Y_{ij}$$

If some of the measures are small, the recommended transformation is

$$(4.26) \qquad\qquad Y'_{ij} = \log (Y_{ij} + 1)$$

The interpretation of the results of analyses performed on transformed data presents some problems since the transformation changes relationships observed among the statistics for the original data.   Consider the following example, in which the ordinality of group means is reversed under a square root transformation.   For simplicity, we assume the following two groups of two scores each:

	A_1	A_2
	4	25
	64	36
$\overline{Y}_{.j} =$	34	30.5

Taking the square root of each score, we obtain

	A_1	A_2
	2	5
	8	6
$\overline{Y}_{.j} =$	5	5.5

The rank order of the means has been reversed.   If we limit any inferential statements to the μ'_j, the treatment population means for the transformed data, we are on safe ground.   However, many psychologists would object that they desire to draw conclusions about the μ_j, the treatment population mean computed on the original scale.   One solution is to take $\overline{Y}_j'^2$ as the estimate of μ_j.   Our inferences would then be based on the analysis of transformed data, but applied to the parameters on a reconverted scale.   For example, our point estimates of μ_1 and μ_2 would be 25 and 30.25, respectively (rather than 34 and 30.5).   Bartlett† succinctly summarizes the justification for this approach.   "If the variability in the data varies with the mean level

---

* G. W. Snedecor, *Statistical Methods*, 5th ed. (Ames: Iowa State Univ. Press, 1956), pp. 318–319.

† M. S. Bartlett, "The Use of Transformations," *Biometrics*, 3:39–52 (1947).

for different blocks or groups, an unweighted average of the observed treatment responses is not necessarily the best estimate of the true treatment response, and the average on the transformed scale will often be the better estimate when reconverted to the original scale." It should be clear that the reconverted mean will be a better estimate than the original unconverted mean only if the transformation provided a stability of variance lacking in the original data.

In addition to reducing heterogeneity of variance, transformations generally result in a closer approximation to the normal distribution. Furthermore, they are most useful in more complex designs, where it is desirable to eliminate certain effects of combinations of variables which are unaccounted for by the usual analysis of variance models. We reserve discussion of this problem for Chapter 7, when the relevant designs will first be met. For further information on transformations, including additional transformations and estimates of what the variance will be on the new scale, see Bartlett's (1947) paper.

A second approach to the data when the assumptions have been violated and when the experimenter feels that estimates derived from the Norton study are not sufficient would be the use of nonparametric statistics. Siegel* has strongly recommended the more widespread use of nonparametric statistics on the grounds that the assumptions of analysis of variance are generally violated. However, we feel that the use of nonparametric statistics should usually be limited to instances in which the data are originally in the form of ranks or in the form of frequency counts, as in contingency table problems, or when a quick approximate indication of significance is required. An extensive discussion of the pros and cons of nonparametric statistics and of their advantages and disadvantages relative to those of analysis of variance is beyond the scope of this book; the topic is covered by Siegel, Gaito,† and Anderson,‡ among others. The major reason for the author's restraint in utilizing nonparametric statistics is simply that they are not versatile enough, that the person who uses the nonparametric approach is limited in the designs he can use and in the questions he can ask of his data.

4.2.4 *F* ratios less than 1

If the null hypothesis is correct, the average F ratio is 1, and on the basis of sampling variability one may expect occasional F ratios of less than 1. Such occurrences are merely regarded as support for the null hypothesis. However, the occurrence of F's so small that their reciprocals are significant or

---

* S. Siegel, *Nonparametric Statistics for the Behavioral Sciences* (New York: McGraw-Hill, 1956).

† J. Gaito, "Nonparametric Methods in Psychological Research," *Psychological Report*, 5:115–125 (1959).

‡ N. H. Anderson, "Scales and Statistics: Parametric and Nonparametric," *Psychological Bulletin*, 58:305–316 (1961).

the occurrence of many F's less than 1 in a single analysis of variance merits further consideration. Such findings suggest that the model underlying the analysis of variance has in some way been violated. A frequent occurrence is the presence of some systematic effect which is not described by the analysis of variance model and which is consequently not accounted for in the analysis of the data. For example, if all experimental groups consist of some subjects run by one experimenter and some subjects run by another experimenter, within-groups variability may be increased without a concomitant increase in between-groups variability. If the systematic factor can be designated, its contribution to the error variance can often be removed with the loss of a few df's in the error term.

4.3 THE ANALYSIS OF VARIANCE

Having considered the relevant theory, we now turn to the actual data analysis process. It will be shown that SS_A and $SS_{S/A}$ account for the total variability in the data, and raw score formulas for these quantities will be developed. Finally, these formulas will be applied in the analysis of a sample set of data.

4.3.1 Components of variability

Consider the following identity, which states that the deviation of a score from the grand mean consists of two components: (a) the deviation of a score from the mean of its experimental group, and (b) the deviation of the group mean from the grand mean.

$$(4.27) \qquad Y_{ij} - \bar{Y}_{..} = (Y_{ij} - \bar{Y}_{.j}) + (\bar{Y}_{.j} - \bar{Y}_{..})$$

Squaring both sides of Equation (4.27) results in

$$(4.28) \quad (Y_{ij} - \bar{Y}_{..})^2 = (Y_{ij} - \bar{Y}_{.j})^2 + (\bar{Y}_{.j} - \bar{Y}_{..})^2 + 2(Y_{ij} - \bar{Y}_{.j})(\bar{Y}_{.j} - \bar{Y}_{..})$$

If we sum over i and j for both sides of Equation (4.28), remembering the notational rules presented earlier, the result is

$$(4.29) \quad \sum_i^n \sum_j^a (Y_{ij} - \bar{Y}_{..})^2 = \sum_i^n \sum_j^a (Y_{ij} - \bar{Y}_{.j})^2 + n \sum_j^a (\bar{Y}_{.j} - \bar{Y}_{..})^2$$
$$+ 2 \sum_i^n \sum_j^a (Y_{ij} - \bar{Y}_{.j})(\bar{Y}_{.j} - \bar{Y}_{..})$$

The cross-products term, $\sum_i^n \sum_j^a (Y_{ij} - \bar{Y}_{.j})(\bar{Y}_{.j} - \bar{Y}_{..})$, equals zero. This can be proved by rearranging terms.

$$(4.30) \quad \sum_i^n \sum_j^a (Y_{ij} - \bar{Y}_{.j})(\bar{Y}_{.j} - \bar{Y}_{..}) = \sum_j \left[(\bar{Y}_{.j} - \bar{Y}_{..}) \sum_i (Y_{ij} - \bar{Y}_{.j}) \right]$$
$$= \sum_j (\bar{Y}_{.j} - \bar{Y}_{..})(0)$$
$$= 0$$

Consider Equation (4.29) again, ignoring the cross-products term which has been proven equal to zero. The term $\sum_i \sum_j (Y_{ij} - \overline{Y}_{..})^2$ is the numerator of the variance of all scores about the grand mean and will henceforth be referred to as the total sum of squares (SS_{tot}). The term $n \sum_j (\overline{Y}_{.j} - \overline{Y}_{..})^2$ is n times the numerator of the variance of the group means about the grand mean. This is usually (and ungrammatically) referred to as the between-groups sum of squares (SS_A). The term $\sum_i \sum_j (Y_{ij} - \overline{Y}_{.j})^2$ is the within-groups sum of squares ($SS_{S/A}$, the subscript representing "subjects within levels of A").

The formulas presented above define the quantities SS_{tot}, SS_A, and $SS_{S/A}$. In practice, they are clumsy to work with and it is helpful to transform these formulas into raw score formulas, simplifying the computations. This was previously done for the $SS_{S/A}$ in Chapter 3. Using the same general procedure, we can obtain raw score formulas for SS_{tot} and SS_A. From the development in Chapter 3,

$$(4.31) \qquad SS_{S/A} = \sum_i^n \sum_j^a Y_{ij}^2 - \sum_j^a \frac{\left(\sum_i^n Y_{ij} \right)^2}{n}$$

In the same manner,

$$
\begin{aligned}
SS_{tot} &= \sum_i^n \sum_j^a (Y_{ij} - \overline{Y}_{..})^2 \\
&= \sum_i^n \sum_j^a (Y_{ij}^2 + \overline{Y}_{..}^2 - 2Y_{ij}\overline{Y}_{..}) \\
&= \sum_j^a \left(\sum_i^n Y_{ij}^2 + n\overline{Y}_{..}^2 - 2\overline{Y}_{..} \sum_i^n Y_{ij} \right) \\
(4.32) \qquad &= \sum_i^n \sum_j^a Y_{ij}^2 + an\overline{Y}_{..}^2 - 2\overline{Y}_{..} \sum_i^n \sum_j^a Y_{ij} \\
&= \sum_i^n \sum_j^a Y_{ij}^2 + an \frac{\left(\sum_i^n \sum_j^a Y_{ij} \right)^2}{a^2 n^2} - 2 \frac{\left(\sum_i^n \sum_j^a Y_{ij} \right)\left(\sum_i^n \sum_j^a Y_{ij} \right)}{an} \\
&= \sum_i^n \sum_j^a Y_{ij}^2 - \frac{\left(\sum_i^n \sum_j^a Y_{ij} \right)^2}{an}
\end{aligned}
$$

and

$$SS_A = n \sum_j^a (\overline{Y}_{.j} - \overline{Y}_{..})^2$$

$$(4.33)$$

$$= n \sum_j^a (\overline{Y}_{.j}^2 + \overline{Y}_{..}^2 - 2\overline{Y}_{..}\overline{Y}_{.j})$$

$$= n \sum_j^a \bar{Y}_{.j}^2 + an \bar{Y}_{..}^2 - 2n \bar{Y}_{..} \sum_j^a \bar{Y}_{.j}$$

$$\left(\begin{matrix}4.33\\ \text{cont.}\end{matrix}\right) \quad = n \sum_j^a \frac{\left(\sum_i^n Y_{ij}\right)^2}{n^2} + an \frac{\left(\sum_i^n \sum_j^a Y_{ij}\right)^2}{a^2 n^2} - 2n \frac{\left(\sum_i^n \sum_j^a Y_{ij}\right)}{an} \sum_j^a \frac{\left(\sum_i^n Y_{ij}\right)}{n}$$

$$= \sum_j^a \frac{\left(\sum_i^n Y_{ij}\right)^2}{n} - \frac{\left(\sum_i^n \sum_j^a Y_{ij}\right)^2}{an}$$

4.3.2 Summarizing the analysis of variance

Table 4-1 summarizes much of the material presented thus far. The first column on the left contains the *sources of variance (SV)*. These follow from Equation (4.1), which states that the deviation of a score from the population mean consists of a treatment component (*A*) and a component due to individual differences (*S/A*).

The second column from the left in Table 4-1 contains the *df* associated with each *SV*. In deriving the expected mean squares (*EMS*), we noted that the *df* associated with the *A* effect are $a - 1$, those associated with *S/A* are $a(n - 1)$. Let us consider why this is so.

Suppose that we are asked to choose four numbers which sum to 100. The first three numbers chosen can be any three finite numbers. However, the fourth number must be 100 minus the sum of the first three numbers; only three numbers are chosen freely. For example, if the first three numbers chosen are 41, 3, and -18, the fourth number, k_4, must be $100 - 41 - 3 - (-18) = 74$. We characterize this situation by saying that there is one restriction on the data, causing us to lose one *df*. If it is required that the first two numbers chosen sum to 50 and all four sum to 100, there are two restrictions on the data and two *df* are thus lost. Only two numbers may be freely chosen. Analogous geometrical examples exist. Suppose that one is told to draw a triangle, the only restriction being that the figure must be a closed three-sided one. This restriction causes the loss of one *df*; while the first two sides may be of any length and form any angle, for example,

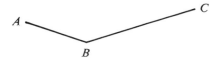

the third side must be a line connecting the points *A* and *C*. From these examples, we draw the generalization:

(4.34)   *df* = number of independent observations
= total number of observations minus the number of restrictions on the observations

TABLE 4-1
Analysis of variance for the completely randomized one-factor design

SV	df	SS	MS	EMS *	F
Total	$an - 1$	$\sum_i^n \sum_j^a Y_{ij}^2 - \dfrac{\left(\sum_i^n \sum_j^a Y_{ij}\right)^2}{an}$			
A (between groups)	$a - 1$	$\sum_j^a \dfrac{\left(\sum_i^n Y_{ij}\right)^2}{n} - \dfrac{\left(\sum_i^n \sum_j^a Y_{ij}\right)^2}{an}$	$\dfrac{SS_A}{a - 1}$	$\sigma_e^2 + n\theta_A^2$	$\dfrac{MS_A}{MS_{S/A}}$
S/A (within groups)	$a(n - 1)$	$\sum_i^n \sum_j^a Y_{ij}^2 - \sum_j^a \dfrac{\left(\sum_i^n Y_{ij}\right)^2}{n}$	$\dfrac{SS_{S/A}}{a(n - 1)}$	σ_e^2	

$$* \theta_A^2 = \frac{\sum (\mu_j - \mu)^2}{a - 1}$$

Next this line of reasoning is extended to statistical tests by noting that the estimation of a population parameter places a restriction on the data. The computation of the variance of a group of scores involves the summing of squared deviations about the group mean, imposing the restriction that $\sum_i Y_i = n\bar{Y}$, or $\sum_i (Y_i - \bar{Y}) = 0$. Consequently, the variance of a single group of scores is based on $n - 1$ *df*. In the computation of $MS_{S/A}$, a such quantities are calculated, resulting in $a(n - 1)$ *df*. In computing the MS_A we encounter the restriction that $\sum_j \bar{Y}_{\cdot j} = a\bar{Y}_{\cdot\cdot}$. We therefore have $a - 1$ *df*.

The role of *df* may be clearer if the above development for the F test is contrasted with that for the normal deviate, or z, test, where $z = (\bar{Y} - \mu)/(\sigma/\sqrt{n})$. Note that the population standard deviation is *known rather than estimated* and consequently there is no restriction on the data. The concept of *df* is not relevant to this test. An alternative way of viewing the relevance or irrelevance of *df* to a statistical test is to look at the distribution of the statistic. The shape of the normal curve is not a function of the number of observations, while that of the F distribution is affected by the numerator and denominator *df*.

The importance of *df* does not lie only in the fact that they are necessary components of the F ratio and determiners of the F distribution. These quantities provide a check on the SV in more complex designs where a source may be overlooked or the variance wrongly analyzed in some other manner. The check assumes that we have the correct *df* for each listed source, in which case they must sum to the total number of scores minus one. Furthermore, the *df* provide an alternative basis for arriving at raw score formulas for the SS. This point will be considered next.

The formulas for the SS were previously derived in Section 4.3.1. For more complex designs such a procedure is tedious, and it is therefore desirable to establish some simple rule which will make it possible to quickly set down SS formulas. The rule should generalize to all the terms of the analysis, and to analyses for any design. Such a rule follows if one notes the isomorphism existing between *df* and SS. There is a *df* for each squared quantity involved in the computations of SS, and any operation applied to the *df* is applied to the squared quantities. Consider the $SS_{S/A}$ first:

(a) Expand the *df* expression.

$$df_{S/A} = a(n - 1) = an - a$$

(b) Write an expression in terms of squared quantities which corresponds to the above result.

$$\sum_i^n \sum_j^a (\quad)^2 - \sum_j^a (\quad)^2$$

(c) Any summation operations which are not indicated outside the parentheses should be indicated within the parentheses. All indices of summation should appear somewhere in the formula.

$$\sum_{i}^{n} \sum_{j}^{a} (Y_{ij})^2 - \sum_{j}^{a} \left(\sum_{i}^{n} Y_{ij} \right)^2$$

(d) Divide each quantity by the number of scores within the parentheses.

$$SS_{S/A} = \sum_{i}^{n} \sum_{j}^{a} (Y_{ij})^2 - \frac{\sum_{j}^{a} \left(\sum_{i}^{n} Y_{ij} \right)^2}{n}$$

For the SS_A, the four steps are:

(a) $df_A = a - 1$

(b) $\sum_{j}^{a} (\quad)^2 - (\quad)^2$

(c) $\sum_{j}^{a} \left(\sum_{i}^{n} Y_{ij} \right)^2 - \left(\sum_{j}^{a} \sum_{i}^{n} Y_{ij} \right)^2$

(d) $SS_A = \dfrac{\sum_{j}^{a} \left(\sum_{i}^{n} Y_{ij} \right)^2}{n} - \dfrac{\left(\sum_{j}^{a} \sum_{i}^{n} Y_{ij} \right)^2}{an}$

The SS_{tot} is left as an exercise for the student.

The entries in the MS column of Table 4-1 are the ratios of SS to df. The MS_A is n times the variance of the group means about the grand mean, and the $MS_{S/A}$ is the average over groups of the variances of scores about group means. The EMS have been derived previously (Section 4.2.1) and have been shown to justify the use of the F ratio as a test statistic.

4.3.3 Numerical examples

Table 4-2 contains speeds of traversing a runway, in $ft./sec.$, for four groups of eight rats. All rats were allowed access to a solution of sucrose for 20 sec. at the end of each run. The groups differed with respect to the percentage of sucrose in the solution.

The first step in the analysis is to obtain $\sum_i Y_{ij}$ and $\sum_i Y_{ij}^2$ for each group, i.e., for each value of j. The two sums can be obtained simultaneously on most desk calculators. They provide the basic ingredients for both the test of homogeneity of variance and the F test of the null hypothesis that the μ_j are equal. We first examine the null hypothesis that the variances are homogeneous.

The variances are computed according to Equation (4.35), and are entered in Table 4-2.

(4.35)
$$s_j^2 = \frac{\sum_i Y_{ij}^2 - \left(\sum_i Y_{ij} \right)^2 / n}{n - 1}$$

As an example of the computations, $s_1^2 = [86.54 - (24)^2/8]/7 = 2.08$. In practice, we would not statistically test the homogeneity of variance assumption with the present data. The variances are clearly not dissimilar enough

2.4
2.4
5.4
.56

-2   .0. 8

or four groups of rats in a runway study

	Per Cent Sucrose in Water			
	8	16	32	64
	1.4	3.2	6.2	5.8
	2.0	6.8	3.1	6.6
	3.2	5.0	3.2	6.5
	1.4	2.5	4.0	5.9
	2.3	6.1	4.5	5.9
	4.0	4.8	6.4	3.0
	5.0	4.6	4.4	5.9
	4.7	4.2	4.1	5.6
$\sum_i Y_{ij} = 24.0$		37.2	35.9	45.2
$\bar{Y}_j = 3.00$		4.65	4.50	5.65
$\sum_i Y_{ij}^2 = 86.54$		186.78	171.67	264.24
$S_{y_i}^2 = 2.08$		1.97	1.51	1.27

to markedly influence the distribution of mean squares. However, for illustrative purposes, we will consider two previously mentioned tests of

$$H_0: \sigma_1 = \sigma_2 = \sigma_3 = \sigma_4$$

(a) *Hartley's test.* Compute the statistic F_{max}, the ratio of the largest to the smallest group variance. In our example, $F_{max} = 2.08/1.27 = 1.64$. The distribution of F_{max} depends upon a, the number of treatments, and $n - 1$, the number of df upon which each variance is based. These parameters have the values 4 and 7 in the present set of data. Turning to Table A-6 in the Appendix, we find that for our parameter values F_{max} must be equal to or greater than 8.44 in order to allow rejection of the homogeneity of variance assumption at the .05 significance level. Clearly, the assumption may be accepted.

(b) *Cochran's test.* Compute the statistic C, the largest variance divided by the sum of the variances. In our example, $C = 2.08/6.83 = .305$. The parameters of the sampling distribution of C are a and $n - 1$, as they were for the distribution of F_{max}. Turning to Table A-7, we find that the value of C required for significance at the 5 per cent level is .5365. Again the assumption of homogeneity of variance is tenable.

Now we may proceed to the actual analysis of variance. According to Equation (4.32), $SS_{tot} = \sum_i \sum_j Y^2 - (\sum_i \sum_j Y)^2/an$. Since terms like $(\sum_i \sum_j Y)^2/an$ appear in many components of all analyses of variance, a special notation is used. Such terms are called *correction terms* and are designated by C, where

$$(4.36) \qquad C = \frac{\text{(sum of all scores in the data matrix)}^2}{\text{total number of scores}}$$

In our example,

$$C = \frac{(24.0 + 37.2 + 35.9 + 45.2)^2}{32} = 632.79$$

and

$$SS_{\text{tot}} = 86.54 + 186.78 + 171.67 + 264.24 - 632.79$$
$$= 709.23 - 632.79$$
$$= 76.44$$

According to Equation (4.33),

$$SS_A = \frac{\sum\limits_{j}\left(\sum\limits_{i} Y\right)^2}{n} - C$$

$$= \frac{(24.0)^2 + (37.2)^2 + (35.9)^2 + (45.2)^2}{8} - 632.79$$

$$= 661.46 - 632.79$$

$$= 28.67$$

The $SS_{S/A}$ may be obtained as the residual variability,

$$SS_{S/A} = SS_{\text{tot}} - SS_A$$
$$(4.37) \qquad\qquad = 76.44 - 28.67$$
$$= 47.77$$

and, as a check, by pooling the sums of squares for each group,

$$SS_{S/A} = \sum_{j}\left[\sum_{i} Y^2 - \frac{\left(\sum\limits_{i} Y\right)^2}{n}\right]$$

$$(4.38) \qquad = \left(86.54 - \frac{(24.0)^2}{8}\right) + \cdots + \left(264.24 - \frac{(45.2)^2}{8}\right)$$

$$= 47.77$$

The first procedure corresponds to $(an - 1) - (a - 1)$ df, the second to $(n - 1) + \cdots + (n - 1)$. The result in both instances is $a(n - 1)$; correspondingly, the two computations on SS should yield identical results.

The MS and the F ratio are now easily computed.

$$MS_A = \frac{SS_A}{a - 1} \qquad\qquad MS_{S/A} = \frac{SS_{S/A}}{a(n - 1)}$$

$$= \frac{28.67}{3} \qquad\qquad\qquad = \frac{47.77}{28}$$

$$= 9.56 \qquad\qquad\qquad\quad = 1.71$$

$$F = \frac{MS_A}{MS_{S/A}}$$

$$= \frac{9.56}{1.71}$$

$$= 5.59$$

The results of our analysis are summarized in Table 4-3. Turning to Table A-5, we find that for 3 and 28 *df* an *F* of 4.57 is required for significance at the .01 level. Since our computed *F* exceeds this critical value, we feel justified in concluding that the treatment population means differ. The statement "$p < .01$" indicates that if H_0 is true, the observed *F* of 5.59 will occur in less than 1 per cent of the replications of the experiment.

TABLE 4-3

Analysis of variance for data from a completely randomized one-factor experiment

SV	df	SS	MS	F
Total	31	76.44		
A	3	28.67	9.56	5.59 *
S/A	28	47.77	1.71	
				* $p < .01$

In handling actual experimental data, the analysis would not be concluded at this point. Many interesting questions are still unanswered. Do all four means differ significantly from one another? Or are the 16 per cent and 32 per cent treatments essentially equivalent as a quick look at the data suggests? If the treatment means are plotted as a function of concentration, what type of equation best describes the relationship? In order to deal with such questions a number of additional conceptual and computational factors must be considered. Treatment of these questions is reserved for Chapters 13 and 14.

Throughout this chapter the presentation has been restricted to the case where *n* is equal for all groups, since both derivations of expectations and computations in the analysis of variance are simpler under this condition. This restriction will now be removed in order to present computations for the unequal *n* case, in which n_j, the number of subjects in the *j*th treatment group, varies over levels of *j*. Before considering the computations, we note that the analysis of variance model is fundamentally the same as previously; the major difference in the theoretical development is that now

(4.39) $$E(MS_A) = \sigma_e^2 + \frac{\sum_j n_j(\mu_j - \mu)^2}{a - 1}$$

When n_j is constant over j, we have the previously presented EMS. In both cases, the F ratio involves the MS_A and the $MS_{S/A}$.

Table 4-4 contains data for the runway experiment previously analyzed, with some scores randomly discarded from the data matrix of Table 4-2. The Hartley and Cochran tests of homogeneity of variance are performed as previously; the only difference is that the largest value of n_j (8, in this case) is

TABLE 4-4

Data for the runway experiment with unequal n

| | Per Cent Sucrose in Water | | | |
	8	16	32	64
	1.4	3.2	6.2	5.8
	1.4	5.0	3.2	6.6
	5.0	2.5	4.5	6.5
	2.0	6.4	4.4	5.9
	2.3	4.8	4.1	5.9
		4.2		3.0
				5.9
				5.6
$\sum_i Y_{ij} =$	12.1	26.1	22.4	45.2
$n_j =$	5	6	5	8
$\bar{Y}_j =$	2.42	4.35	4.48	5.65
$\sum_i Y_{ij}^2 =$	38.21	123.13	105.10	264.24
$S_{y_j}^2 =$	2.23	1.92	1.19	1.27

used to enter the F_{max} and C tables. For the Hartley test, $F_{max} = 2.23/1.11 = 2.35$, which again falls far short of the critical value required for significance at the .01 level. In the case of Cochran's test, $C = 2.23/6.45 = .382$, which also supports the assumption of homogeneity of variance. We proceed to the analysis of variance.

Following Equation (4.36), we compute the correction term,

$$C = \frac{(12.1 + 26.1 + 22.4 + 45.2)^2}{(5 + 6 + 5 + 8)}$$

$$= \frac{(105.8)^2}{24}$$

$$= 466.40$$

The SS_{tot} are now computed as previously:

$$SS_{tot} = 38.21 + 123.13 + 105.10 + 264.24 - C$$
$$= 64.28$$

The revised equation for the SS_A for the unequal n case is

(4.40)
$$SS_A = \sum_j \frac{\left(\sum_i Y\right)^2}{n_j} - C$$

Therefore, we have

$$SS_A = \frac{(13.1)^2}{5} + \frac{(26.1)^2}{6} + \frac{(22.4)^2}{5} + \frac{(45.2)^2}{8} - C$$

$$= 32.15$$

The $SS_{S/A}$ may again be computed as a residual.

$$SS_{S/A} = SS_{tot} - SS_A$$
$$= 32.13$$

The mean squares are then computed as before, and F is again the ratio of mean squares.

$$MS_A = \frac{32.15}{3} \qquad MS_{S/A} = \frac{32.13}{(4 + 5 + 4 + 7)}$$

$$= 10.72 \qquad = 1.61$$

$$F = 6.66$$

Entering Table A-5 with 3 and 20 df, we find that the critical value at the 1 per cent level, 4.94, is again exceeded by the obtained F. The analysis is summarized in Table 4-5.

TABLE 4-5

Analysis of variance for data from a completely randomized one-factor experiment with unequal n

SV	df	SS	MS	F
Total	23	64.28		
A	3	32.15	10.72	6.66 *
S/A	20	32.13	1.61	
				*$p < .01$

4.4 POWER OF THE F TEST

The power of the F test is usually plotted against an alternative measured by ϕ, where ϕ^2 is an F ratio based on the population; i.e., it is n times the variance among treatment population means divided by the population error variance. Thus,

(4.41)
$$\phi^2 = \frac{n \sum_j (\mu_j - \mu)^2 / a}{\sigma_e^2}$$

Turning to Table A-8 in the Appendix, we see that power is graphed as a function of ϕ for several combinations of df and α levels. Note that power increases with increasing values of ϕ, df_1, df_2, and α. These relationships have been previously discussed in Chapter 2. Note also that for any constant variance among the treatment population means, power will increase as error variance decreases, for ϕ will vary inversely with σ, as is apparent from Equation (4.41).

The power functions of Table A-8 provide a basis for deciding on the number of subjects to be included in the experiment. For appropriate use of the table, we require that the following be selected or estimated:

(a) *The α level.* This reflects our willingness to risk Type I errors.

(b) *The level of power.* This is the probability of rejecting a false null hypothesis. This value is not selected in the same way that α is, for power varies as a function of ϕ and the exact value of this latter quantity is unknown. However, one can select a probability of rejecting H_0, given that ϕ is equal to or greater than some critical value, ϕ'.

(c) *The error variance, σ_e^2.* Previous experimentation or a pilot study with the dependent variable of interest will provide an estimate of σ_e^2. If several estimates are available, the largest should be chosen. The larger the value of σ_e^2, the larger will be the value of n required to achieve a given level of power.

(d) *The critical variance among treatment population means.* This is the minimum value of $\sum (\mu_j - \mu)^2/a$ that it is important to detect.

The following example should illustrate how the above factors combine to permit a selection of n. We assume

$$a = 4$$
$$\alpha = .01$$
$$\text{power} = .80$$
$$\sigma_e^2 = 200$$

$$\frac{\sum (\mu_j - \mu)^2}{4} = 125$$

The last figure was arrived at by assuming that it was important to reject H_0 if the successive μ_j were ten or more units apart. Then,

$$\mu_1 = \mu - 15$$
$$\mu_2 = \mu - 5$$
$$\mu_3 = \mu + 5$$
$$\mu_4 = \mu + 15$$

and $\sum (\mu_j - \mu)^2/4 = (1/4)[(-15)^2 + (-5)^2 + (5)^2 + (15)^2] = 125$. We may now calculate $\phi' = \sqrt{n(125)/200} = .79\sqrt{n}$. We require a value of n such that the quantities $\phi' = .79\sqrt{n}$, $\alpha = .01$, $df_1 = 3$, and $df_2 = 4(n-1)$ result in power $= .80$. Turning to the chart for $df_1 = 3$ and $\alpha = .01$, we consider various values of n. When $n = 8$, ϕ' is approximately equal to 2.2, and $df_2 = 28$. The curve for $df_1 = 3$, $df_2 = 28$, and $\alpha = .01$ crosses the point

$\phi' = 2.2$, power $= .80$. Therefore, we decide on eight subjects for each group.

4.5 CONCLUDING REMARKS

Direct applications of the one-dimensional design are infrequent in psychological research. Many studies involve repeated measurements on subjects, necessitating the parceling out of subject effects in addition to treatment effects. Even studies in which there are no repeated measurements usually involve more than one treatment variable. Nevertheless, the material in the present chapter is extremely important. Within the context of a relatively simple design, we have considered notation, derivations, computations, null hypothesis testing, and the model underlying the use of the F test, all of which are involved in subsequent chapters. A thorough comprehension of the material of the present chapter will facilitate understanding of the more complicated designs and analyses of subsequent chapters.

EXERCISES

4.1 In deriving *EMS* we assume that $\sum_j^a \alpha_j = 0$. However, we do not assume that $\sum_i^n \sum_j^a \epsilon_{ij} = 0$, but rather that

$$E\left(\sum_i^n \sum_j^a \epsilon_{ij} = 0 \right)$$

Why does this distinction between α and ϵ_{ij} exist? How would the situation change if the a levels of the variable A were randomly selected from a population of levels?

4.2 Show the steps in going from Equation (4.4) to Equation (4.5), using the procedures of Chapter 3.

4.3 Prove that the $SS_{S/A}$ is unchanged by the addition of a constant to all the scores of any one group. What does this imply about the relationship of $SS_{S/A}$ and SS_A?

4.4 Prove Equations (4.14c) and (4.14e).

4.5 Do analyses of variance on the following sets of data:

(a)

	A_1	A_2	A_3
	28	38	64
	23	39	73
	21	57	61
	38	36	48
	38	38	72
	49	48	52
	28	52	54
	33	40	60
	34	39	54
	29	45	60

(b)	A_1	A_2	A_3	A_4	A_5
	24	48	42	96	73
	07	91	82	67	81
	46	63	75	88	33
	45	69	76	24	44
	97	26		92	94
		22		83	77
		45			60
					89
					25

4.6 In an attempt to determine the effect of time in therapy upon schizophrenic patients in a state hospital, the clinical staff agree on the following experiment. n subjects will be individually treated on a daily basis for one year, n subjects will be treated for six months, and n others will receive no special therapy. As a measure of the success of therapy, the clinicians will use a 100-point scale which differentially weights several aspects of personality and which has proven sensitive to experimental manipulations in other studies. They agree that each six months of the individual therapy should produce a mean gain of at least ten points for the technique to be worth the staff's time. They set $\alpha = .01$, $\beta = .10$, and on the basis of previous research estimate σ_e^2 to be 225. How many patients are required for the study?

SUPPLEMENTARY READINGS

A brief introduction to the theory of least squares is available to the mathematically sophisticated reader in

KEMPTHORNE, O., *Design and Analysis of Experiments*. New York: Wiley, 1952.

In 1947, the Biometrics society published a classic issue containing discussions of the assumptions of analysis of variance, the consequences of violating these assumptions, and what to do about transforming data that do not meet the assumptions. The three papers are

BARTLETT, M. S., "The Use of Transformations," *Biometrics*, 3:39–52 (1947).
COCHRAN, W. G., "Some Consequences When Assumptions for the Analysis of Variance Are Not Satisfied," *Biometrics*, 3:22–38 (1947).
EISENHART, C., "The Assumptions Underlying the Analysis of Variance," *Biometrics*, 3:1–21 (1947).

An excellent discussion of degrees of freedom is provided by

WALKER, H. M., "Degrees of Freedom," *Journal of Educational Psychology*, 31:253–269 (1940).

COMPLETELY RANDOMIZED

MULTI-FACTOR DESIGNS

5

5.1 INTRODUCTION

The modern theory of experimental design permits the experimenter to study a number of independent variables, or factors, within the same experiment. This has two major advantages. It is efficient, saving the time and effort of the experimenter, and, equally important, it permits him to investigate the joint effects of variables. This chapter deals with the analysis of data from completely randomized designs involving more than a single factor. In such designs subjects are randomly assigned to combinations of treatment levels. The advantages and disadvantages of the completely randomized one-factor design were cited in the preceding chapter; that discussion is relevant for the designs of this chapter as well. It is again assumed that the levels of each variable have been arbitrarily, rather than randomly, selected.

As an example of the type of design which will be presented, consider the following experiment. We are interested in comparing the effects of four different amounts of reward, of three different delays of reward, and of the 12 combinations of amount and delay upon discrimination learning in rats. Each of 120 rats is randomly assigned to one of the 12 combinations of amount and delay of reward, with the restriction that there be exactly ten rats exposed to each combination. Ten rats might receive one food pellet 1 sec. after a correct response, ten rats might receive two food pellets 3 sec. after a correct response, and so on. In general, such a design involves the random assignment of n (10, in our example) subjects to each of ab ($4 \times 3 = 12$, in our example) combinations of treatment levels. The layout of such a design is presented in Table 5-1. The first subscript, represented by i in the general case, indexes the subjects within each treatment cell and varies from 1 to n. The second subscript, j, indexes the levels of the independent variable A and varies from 1 to a. The third subscript, k, indexes the levels of the variable B and varies from 1 to b. Thus, there are a levels of A, b levels of B, ab cells corresponding to the ab treatment combinations, with abn scores, n in each cell. In this chapter, we consider the analysis of variance for this design and for similar designs which differ only in the number of independent variables.

5.2 A MODEL FOR THE COMPLETELY RANDOMIZED TWO-FACTOR DESIGN

The ab experimental groups of n subjects may be considered as ab random samples, one from each of ab treatment populations. These treatment populations are assumed to have been drawn from the same infinitely large parent population; thus, any differences among the ab distributions are attributable solely to differences among the treatment effects. The mean of the treatment population defined by the jth level of treatment A and the kth level of treatment B is μ_{jk}. The mean of the population consisting of all scores obtained under the jth level of A is $\mu_j = \sum_k^b \mu_{jk}/b$. The mean of all scores obtained under the kth level of B is $\mu_k = \sum_j^a \mu_{jk}/a$. The mean of all scores in the treatment population is $\mu = \sum_{jk}^{ab} \mu_{jk}/ab$. Equivalently, μ is the mean of the parent population prior to the establishment of the treatment populations.

The observed data are related to the population parameters by the following equation:

$$(5.1) \qquad Y_{ijk} = \mu + \alpha_j + \beta_k + (\alpha\beta)_{jk} + \epsilon_{ijk}$$

where Y_{ijk} is the score of the ith subject in the jth treatment level of A and the kth treatment level of B,

$$\alpha_j = \mu_j - \mu, \text{ the } \textit{main effect} \text{ of treatment } A_j$$
$$\beta_k = \mu_k - \mu, \text{ the } \textit{main effect} \text{ of treatment } B_k$$
$$(\alpha\beta)_{jk} = \mu_{jk} - \mu_j - \mu_k + \mu, \text{ the } \textit{interaction effect} \text{ of treatments } A_j \text{ and } B_k$$
$$\epsilon_{ijk} = Y_{ijk} - [\mu + \alpha_j + \beta_k + (\alpha\beta)_{jk}]$$
$$= Y_{ijk} - \mu_{jk}, \text{ the error component}$$

The quantities involved in Equation (5.1) are similar to those encountered in Chapter 4, with the exception of the interaction, which therefore merits further definition. Note that

$$(5.2) \qquad (\mu_{jk} - \mu_j - \mu_k + \mu) = (\mu_{jk} - \mu) - (\mu_j - \mu) - (\mu_k - \mu)$$

In words, the interaction effect, $(\alpha\beta)_{jk}$, is the combined effect of the jth level of A and the kth level of B, which cannot be accounted for by α_j and β_k, the independent effects of A_j and B_k. The effects, α_j and β_k, are usually referred to as *main effects* in contrast with the *interaction effect*, $(\alpha\beta)_{jk}$. The inter-

TABLE 5-1

Data matrix for a two-factor design

	B_1	B_2	$\cdots$	B_k	$\cdots$	B_b
	Y_{111}	Y_{112}		Y_{11k}		Y_{11b}
	Y_{211}	Y_{212}		Y_{21k}		Y_{21b}
A_1	$\vdots$	$\vdots$		$\vdots$		$\vdots$
	Y_{i11}	Y_{i12}		Y_{i1k}		Y_{i1b}
	$\vdots$	$\vdots$		$\vdots$		$\vdots$
	Y_{n11}	Y_{n12}		Y_{n1k}		Y_{n1b}
	Y_{121}	Y_{122}		Y_{12k}		Y_{12b}
	Y_{221}	Y_{222}		Y_{22k}		Y_{22b}
A_2	$\vdots$	$\vdots$		$\vdots$		$\vdots$
	Y_{i21}	Y_{i22}		Y_{i2k}		Y_{i2b}
	$\vdots$	$\vdots$		$\vdots$		$\vdots$
$\vdots$						
	Y_{1j1}	Y_{1j2}		Y_{1jk}		Y_{1jb}
	Y_{2j1}	Y_{2j2}		Y_{2jk}		Y_{2jb}
A_j	$\vdots$	$\vdots$		$\vdots$		$\vdots$
	Y_{ij1}	Y_{ij2}		Y_{ijk}		Y_{ijb}
	$\vdots$	$\vdots$		$\vdots$		$\vdots$
$\vdots$						
	Y_{1a1}	Y_{1a2}		Y_{1ak}		Y_{1ab}
	Y_{2a1}	Y_{2a2}		Y_{2ak}		Y_{2ab}
	$\vdots$	$\vdots$		$\vdots$		$\vdots$
A_a	Y_{ia1}	Y_{ia2}		Y_{iak}		Y_{iab}
	$\vdots$	$\vdots$		$\vdots$		$\vdots$

action effect and its relation to main effects will be considered further in Section 5.3.2.

It follows from Equation (5.1) that the variability in our observed data matrix (Table 5-1) has several sources. These are:

(a) α_j, *the effect of treatment* A_j. This effect is a constant component of all scores obtained under A_j, but may vary over levels of j. If the a levels of A are arbitrarily selected as assumed, they exhaust the population of levels of A and therefore $\sum_j \alpha_j = 0$. One null hypothesis which will be tested is that

$$\alpha_1 = \alpha_2 = \cdots = \alpha_j = \cdots = \alpha_a = 0$$

(b) β_k, *the effect of treatment B_k.* This effect is a constant component of all scores obtained under B_k, but may vary over levels of k. We assume that $\sum_k \beta_k = 0$. We will test the null hypothesis that

$$\beta_1 = \beta_2 = \cdots = \beta_k = \cdots = \beta_b = 0$$

(c) $(\alpha\beta)_{jk}$, *the interaction effect of A_j and B_k.* This effect is a constant component of all scores obtained under A_j and B_k, but may vary over the levels of j and k. We assume that $\sum_j \sum_k (\alpha\beta)_{jk} = 0$. The relevant null hypothesis is that

$$(\alpha\beta)_{12} = (\alpha\beta)_{13} = \cdots = (\alpha\beta)_{jk} = \cdots = (\alpha\beta)_{ab} = 0$$

(d) ϵ_{ijk}, *the error component* which is not accounted for by the systematic manipulation of the variables A and B. This is the only source of variance within the cells that correspond to the treatment combinations. We assume that the ϵ_{ijk} are independently and normally distributed with mean of zero and variance σ_e^2 within each treatment population defined by a combination of levels of A and B.

On the basis of the model presented, we may derive parameter estimates, expected mean squares, and F tests of the null hypotheses stated above. The development is similar to that of Section 4.2.1 for the one-factor design. The relevant parameter estimates are:

$$\hat{\mu} = \frac{\sum_i \sum_j \sum_k Y_{ijk}}{abn}$$

$$= \bar{Y}_{...}$$

$$\hat{\mu}_j = \frac{\sum_i \sum_k Y_{ijk}}{bn}$$

(5.3) $$= \bar{Y}_{.j.}$$

$$\hat{\mu}_k = \frac{\sum_i \sum_j Y_{ijk}}{an}$$

$$= \bar{Y}_{..k}$$

$$\hat{\mu}_{jk} = \frac{\sum_i Y_{ijk}}{n}$$

$$= \bar{Y}_{.jk}$$

The expected mean squares and F tests will be considered in the next section as part of the general discussion of the analysis of variance.

5.3 THE ANALYSIS OF VARIANCE FOR THE COMPLETELY RANDOMIZED TWO-FACTOR DESIGN

The sources of variability in our data are specified by Equation (5.1). A general way of proceeding to obtain the appropriate sums of squares is to substitute parameter estimates for parameters in the basic equation. Thus, beginning with Equation (5.1),

$$Y_{ijk} = \mu + \alpha_j + \beta_k + (\alpha\beta)_{jk} + \epsilon_{ijk}$$

and substituting from Equation (5.3), we arrive at the following identity:

(5.4)
$$Y_{ijk} = \bar{Y}_{...} + (\bar{Y}_{.j.} - \bar{Y}_{...}) + (\bar{Y}_{..k} - \bar{Y}_{...})$$
$$+ (\bar{Y}_{.jk} - \bar{Y}_{.j.} - \bar{Y}_{..k} + \bar{Y}_{...}) + (Y_{ijk} - \bar{Y}_{.jk})$$

Subtracting $\bar{Y}_{...}$ from both sides of Equation (5.4) and squaring both sides yields

(5.5)
$$(Y_{ijk} - \bar{Y}_{...})^2 = (\bar{Y}_{.j.} - \bar{Y}_{...})^2 + (\bar{Y}_{..k} - \bar{Y}_{...})^2$$
$$+ (\bar{Y}_{.jk} - \bar{Y}_{.j.} - \bar{Y}_{..k} + \bar{Y}_{...})^2$$
$$+ (Y_{ijk} - \bar{Y}_{.jk})^2 + 2(\bar{Y}_{.j.} - \bar{Y}_{...})(\bar{Y}_{..k} - \bar{Y}_{...})$$
$$+ 2(\bar{Y}_{.j.} - \bar{Y}_{...})(\bar{Y}_{.jk} - \bar{Y}_{.j.} - \bar{Y}_{..k} + \bar{Y}_{...})$$
$$+ 2(\bar{Y}_{.j.} - \bar{Y}_{...})(Y_{ijk} - \bar{Y}_{.jk})$$
$$+ 2(\bar{Y}_{..k} - \bar{Y}_{...})(\bar{Y}_{.jk} - \bar{Y}_{.j.} - \bar{Y}_{..k} + \bar{Y}_{...})$$
$$+ 2(\bar{Y}_{..k} - \bar{Y}_{...})(Y_{ijk} - \bar{Y}_{.jk})$$
$$+ 2(\bar{Y}_{.jk} - \bar{Y}_{.j.} - \bar{Y}_{..k} + \bar{Y}_{...})(Y_{ijk} - \bar{Y}_{.jk})$$

After summing over the indices, i, j, and k, the cross-product terms vanish (the proof of this will be left to the student). They will therefore be ignored in the remainder of this derivation. Summing over i, we obtain

(5.6)
$$\sum_i^n (Y_{ijk} - \bar{Y}_{...})^2 = n(\bar{Y}_{.j.} - \bar{Y}_{...})^2 + n(\bar{Y}_{..k} - \bar{Y}_{...})^2$$
$$+ n(\bar{Y}_{.jk} - \bar{Y}_{.j.} - \bar{Y}_{..k} + \bar{Y}_{...})^2 + \sum_i (Y_{ijk} - \bar{Y}_{.jk})^2$$

Next, summing over j, the result is

(5.7)
$$\sum_i^n \sum_j^a (Y_{ijk} - \bar{Y}_{...})^2 = n \sum_j^a (\bar{Y}_{.j.} - \bar{Y}_{...})^2 + an(\bar{Y}_{..k} - \bar{Y}_{...})^2$$
$$+ n \sum_j^a (\bar{Y}_{.jk} - \bar{Y}_{.j.} - \bar{Y}_{..k} + \bar{Y}_{...})^2 + \sum_i^n \sum_j^a (Y_{ijk} - \bar{Y}_{.jk})^2$$

Finally, summing over k, we have

$$\sum_i^n \sum_j^a \sum_k^b (Y_{ijk} - \bar{Y}_{...})^2 = bn \sum_j^a (\bar{Y}_{.j.} - \bar{Y}_{...})^2$$

(sum of squares total, SS_{tot})   (sum of squares for A, SS_A)

$$+ an \sum_k^b (\bar{Y}_{..k} - \bar{Y}_{...})^2$$

(sum of squares for B, SS_B)

(5.8)

$$+ n \sum_j^a \sum_k^b (\bar{Y}_{.jk} - \bar{Y}_{.j.} - \bar{Y}_{..k} + \bar{Y}_{...})^2$$

(sum of squares for interaction, SS_{AB})

$$+ \sum_i^n \sum_j^a \sum_k^b (Y_{ijk} - \bar{Y}_{.jk})^2$$

(sum of squares within groups, $SS_{S/AB}$)

Equation (5.8) states that the total variability is to be partitioned into four parts: variability due to A, variability due to B, variability due to the joint effect of A and B, and variability due to error. This analysis is not the only one possible, but rather the one appropriate for our particular model [Equation (5.1)]. For example, if we were to assume the absence of interaction, our model would assert that

$$(5.9) \qquad Y_{ijk} = \mu + \alpha_j + \beta_k + \epsilon_{ijk}$$

and the identity which forms the basis for our analysis would be

$$(5.10) \qquad (Y_{ijk} - \bar{Y}_{...}) = (\bar{Y}_{.j.} - \bar{Y}_{...}) + (\bar{Y}_{..k} - \bar{Y}_{...}) \\ + (Y_{ijk} - \bar{Y}_{.j.} - \bar{Y}_{..k} + \bar{Y}_{...})$$

In this case, the total variability would be partitioned into three parts due to the A effect, the B effect, and error variability. The point of these comments is that the analysis of variance is not an arbitrary set of computations, but a logical consequence of the experimenter's assumptions about the relationships between his data and the parameters of the population from which he has sampled.

5.3.1 Summarizing the analysis of variance

Table 5-2 summarizes the analysis of variance for the completely randomized two-factor design. The source of variance (SV) column reflects the partitioning described above and, as was stated, is a direct consequence of Equation (5.1). For the A main effect there are $a - 1$ df because of the requirement that the sum of the deviations of the a treatment means about the grand mean must be zero. For a similar reason, the df for the B main effect are $b - 1$. In the case of the AB interaction, we begin with $ab - 1$ df, because of the requirement that the sum of the deviations of the ab cell means. about the grand mean must be zero. Removal of the variability among the cell means that is due to the A and B effects causes the loss of $a - 1$ and $b - 1$ df. Because of the removal of this variability, the row and column means of Table 5-1 are no longer free to vary, and the corresponding df are lost. Thus, restrictions placed on the variability of the cell means by the grand mean and by the removal of the A and B effects yield

$$(5.11) \qquad \begin{aligned} df_{AB} &= ab - 1 - (a - 1) - (b - 1) \\ &= (a - 1)(b - 1) \end{aligned}$$

The df associated with S/AB can be viewed as the result of taking the deviations of n scores about their cell mean, yielding $n - 1$ df, then summing this result over the ab cells, yielding $ab(n - 1)$ df. Alternatively, noting that the variability due to S/AB is a residual from the total after removal of the variability due to A, B, and AB, we have

$$(5.12) \qquad \begin{aligned} df_{S/AB} &= abn - 1 - (a - 1) - (b - 1) - (a - 1)(b - 1) \\ &= ab(n - 1) \end{aligned}$$

TABLE 5-2

Analysis of variance for a two-factor design

SV	df	SS	MS	EMS	F
Total	$abn - 1$	$\sum\limits_i^n \sum\limits_j^a \sum\limits_k^b Y^2 - C\,{}^*$			
A	$a - 1$	$\dfrac{\sum\limits_j^a \left(\sum\limits_i^n \sum\limits_k^b Y\right)^2}{nb} - C$	$\dfrac{SS_A}{a-1}$	$\sigma_e^2 + nb\theta_A^2$	$\dfrac{MS_A}{MS_{S/AB}}$
B	$b - 1$	$\dfrac{\sum\limits_k^b \left(\sum\limits_i^n \sum\limits_j^a Y\right)^2}{na} - C$	$\dfrac{SS_B}{b-1}$	$\sigma_e^2 + na\theta_B^2$	$\dfrac{MS_B}{MS_{S/AB}}$
AB	$(a-1)(b-1)$	$\dfrac{\sum\limits_j^a \sum\limits_k^b \left(\sum\limits_i^n Y\right)^2}{n} - C - SS_A - SS_B$	$\dfrac{SS_{AB}}{(a-1)(b-1)}$	$\sigma_e^2 + n\theta_{AB}^2$	$\dfrac{MS_{AB}}{MS_{S/AB}}$
S/AB	$ab(n-1)$	$SS_{\text{tot}} - SS_A - SS_B - SS_{AB}$	$\dfrac{SS_{S/AB}}{ab(n-1)}$	σ_e^2	

$$* C = \frac{\left(\sum\limits_i^n \sum\limits_j^a \sum\limits_k^b Y\right)^2}{nab}$$

Test $H_0: \alpha_1 = \alpha_2 = \cdots = \alpha_a = 0$

$F = MS_A / MS_{S/AB}$

87

As a third alternative, we note that the total variability among scores must be due either to variability among cell means or variability among scores in the same cell. Therefore, the variability within cells equals the total minus the between-cells variability, or

(5.13)
$$df_{S/AB} = abn - 1 - (ab - 1)$$
$$= ab(n - 1)$$

The computational formulas in the SS column may be derived from the components of Equation (5.8), as was done in Chapter 4. Each term is expanded, the summations are carried out, raw score formulas are substituted for the means, and the expressions are simplified as far as possible. However, this lengthy procedure can be bypassed by again noting the isomorphism of df and squared quantities. The term $a - 1$ in the df column suggests the sum of a squared quantities minus the correction term, or

$$\sum_{j}^{a} (\ )^2 - C$$

Remembering that any summations not represented outside the parentheses must appear inside, we have

$$\sum_{j}^{a} \left(\sum_{i}^{n} \sum_{k}^{b} Y_{ijk} \right)^2 - C$$

Finally, we divide by the number of scores inside the parentheses, yielding

(5.14)
$$SS_A = \frac{\sum_{j}^{a} \left(\sum_{i}^{n} \sum_{k}^{b} Y_{ijk} \right)^2}{bn} - C$$

The SS_B follow in a similar manner. Two equivalent formulas are available for SS_{AB}. Expanding $(a - 1)(b - 1)$ yields $ab - a - b + 1$, which suggests

(5.15)
$$SS_{AB} = \frac{\sum_{j}^{a} \sum_{k}^{b} \left(\sum_{i}^{n} Y_{ijk} \right)^2}{n} - \frac{\sum_{j}^{a} \left(\sum_{i}^{n} \sum_{k}^{b} Y_{ijk} \right)^2}{bn} - \frac{\sum_{k}^{b} \left(\sum_{i}^{n} \sum_{j}^{a} Y_{ijk} \right)^2}{an} + C$$

Since the df_{AB} also equals $(ab - 1) - (a - 1) - (b - 1)$, we might have

(5.16)
$$SS_{AB} = \frac{\sum_{j}^{a} \sum_{k}^{b} \left(\sum_{i}^{n} Y_{ijk} \right)^2}{n} - C - SS_A - SS_B$$

The $ab(n - 1)$ df suggest calculating $SS_{S/AB}$ by computing a sum of squared deviations for each cell, and then pooling over cells. More simply, $abn - ab$ suggests

(5.17)
$$SS_{S/AB} = \sum_{i}^{n} \sum_{j}^{a} \sum_{k}^{b} Y_{ijk}^2 - \frac{\sum_{j}^{a} \sum_{k}^{b} \left(\sum_{i}^{n} Y_{ijk} \right)^2}{n}$$

Alternatively, remembering that

$$df_{S/AB} = (abn - 1) - (a - 1) - (b - 1) - (a - 1)(b - 1),$$

we have

(5.18) $$SS_{S/AB} = \sum_i^n \sum_j^a \sum_k^b Y_{ijk}^2 - C - SS_A - SS_B - SS_{AB}$$

The degrees of freedom not only suggest the proper computational formula; they suggest alternative formulas which in turn provide checks on our computation.

The MS column is again the result of dividing the entries in the SS column by the corresponding entries in the df column. The entries under EMS consist of σ_e^2, plus a term, θ^2, representing the corresponding SV. The θ^2 term is multiplied by the number of levels of all variables which are not represented in the subscript. The θ^2 terms are defined as follows:

(5.19) $$\theta_A^2 = \frac{\sum_j^a (\mu_j - \mu)^2}{a - 1}$$

(5.20) $$\theta_B^2 = \frac{\sum_k^b (\mu_k - \mu)^2}{b - 1}$$

(5.21) $$\theta_{AB}^2 = \frac{\sum_j^a \sum_k^b (\mu_{jk} - \mu_j - \mu_k + \mu)^2}{(a - 1)(b - 1)}$$

The notation θ^2 indicates that the subscripted variable is fixed. This follows from the definitions, Equations (5.19) to (5.21), where the squared deviations are pooled only over the levels of A appearing in the experiment. In contrast, σ_e^2 represents the variance of effects for a population of levels of which those in the experiment are only a random sample.

The appropriate F tests are also listed in Table 5-2. The logic is exactly that discussed in Chapter 4; we require an error term which consists of all the components of the numerator except the null hypothesis term. Then, if H_0 is true, $E(F)$ will equal 1. The null hypothesis that the μ_j are all equal (i.e., $\theta_A^2 = 0$) is tested by an F distributed on $a - 1$ df and $ab(n - 1)$ df. A significant value of F leads to a relatively restricted conclusion. It does not indicate that the levels of A differ in their effects at any given level of B or at any level of B other than those used in this particular experiment, but rather that, *averaged over the levels of B used in the present study*, there is an effect due to A. If the experimenter is interested in comparing the effects of A at a particular level of B, then a sum of squares for A should be computed only for the data at that level of B. This sum of squares should then be divided by $a - 1$ and tested against the usual error term, $MS_{S/AB}$. Such a test is a test of a *simple effect* of A, as contrasted with the overall test of the main effect of A. The null hypothesis that θ_B^2 equals zero is tested by an F distributed on $b - 1$ and $ab(n - 1)$ df. Rejection of the null hypothesis indicates that the μ_k differ, where μ_k is the mean of the kth treatment population of B, obtained by averaging over all treatment populations of A. If we wish to compare the means of the B treatment populations at one particular level of A, we are again interested in testing simple effects, and the procedure previously described is applicable. The null hypothesis that θ^2_{AB} equals zero is tested by an F distributed on $(a - 1)(b - 1)$ and $ab(n - 1)$ df. Its rejection indicates that variability remains among the $\mu_{.jk}$ after removal of variability due to the effects of A and B.

5.3.2 Two-factor interactions

The two-factor interaction merits a more detailed interpretation than has thus far been provided. We begin with Equation (5.22), which follows from Equation (5.1):

$$(5.22) \qquad \bar{Y}_{.jk} = \mu + \alpha_j + \beta_k + (\alpha\beta)_{jk} + \frac{\sum_i \epsilon_{ijk}}{n}$$

Substituting sample estimates of population parameters and transposing terms, we obtain

$$(5.23) \qquad \widehat{(\alpha\beta)}_{jk} = \bar{Y}_{.jk} - (\bar{Y}_{.j.} - \bar{Y}_{...}) - (\bar{Y}_{..k} - \bar{Y}_{...}) - \bar{Y}_{...}$$

the estimate of the interaction effect of the jkth treatment combination (note that $\sum_i (Y_{ijk} - \bar{Y}_{.jk})/n = 0$). As an example, we next apply Equation (5.23) to the set of sample means in Table 5-3. If, in accord with Equation (5-23),

TABLE 5-3

A 3 × 3 table of means

	B_1	B_2	B_3	$\bar{Y}_{.j.}$	$\bar{Y}_{.j.} - \bar{Y}_{...}$
A_1	2.5	3.0	3.5	3.0	−3.0
A_2	5.0	7.0	9.0	7.0	+1.0
A_3	4.5	8.0	11.5	8.0	+2.0
$\bar{Y}_{..k}$	4.0	6.0	8.0	$\bar{Y}_{...} = 6.0$	

we remove the estimate of α_j from each cell mean, the result—Table 5-4—consists of the quantities $\bar{Y}_{.jk} - (\bar{Y}_{.j.} - \bar{Y}_{...})$. Note that the two df for A are literally lost; the row means are no longer free to vary but instead stand equal to each other and to the grand mean. Further, note that the column means are unchanged by this manipulation of the data, demonstrating the independence of row and column effects.

TABLE 5-4

Table 5-3 after removal of variability due to A

	B_1	B_2	B_3	$\overline{Y}_{.j.}$
A_1	5.5	6.0	6.5	6.0
A_2	4.0	6.0	8.0	6.0
A_3	2.5	6.0	9.5	6.0
$\overline{Y}_{..k}$	4.0	6.0	8.0	$\overline{Y}_{...} = 6.0$
$\overline{Y}_{..k} - \overline{Y}_{...}$	-2.0	0	$+2.0$	

Next, remove ($\overline{Y}_{..k} - \overline{Y}_{...}$), the estimate of β_k, from each entry in Table 5-4. The result is Table 5-5, in which there are no *df* for rows or columns. If we now complete the process described by Equation (5.23), subtracting $\overline{Y}_{...}$ from all entries in Table 5-5, we obtain

$$\begin{bmatrix} 1.5 & 0 & -1.5 \\ 0 & 0 & 0 \\ -1.5 & 0 & 1.5 \end{bmatrix}$$

The entries in the above matrix are the estimates of $(\alpha\beta)_{jk}$. The important thing to note is that they are not all zero, that there is variability among the effects of treatment combinations even after removal of the variability in the data that is due to A and B effects. If this variability is significantly greater than that due to individual differences (S/AB), one says that interaction effects are present in the data.

TABLE 5-5

Table 5-3 after removal of variability due to A and B

	B_1	B_2	B_3	$\overline{Y}_{.j.}$
A_1	7.5	6.0	4.5	6.0
A_2	6.0	6.0	6.0	6.0
A_3	4.5	6.0	7.5	6.0
$\overline{Y}_{..k}$	6.0	6.0	6.0	$\overline{Y}_{...} = 6.0$

The entries in Tables 5-3 to 5-5 are graphically presented in Figure 5-1. On the left, the entries are plotted as a function of the levels of B with A as the parameter, and on the right, the entries are plotted as a function of A with B as the parameter. If all interaction effects were identically zero, the nine means would lie on a straight line with slope of zero in the final plots at the bottom of the figure. The failure of this to occur suggests that all the variability among the cell means is not accounted for by A and B effects and

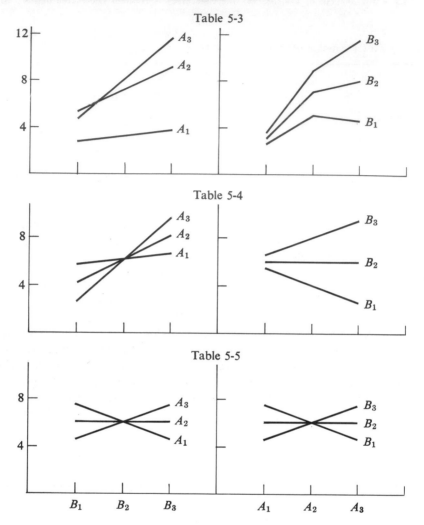

FIGURE 5-1   Graphic representation of Tables 5-3 to 5-5

that interaction effects contribute to the variability among cell means (assuming that the deviations from a line with zero slope are significant).

Tables 5-4 and 5-5 and their graphic representations clarify one interpretation of interaction; namely, it is the variability among cell means which still remains when variability due to the main effects are removed.   However, we ordinarily want to make some statement about interaction effects in terms of the tabulation or plot of the original cell means, i.e., in terms of Table 5-3 and its graphic representation.   Assuming that the data are error-free (or equivalently, that the cell means are means of populations rather than samples), what do the unadjusted means reveal about the presence or absence, as well as the direction, of interaction? To answer this question, first note that the quantity

$$(\bar{Y}_{.jk} - \bar{Y}_{.jk'}) - (\bar{Y}_{.j'k} - \bar{Y}_{.j'k'})$$

is constant throughout adjustments for main effects. For example, in Table 5-3,

$$(\bar{Y}_{.11} - \bar{Y}_{.12}) - (\bar{Y}_{.21} - \bar{Y}_{.22}) = (2.5 - 3.0) - (5.0 - 7.0)$$

$$= 1.5$$

and after adjusting for row effects, we have in Table 5-4,

$$(5.5 - 6.0) - (4.0 - 6.0) = 1.5$$

and after further adjustment for column effects, we have in Table 5-5,

$$(7.5 - 6.0) - (6.0 - 6.0) = 1.5$$

As a second example, for $j = 1$, $k = 2$, $j' = 3$, and $k' = 3$, we have in Table 5-3,

$$(3.0 - 3.5) - (8.0 - 11.5) = 3.0$$

and in Table 5-4,

$$(6.0 - 6.5) - (6.0 - 9.5) = 3.0$$

and in Table 5-5,

$$(6.0 - 4.5) - (6.0 - 7.5) = 3.0$$

It follows from our previous comments that if there are no interaction effects in the data, all comparisons of the sort just exemplified must be zero for Table 5-5. More explicitly, zero interaction means that the twice-adjusted means are all identical (or, in the case of sample data, not significantly different from each other), and therefore any differences between differences in Table 5-5 must be zero (or not significantly different from zero). But we have just pointed out that the result of any particular comparison of differences is the same for all three tables. Therefore, zero interaction signifies that

(5.24) $$(\bar{Y}_{.jk} - \bar{Y}_{.jk'}) - (\bar{Y}_{.j'k} - \bar{Y}_{.j'k'}) = 0$$

for all values of j, j', k, and k'. In the case of sample data, the equal-sign would be read as "is not significantly different from."

An example of a set of unadjusted cell means for which Equation (5.24) holds is

$$\begin{bmatrix} 1 & 3 & 5 \\ 5 & 7 & 9 \\ 6 & 8 & 10 \end{bmatrix}$$

If these data are adjusted for row and column effects, one finds that all entries are equal to the grand mean, suggesting that all variability among cell means is due to row and column effects and no interaction occurs. The same conclusion is reached by determining that Equation (5.24) holds for the above data matrix. It is instructive to plot this data set as is done in Figure 5-2.

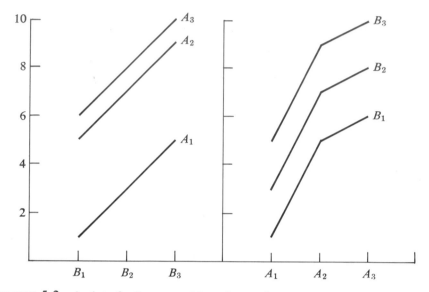

FIGURE 5-2 A plot of cell means with no interaction present

The notable aspect of the two plots is that the curves are parallel, a necessary consequence of Equation (5.24). In terms of the plot of data, *interaction is a significant departure from parallelism*. The spread among the means for the levels of one variable changes as a function of the level of the second variable. Alternatively, interaction may be viewed as significant variability among simple effects. The simple effects of one variable are not constant at all levels of the second and are therefore not all equal to the main effect.

Although the main and interaction effects are independent, an adequate interpretation of the data requires joint consideration of all three. Consider the two examples in Figure 5-3. For simplicity, again assume errorless data or, in other words, assume that the cell means are population means and any nonzero effects are therefore significant. In the left side of Figure 5-3 there are no A or AB effects, but the B effect is significant. Compare this with the right side, in which there is again no A effect, there is again a B effect, but this time there is also an AB interaction effect. The statement that there is no A effect has the same formal meaning for both data plots; averaging over both levels of B, the means for the three levels of A do not differ. However, in the data on the left there is no A effect at any level of B, while on the right

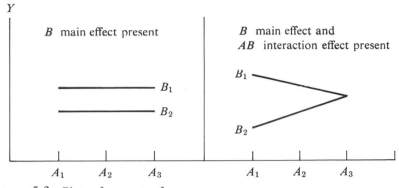

FIGURE 5-3   Plots of two sets of means

there are simple A effects at both B_1 and B_2; these effects are in opposite directions and tend to cancel each other out.   Clearly, if one is to obtain an accurate picture of the relationship among treatment population means, the total set of effects must be considered.   Thus, knowing that B is a significant source of variance is not enough; it is only when the condition of the A and AB effects is noted that an intelligent discussion of the data can begin.

5.3.3 Behavioral and statistical hypotheses

An understanding of statistical effects is incomplete without some feeling for their relationship to behavioral hypotheses.   Although there are no rules for the translation of hypotheses about behavior into hypotheses about statistical effects, we will attempt to exemplify the process.

Consider the following experiment.   On each of 100 trials, each subject has a choice between gambling and not gambling.   There are two independent variables: A, the amount which can be won or lost on a gamble, and B, the consequences of not gambling.   The levels of A are:

$A_1 = 5 \text{\textcent}$ is won or lost on a gamble
$A_2 = 15 \text{\textcent}$ is won or lost on a gamble
$A_3 = 25 \text{\textcent}$ is won or lost on a gamble

On each gamble the subject has an equal chance of winning or losing.   The levels of B are:

$B_1 = $ the subject always pays out $1 \text{\textcent}$ on trials on which he does not gamble
$B_2 = $ the subject always receives $1 \text{\textcent}$ on trials on which he does not gamble

One theory of choice behavior would predict the following:

(a) The percentage of gambles (P) will increase as the amount risked (the levels of A) increases when the consequence of not gambling is a sure gain (B_2).

(b) P will decrease as the amount risked increases when the consequence of not gambling is a sure loss (B_1).

(c) P will increase (when the alternative is B_2) over the levels of A at about the same rate that P will decrease (when the alternative is B_1) over the levels of A.

(d) P will be greater when the alternative to gambling is a sure loss (B_1) than when it is a sure gain (B_2), regardless of the level of A.

These hypotheses about the performances of subjects would be confirmed if the plot of the means for the AB combinations looked like the right-hand side of Figure 5-3. Thus, the translation into statistical hypotheses would be as follows:

(a′) There will be a significant AB interaction (from (a) and (b) above).

(b′) The A main effect will not be significant (from (c) above).

(c′) The B main effect will be significant (from (d) above).

If hypotheses (a′), (b′), and (c′) are verified and if, in addition, the effects are in the predicted direction, our behavioral hypotheses are supported.

Let us consider a second example of the relationship between behavioral and statistical hypotheses. Schizophrenics and normal subjects, equated on an intelligence test, are required to perform on a concept formation task. Two sets of stimuli are used; both involve the same concepts. One set contains pictures which express social approval (e.g., woman patting boy on head) and the second set contains pictures expressing social disapproval (e.g., woman shaking finger at boy). Certain theories of personality and intellectual performance might lead to the following hypotheses:

(a) Normal subjects will take fewer trials to attain the relevant concept than will schizophrenics, whichever stimulus set is the basis for comparison.

(b) The performances of normal subjects will not be influenced by the type of stimulus set (approving or disapproving pictures).

(c) Schizophrenics will perform less well on the disapproving than on the approving set of pictures.

If all three hypotheses were correct, the data might look something like the plot in Figure 5-4. The following results are hypothesized for the statistical analysis:

(a′) There will be a significant main effect due to the personality variable (from (a) above).

(b′) There will be a significant main effect due to stimulus sets (from (b) and (c) above).

(c′) There will be a significant interaction of personality and stimulus sets (from (b) and (c) above).

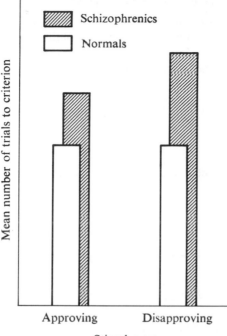

FIGURE 5-4 Performance of schizophrenic and normal subjects on a concept formation task

It is a good idea to go through the process just exemplified before the collection of data. The experimenter should try to visualize the sorts of results which might be obtained and should consider which sources of variance in the analysis will reflect these results. This type of activity will help ensure that the experimental design makes possible adequate tests of the behavioral hypotheses or provides answers to the questions posed. In addition, this type of thinking promotes a feeling for the relationship of data to psychological processes. Remember, the end goal of experimentation is not a statistical statement (e.g., the stimulus set variable is a significant source of variance), but rather a statement about behavior (e.g., stimuli which express social disapproval are less readily categorized than stimuli expressing approval by a population consisting of schizophrenic and normal subjects).

It is also important to plot the data once it is obtained and to study carefully the plot of data. Plot the same set of cell means several ways, as was done in Figures 5-1 and 5-2. Plot the means at the levels of *B*, averaging over the levels of *A*, in order to get a picture of the *B* main effect. Look at the *A* main effect by averaging over levels of *B*. Keep these plots at hand while reading the entries in the analysis of variance table.

5.3.4 A numerical example for the two-factor design, equal n

Table 5-6 presents data from an experiment involving two independent variables, A and B. As a first step in the analysis, obtain the sum of scores and the sum of squared scores for each cell (combination of j and k). These quantities then provide the basis for calculating the cell variances:

$$(5.25) \qquad s_{jk}^2 = \frac{\sum_i Y_{ijk}^2 - \left(\sum_i Y_{ijk}\right)^2 / n}{n - 1}$$

TABLE 5-6

Data from a completely randomized two-factor experiment

	A_1B_1	A_1B_2	A_1B_3	
	7	6	9	
	33	11	12	
	26	11	6	
	27	18	24	
	21	14	7	
	6	18	10	
	14	19	1	
	19	14	10	
$\sum_i Y_{i1k} = 153$	111	79	$\sum_i \sum_k Y_{i1k} = 343$
$\sum_i Y_{i1k}^2 = 3{,}577$	1,679	1,087	
$s_{1k}^2 = 92.982$	19.839	43.839	

	A_2B_1	A_2B_2	A_2B_3	
	42	28	13	
	25	6	18	
	8	1	23	
	28	15	1	
	30	9	3	
	22	15	4	
	17	2	6	
	32	37	2	
$\sum_i Y_{i2k} = 204$	113	70	$\sum_i \sum_k Y_{i2k} = 387$
$\sum_i Y_{i2k}^2 = 5{,}934$	2,725	1,088	
$s_{2k}^2 = 104.571$	161.268	67.929	
$\sum_j \sum_i Y_{ijk} = 357$	224	149	$\sum_i \sum_j \sum_k Y_{ijk} = 730$

An example of this computation is

$$s_{21}^2 = \frac{5{,}934 - (204)^2/8}{7}$$

$$= 104.571$$

Having computed the cell variances, proceed to test the null hypothesis that

$$\sigma_{11} = \sigma_{12} = \cdots = \sigma_{jk} = \cdots = \sigma_{23}$$

Following the Hartley procedure, select the largest and smallest cell variances and compute their ratio. The result is $F_{max} = 161.3/19.8 = 8.129$. In Table A-6 the critical value of F_{max} is found to be 10.8 for α equal to .05, and six variances each on 7 df. There are therefore no grounds for rejecting the assumption of homogeneity of variance.

The sums of squares formulas of Table 5-2 may now be applied. The correction term is again the sum of all scores squared, and divided by the total number of scores, thus,

$$C = \frac{(730)^2}{48}$$

$$= 11{,}102.080$$

The SS_{tot} is

$$SS_{tot} = 3{,}577 + \cdots + 2{,}725 - C$$

$$= 16{,}090 - C$$

$$= 4{,}987.920$$

Next,

$$SS_A = \frac{(343)^2 + (387)^2}{24} - C$$

$$= 11{,}142.417 - C$$

$$= 40.337$$

Similarly,

$$SS_B = \frac{(357)^2 + (224)^2 + (149)^2}{16} - C$$

$$= 12{,}489.125 - C$$

$$= 1{,}387.045$$

The calculation of the total sum of squares is the same as it was for the one-factor design of Chapter 4. In fact, for any design, SS_{tot} is the sum of all squared scores minus the correction term. The sum of squares for the A treatment variable is also computed in the same manner as in Chapter 4. In general, the design is collapsed so that it consists of a groups of scores and then the SS_A is computed as would be done for a one-factor design. In our example, we ignore the B variable and view the design as consisting of two groups of 24 (in general, bn) scores each. To compute SS_B we ignore the A variable and view the design as a one-factor design consisting of three groups of 16 scores (in general, b groups of an scores). This is exactly what has been done in the immediately preceding computations.

To calculate the SS_{AB} one might first calculate the sum of squares for the cell means, which will be denoted by $SS_{\overline{AB}}$. Essentially, the design is again viewed as a one-factor design, this time consisting of six (ab) groups of eight (n) scores each. Consequently

$$SS_{\overline{AB}} = \frac{(153)^2 + (111)^2 + \cdots + (70)^2}{8} - C$$

$$= 12{,}657.000 - C$$

$$= 1{,}554.92$$

Next, remove that portion of the variability among cells due to A and B effects, resulting in

$$SS_{AB} = 1{,}554.92 - SS_A - SS_B$$

$$= 127.538$$

The above is the procedure described in the sum of squares column of Table 5-2. An alternative approach is to use Equation (5.15), which follows from the expanded df, $ab - a - b + 1$. Thus,

$$SS_{AB} = \frac{\sum\limits_{j}^{2}\sum\limits_{k}^{3}\left(\sum\limits_{i}^{8} Y_{ijk}\right)^2}{8} - \frac{\sum\limits_{j}^{2}\left(\sum\limits_{i}^{8}\sum\limits_{k}^{3} Y_{ijk}\right)^2}{24} - \frac{\sum\limits_{k}^{3}\left(\sum\limits_{i}^{8}\sum\limits_{j}^{2} Y_{ijk}\right)^2}{16} + C$$

$$= 12{,}657.000 - 11{,}142.417 - 12{,}489.125 + 11{,}102.080$$

$$= 127.538$$

Now the sum of squares for the error term, S/AB, is required. This may be computed as a residual from the total variability, i.e.,

$$SS_{S/AB} = SS_{\text{tot}} - SS_A - SS_B - SS_{AB}$$

$$= 3{,}433.000$$

As an alternative, the error sum of squares might be computed as the difference between the total and between-cells variability, as in Equation (5.17):

$$SS_{S/AB} = SS_{\text{tot}} - SS_{\overline{AB}}$$

$$= 4{,}987.920 - 1{,}554.92$$

$$= 3{,}433.000$$

A third approach to the calculation of $SS_{S/AB}$ stems from the fact that the $MS_{S/AB}$ is equal to the average cell variance. Therefore,

(5.26) $$MS_{S/AB} = \sum_{j}\sum_{k} s^2_{jk/ab}$$

and by substituting and transposing terms,

$$SS_{S/AB} = (n - 1) \sum_j \sum_k s_{jk}^2$$

(5.27)
$$= 7(490.428)$$
$$= 3{,}432.996$$

which is correct within a slight rounding error. These alternative methods provide a *partial* check on the calculations. Thus, an error in calculating SS_A might affect the residual method of obtaining the error sum of squares and not affect the third method used. On the other hand, an error in squaring the individual scores would lead to the same result with all approaches. Knowledge of these alternative calculations is also worthwhile because there are situations in which the within-cells variability must be obtained prior to the calculation of treatment effects. An instance of this will be noted in the discussion of calculations for the case of unequal n. An additional reason for demonstrating these alternative calculations is to emphasize the underlying identity of several conceptualizations of within-cells variability—it is residual when all treatment effects have been accounted for, it is the difference in variability among and within cells, and it is the average within-cells variability.

The mean squares and the F ratios are now easily computed. Dividing sums of squares by the appropriate df, we obtain the entries in the MS column of Table 5-7. The A, B, and AB mean squares are each tested against

TABLE 5-7

Analysis of variance for data from a two-factor experiment

SV	df	SS	MS	F
Total	47	4,987.92		
A	1	40.34	40.34	.49
B	2	1,387.05	693.52	8.48 *
AB	2	127.54	63.77	.78
S/AB	42	3,433.00	81.74	

$^*p < .01$

the same error term, $MS_{S/AB}$, yielding the ratios reported in the F column. Only the B main effect is significant.

Turn now to Figure 5-5, which shows a plot of the group means. The source of the B main effect is clear; $\overline{Y}_{..k}$ consistently declines as k increases. The figure also suggests that scores are higher under A_2 than under A_1 and that there is an AB interaction, the decline over levels of B appearing to be more rapid under A_2 than under A_1. This sort of result more than any other suggests the importance of the statistical analysis. While inspection of the figure suggests A and AB effects, the statistical analysis reveals that the A and AB variabilities are well within the range which might be expected on the basis of individual differences.

In connection with Figure 5-5, note that this method of graphing the data is appropriate only if B is a quantitative variable. If there is no rationale for

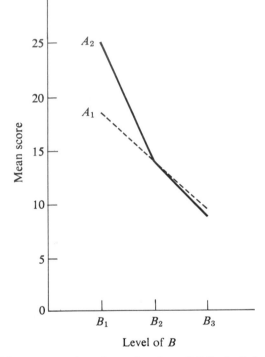

FIGURE 5-5   Mean scores plotted as a function of B for both levels of A

ordering the levels of B, or if there is no rationale for spacing the levels along the abscissa, then a histogram rather than a line graph should be presented. The line graph suggests a function about which one can ask questions of shape and curvature, questions which are only appropriate when the independent variable is a quantitative scaled variable.

5.3.5   Unequal but proportional cell frequencies

Thus far we have considered only the equal n case. If the cell frequencies are unequal but proportional, the analysis must be slightly modified. To define proportionality the following notation is introduced:

n_{jk} = the number of subjects tested under A_j and B_k

$n_{j.}$ = the number of subjects tested under A_j

$\quad = \sum_k n_{jk}$

$n_{.k}$ = the number of subjects tested under B_k

$\quad = \sum_j n_{jk}$

Then there are proportional n's if for any value of j

(5.28)
$$\frac{n_{jk}}{n_{j.}} = C_k$$

where C_k is a constant for the kth level of B. Equivalently, there is proportionality if for any k

(5.29)
$$\frac{n_{jk}}{n_{.k}} = C_j$$

where C_j is a constant for the jth level of B.

For example, suppose that

$n_{11} = 8$	$n_{12} = 6$	$n_{13} = 6$	$n_{1.} = 20$
$n_{21} = 4$	$n_{22} = 3$	$n_{23} = 3$	$n_{2.} = 10$
$n_{.1} = 12$	$n_{.2} = 9$	$n_{.3} = 9$	

Then,

$$\frac{n_{11}}{n_{1.}} = \frac{n_{21}}{n_{2.}} = \frac{2}{5} = C_{.1}$$

$$\frac{n_{12}}{n_{1.}} = \frac{n_{22}}{n_{2.}} = \frac{3}{10} = C_{.2}$$

$$\frac{n_{13}}{n_{1.}} = \frac{n_{23}}{n_{3.}} = \frac{3}{10} = C_{.3}$$

fulfilling the condition set by Equation (5.28). Equivalently,

$$\frac{n_{11}}{n_{.1}} = \frac{n_{12}}{n_{.2}} = \frac{n_{13}}{n_{.3}} = \frac{2}{3} = C_{1.}$$

$$\frac{n_{21}}{n_{.1}} = \frac{n_{22}}{n_{.2}} = \frac{n_{23}}{n_{.3}} = \frac{1}{3} = C_{2.}$$

The analysis of variance for the proportional but unequal n case is carried out as before, always dividing each squared quantity by the number of scores which have been summed to make up the quantity. The difference is that in the equal n case, for example,

$$SS_A = \frac{\sum_j \left(\sum_i \sum_k Y_{ijk} \right)^2}{bn} - C$$

and in the proportional n case, we have

$$SS_A = \frac{\left(\sum_i \sum_k Y_{i1k}\right)^2}{\sum_k n_{1k}} + \cdots + \frac{\left(\sum_i \sum_k Y_{iak}\right)^2}{\sum_k n_{ak}} - C$$

If the n_{jk} are all equal,

$$\sum_k n_{1k} = \cdots = \sum_k n_{ak} = bn$$

and the equations for the equal and proportional cases are identical. The specific formulas for the analysis of variance, proportional n case, are:

(5.30)
$$SS_{\text{tot}} = \sum_i \sum_j \sum_k Y_{ijk}^2 - C$$

(5.31)
$$SS_A = \sum_j \frac{\left(\sum_i \sum_k Y_{ijk}\right)^2}{\sum_k n_{jk}} - C$$

(5.32)
$$SS_B = \sum_k \frac{\left(\sum_i \sum_j Y_{ijk}\right)^2}{\sum_j n_{jk}} - C$$

(5.33)
$$SS_{AB} = \sum_j \sum_k \frac{\left(\sum_i Y_{ijk}\right)^2}{n_{jk}} - C - SS_A - SS_B$$

(5.34)
$$SS_{S/AB} = SS_{\text{tot}} - SS_A - SS_B - SS_{AB}$$

(5.35)
$$C = \frac{\left(\sum_i \sum_j \sum_k Y_{ijk}\right)^2}{\sum_j \sum_k n_{jk}}$$

A word of caution about the preceding equations is in order. If proportionality occurs by chance and the cell frequencies are not truly representative of the frequencies in the treatment populations, the method described will improperly weight some treatment combinations. In this case, the experimenter is better advised to use the *method of unweighted means*, which will be described in the next section.

5.3.6 Disproportionate cell frequencies

The analysis of variance becomes somewhat more complicated if the cell frequencies are not only unequal but also disproportionate. The problem may be best stated in terms of the partitioning of $SS_{\overline{AB}}$, the between-cells sum of squares. We begin with the identity,

(5.36)
$$\overline{Y}_{.jk} - \overline{Y}_{...} = (\overline{Y}_{.j.} - \overline{Y}_{...}) + (\overline{Y}_{..k} - \overline{Y}_{...})$$
$$+ (\overline{Y}_{.jk} - \overline{Y}_{.j.} - \overline{Y}_{..k} + \overline{Y}_{...})$$

Squaring both sides we obtain:

$$(5.37) \quad \begin{aligned}
(\bar{Y}_{.jk} - \bar{Y}_{...})^2 &= (\bar{Y}_{.j.} - \bar{Y}_{...})^2 + (\bar{Y}_{..k} - \bar{Y}_{...})^2 \\
&+ (\bar{Y}_{.jk} - \bar{Y}_{.j.} - \bar{Y}_{..k} + \bar{Y}_{...})^2 \\
&+ 2(\bar{Y}_{.j.} - \bar{Y}_{...})(\bar{Y}_{..k} - \bar{Y}_{...}) \\
&+ 2(\bar{Y}_{.j.} - \bar{Y}_{...})(\bar{Y}_{.jk} - \bar{Y}_{.j.} - \bar{Y}_{..k} + \bar{Y}_{...}) \\
&+ 2(\bar{Y}_{..k} - \bar{Y}_{...})(\bar{Y}_{.jk} - \bar{Y}_{.j.} - \bar{Y}_{..k} + \bar{Y}_{...})
\end{aligned}$$

Summing over the n_{jk} measures in group $A_j B_k$ and then over j and k yields:

$$(5.38) \quad \begin{aligned}
\sum_j \sum_k n_{jk}(\bar{Y}_{.jk} - \bar{Y}_{...})^2 &= \sum_j \sum_k n_{jk}(\bar{Y}_{.j.} - \bar{Y}_{...})^2 + \sum_j \sum_k n_{jk}(\bar{Y}_{..k} - \bar{Y}_{...})^2 \\
&+ \sum_j \sum_k n_{jk}(\bar{Y}_{.jk} - \bar{Y}_{.j.} - \bar{Y}_{..k} + \bar{Y}_{...})^2 \\
&+ 2\sum_j \sum_k n_{jk}(\bar{Y}_{.j.} - \bar{Y}_{...})(\bar{Y}_{..k} - \bar{Y}_{...}) \\
&+ 2\sum_j \sum_k n_{jk}(\bar{Y}_{.j.} - \bar{Y}_{...})(\bar{Y}_{.jk} - \bar{Y}_{.j.} - \bar{Y}_{..k} + \bar{Y}_{...}) \\
&+ 2\sum_j \sum_k n_{jk}(\bar{Y}_{..k} - \bar{Y}_{...})(\bar{Y}_{.jk} - \bar{Y}_{.j.} - \bar{Y}_{..k} + \bar{Y}_{...})
\end{aligned}$$

Consider the cross-product terms. If the n_{jk} are proportional or equal, then by Equation (5.28), $n_{jk} = n_{j.}C_k$ and therefore,

$$(5.39) \quad \begin{aligned}
\sum_j \sum_k n_{jk}(\bar{Y}_{.j.} - \bar{Y}_{...})(\bar{Y}_{..k} - \bar{Y}_{...}) \\
= \sum_j \sum_k n_{j.}C_k(\bar{Y}_{.j.} - \bar{Y}_{...})(\bar{Y}_{..k} - \bar{Y}_{...})
\end{aligned}$$

Rearranging terms, we obtain

$$(5.40) \quad \begin{aligned}
\sum_j \sum_k n_{jk}(\bar{Y}_{.j.} - \bar{Y}_{...})(\bar{Y}_{..k} - \bar{Y}_{...}) \\
= \sum_k C_k(\bar{Y}_{..k} - \bar{Y}_{...}) \sum_j n_{j.}(\bar{Y}_{.j.} - \bar{Y}_{...})
\end{aligned}$$

But

$$\begin{aligned}
\sum_j n_{j.}(\bar{Y}_{.j.} - \bar{Y}_{...}) &= \sum_j n_{j.}\bar{Y}_{.j.} - \bar{Y}_{...}\sum_j n_{j.} \\
&= \sum_j \left(\sum_i \sum_k Y_{ijk} \right) - \bar{Y}_{...} \sum_j \left(\sum_k n_{jk} \right) \\
&= \sum_i \sum_j \sum_k Y_{ijk} - \sum_i \sum_j \sum_k Y_{ijk} \\
&= 0
\end{aligned}$$

and the entire cross-product term therefore vanishes. The remaining cross-product terms in Equation (5.38) can also be shown to vanish by similar manipulations. When the n_{jk} are proportional or equal, the A, B, and AB effects are independent, and Equation (5.38) may be rewritten as

$$(5.41) \quad SS_{\overline{AB}} = SS_A + SS_B + SS_{AB}$$

What if the cell frequencies are not proportional? Then the above proof cannot be carried through; in fact, the cross-product terms will generally not equal zero, and the usually obtained components of $SS_{\overline{AB}}$ will not be independent. With disproportionality, strange things can, and do, happen. For example, $SS_A + SS_B$ can be greater than $SS_{\overline{AB}}$, indicating that some of the components of the between-cells variability are negatively correlated (i.e., some of the cross-product terms must be negative in order for this to happen). Since Equation (5.41) does not hold under disproportionality, and since the usual estimates of population parameters [Equation (5.3)] may be biased, it is necessary to consider alternative computational procedures. The most efficient of such procedures require that least-squares estimates of α_j and β_k be obtained. The calculations generally require much more time and effort than do those of the analysis for equal and proportional frequencies. Fortunately, good approximations can be obtained with less effort for most problems. We will consider two of these approximate techniques. For the more efficient least-squares procedures, see Snedecor.*

In many cases of disproportionality it is reasonable to assume that differences in cell frequencies are chance occurrences, that the treatment populations involved are equal in size. Such would be the case if the deaths of several rats during the running of an experiment resulted in unequal n's. Under these circumstances, the *method of unweighted means* may be used to analyze the data. This method will be illustrated by applying it to the data of Table 5-8, which are a subset of the data of Table 5-6.

STEP 1   Compute $SS_{S/AB}$ from the data of Table 5-8.

$$SS_{S/AB} = SS_{\text{tot}} - SS_{\overline{AB}}$$

$$= \sum_k^b \sum_j^a \sum_i^{n_{jk}} Y_{ijk}^2 - \sum_k^b \sum_j^a \frac{\left(\sum_i Y_{ijk}\right)^2}{n_{jk}}$$

$$= (3{,}577 + 1{,}234 + \cdots + 406) - \left[\frac{(153)^2}{8} + \frac{(82)^2}{6} + \cdots + \frac{(40)^2}{5}\right]$$

$$= 13{,}658 - 10{,}679.915$$

$$= 2{,}978.085$$

STEP 2   Compute the reciprocal of the harmonic mean of the cell entries.

$$\frac{1}{\bar{n}_h} = \left(\frac{1}{ab}\right)\left(\sum_j \sum_k \frac{1}{n_{jk}}\right)$$

(5.42)

$$= \frac{1}{6}\left(\frac{1}{8} + \frac{1}{6} + \cdots + \frac{1}{5}\right)$$

$$= .163$$

---

* G. W. Snedecor, *Statistical Methods*, 5th ed. (Ames: Iowa State Univ. Press, 1956), pp. 388–391.

TABLE 5-8

A two-dimensional data matrix with disproportionate cell frequencies

	A_1B_1	A_1B_2	A_1B_3		
	7	6	9		
	33	11	12		
	26	18	6		
	27	14	24		
	21	19	1		
	6	14	10		
	14				
	19				
$\sum_i Y_{i1k} = 153$		82	62	$\sum_k \sum_i Y_{ijk} = 297$	
$\overline{Y}_{1k} = 19.125$		13.667	10.333	$\sum_k \overline{Y}_{1k} = 43.125$	
$\sum_i Y_{i1k}^2 = 3{,}577$		1,234	938		

	A_2B_1	A_2B_2	A_2B_3		
	42	28	13		
	8	6	10		
	28	1	1		
	30	2	6		
	22	37	10		
	17				
	32				
$\sum_i Y_{i2k} = 179$		74	40	$\sum_j \sum_i Y_{ijk} = 293$	
$\overline{Y}_{2k} = 25.571$		14.800	8.000	$\sum_k \overline{Y}_{2k} = 48.371$	
$\sum_i Y_{i2k}^2 = 5{,}309$		2,194	406		

	A_2B_1	A_2B_2	A_2B_3		
$\sum_j \overline{Y}_{.jk} = 44.696$		28.467	18.333	$\sum_j \sum_k \overline{Y}_{.jk} = 91.496$	
$\sum_j \sum_i Y_{ijk} = 332$		156	109		

STEP 3 Compute the adjusted sum of squares for within groups, $SS'_{S/AB}$.

$$SS'_{S/AB} = \frac{1}{\overline{n}_h} SS_{S/AB}$$

(5.43)

$$= (.163)(2{,}978.085)$$

$$= 485.428$$

STEP 4 Calculate SS_A, SS_B, and SS_{AB} for the cell means rather than for the original data.

$$SS_A = \frac{\sum\limits_{j}\left(\sum\limits_{k} \bar{Y}_{.jk}\right)^2}{b} - \frac{\left(\sum\limits_{j}\sum\limits_{k} \bar{Y}_{.jk}\right)^2}{ab}$$

(5.44)
$$= \frac{(43.125)^2 + (48.371)^2}{3} - \frac{(91.496)^2}{6}$$

$$= 1{,}399.840 - 1{,}395.263$$
$$= 4.577$$

$$SS_B = \frac{\sum\limits_{k}\left(\sum\limits_{j} \bar{Y}_{.jk}\right)^2}{a} - \frac{\left(\sum\limits_{j}\sum\limits_{k} \bar{Y}_{.jk}\right)^2}{ab}$$

(5.45)
$$= \frac{(44.696)^2 + (28.467)^2 + (18.333)^2}{2} - 1{,}395.263$$

$$= 176.838$$

(5.46)
$$SS_{AB} = \sum\limits_{j}\sum\limits_{k} \bar{Y}^2_{.jk} - \frac{\left(\sum\limits_{j}\sum\limits_{k} \bar{Y}_{.jk}\right)^2}{ab} - SS_A - SS_B$$

$$= (19.125)^2 + \cdots + (8.000)^2 - 1{,}395.263 - 4.577 - 176.838$$
$$= 19.561$$

STEP 5 Compute mean squares as in the proportional case, dividing each sum of squares by its df. The df for S/AB are

(5.47)
$$\begin{aligned} df_{S/AB} &= df_{tot} - df_{\overline{AB}} \\ &= (37 - 1) - (6 - 1) \\ &= 31 \end{aligned}$$

To obtain the $MS_{S/AB}$ divide the *adjusted* $SS_{S/AB}$ by $df_{S/AB}$.

The F ratios are formed in the usual manner. The results of the analysis are summarized in Table 5-9 and lead to the same conclusions as does the analysis reported in Table 5-7.

Disproportionate cell frequencies may be representative of treatment population frequencies, particularly when the independent variable is an in-

TABLE 5-9

Analysis of variance for the data of Table 5-8 using the method of unweighted means

SV	df	SS	MS	F
A	1	4.58	4.58	.29
B	2	176.84	88.42	5.64 *
AB	2	19.56	9.78	.62
S/AB (adj)	31	485.43	15.65	
				* $p < .01$

dividual characteristic such as age, sex, socioeconomic status, a personality trait, or intelligence. In such cases, the *method of expected cell frequencies* may provide an approximate analysis. We will apply this method to the data of Table 5-8.

STEP 1 Compute the $SS_{S/AB}$ as in Step 1 of the unweighted means analysis.

$$SS_{S/AB} = SS_{tot} - SS_{\overline{AB}}$$
$$= 2{,}978.085$$

STEP 2 Compute the expected cell frequencies. If $n_{j.}/n_{..}$ is the probability of sampling an individual from population A_j, and if $n_{.k}/n_{..}$ is the probability of sampling an individual from population B_k, then

(5.48)
$$E(n_{jk}) = \left(\frac{n_{j.}}{n_{..}}\right)\left(\frac{n_{.k}}{n_{..}}\right)(n_{..})$$
$$= \frac{n_{j.}n_{.k}}{n_{..}}$$

where $n_{j.}$ and $n_{.k}$ have been previously defined, and $n_{..}$ is the total number of observations in the experiment. These frequencies are tabulated in Table 5-10.

STEP 3 Compute the expected cell totals. Multiply the obtained cell mean (Table 5-8) by its expected denominator, obtained in the previous step. The result is an estimate of what the sum of scores should be for each cell, given the denominator calculated by Equation (5.47). These expected totals are also tabulated in Table 5-10.

STEP 4 Apply Equations (5.31), (5.32), and (5.33), using the frequencies and sums of Table 5-10. Thus,

$$SS_A = \frac{(297.88)^2}{20} + \frac{(291.32)^2}{17} - \frac{(589.20)^2}{37}$$

$$= 46.216$$

$$SS_B = \frac{(331.32)^2}{15} + \frac{(156.08)^2}{11} + \frac{(101.80)^2}{11} - \frac{(589.20)^2}{37}$$

$$= 1{,}092.330$$

$$SS_{AB} = \frac{(155.14)^2}{8.11} + \cdots + \frac{(40.40)^2}{5.05} - \frac{(589.20)^2}{37} - 46.216 - 1{,}092.330$$

$$= 126.504$$

The mean squares and F ratios are presented in Table 5-11, and are consistent with those of preceding analyses for these data.

TABLE 5-10
Expected cell frequencies and sums for the data of table 5-8

		B_1	B_2	B_3	
A_1	$E(n_{1k})$	$\dfrac{(20)(15)}{37} = 8.11$	$\dfrac{(20)(11)}{37} = 5.95$	$\dfrac{(20)(11)}{37} = 5.95$	$n_{1.} = 20$
	$E\left(\sum_i Y_{i1k}\right)$	$(19.13)(8.11) = 155.14$	$(13.67)(5.95) = 81.34$	$(10.33)(5.95) = 61.40$	$E\left(\sum_i \sum_k Y_{i1k}\right) = 297.88$
A_2	$E(n_{2k})$	$\dfrac{(17)(15)}{37} = 6.89$	$\dfrac{(17)(11)}{37} = 5.05$	$\dfrac{(17)(11)}{37} = 5.05$	$n_{2.} = 17$
	$E\left(\sum_i Y_{i2k}\right)$	$(25.57)(6.89) = 176.18$	$(14.80)(5.05) = 74.74$	$(8.00)(5.05) = 40.40$	$E\left(\sum_i \sum_k Y_{i2k}\right) = 291.32$
	$n_{.k}$	15	11	11	$n_{..} = 37$
	$E\left(\sum_i \sum_j Y_{ijk}\right)$	331.32	156.08	101.80	$E\left(\sum_i \sum_j \sum_k Y_{ijk}\right) = 589.20$

TABLE 5-11

Analysis of variance for the data of Table 5-8 using the method of expected cell frequencies

SV	df	SS	MS	F
A	1	46.216	46.216	.48
B	2	1,092.330	546.165	5.69 *
AB	2	126.504	63.252	.58
S/AB	31	2,978.085	96.067	
				* $p < .01$

5.4 A MODEL FOR THE COMPLETELY RANDOMIZED THREE-FACTOR DESIGN

The approach developed in the preceding part of this chapter can be extended to designs involving more than two factors. The layout of a three-factor design is presented in Table 5-12. The independent variables are A, B, and C, and the relevant indices are

$$i = 1, 2, \cdots, n$$
$$j = 1, 2, \cdots, a$$
$$k = 1, 2, \cdots, b$$
$$m = 1, 2, \cdots, c$$

The abc experimental groups of n subjects may be viewed as abc random samples, one from each of abc populations which systematically differ among themselves only with respect to the treatment combination applied. The mean of the treatment population defined by the jth level of A, the kth level of B, and the mth level of C is μ_{jkm}. The mean of the population of all scores obtained under the jth level of A is

$$\mu_j = \frac{\sum\limits_{k}^{b} \sum\limits_{m}^{c} \mu_{jkm}}{bc}$$

Similarly,

$$\mu_k = \frac{\sum\limits_{j}^{a} \sum\limits_{m}^{c} \mu_{jkm}}{ac} \quad \text{and} \quad \mu_m = \frac{\sum\limits_{j}^{a} \sum\limits_{k}^{b} \mu_{jkm}}{ab}$$

The mean of the treatment population defined by the jth level of A and the kth level of B is

$$\mu_{jk} = \frac{\sum\limits_{m}^{c} \mu_{jkm}}{c}$$

TABLE 5-12

Data matrix for a three-dimensional design

		B_1	$\cdots$	B_k	$\cdots$	B_b
		Y_{1111}		Y_{11k1}		Y_{11b1}
		$\vdots$		$\vdots$		$\vdots$
	A_1	Y_{i111}		Y_{i1k1}		Y_{i1b1}
		$\vdots$		$\vdots$		$\vdots$
		Y_{n111}		Y_{n1k1}		Y_{n1b1}
	$\vdots$					
C_1	A_j	Y_{1j11}		Y_{ijk1}		Y_{ijb1}
		$\vdots$		$\vdots$		$\vdots$
	$\vdots$					
	A_a	Y_{ia11}		Y_{iak1}		Y_{iab1}
		$\vdots$		$\vdots$		$\vdots$
$\vdots$						
C_m	A_j	Y_{ij1m}		Y_{ijkm}		Y_{ijbm}
		$\vdots$		$\vdots$		$\vdots$
$\vdots$						
C_c	A_j	Y_{ij1c}		Y_{ijkc}		Y_{ijbc}
		$\vdots$		$\vdots$		$\vdots$

Similarly,

$$\mu_{jm} = \frac{\sum_{k}^{b} \mu_{jkm}}{b} \quad \text{and} \quad \mu_{km} = \frac{\sum_{j}^{a} \mu_{jkm}}{a}$$

The mean of all scores in the *abc* treatment populations is

$$\mu = \frac{\sum_{j}^{a} \sum_{k}^{b} \sum_{m}^{c} \mu_{jkm}}{abc}$$

The observed data are related to the population parameters by the equation

$$\text{(5.49)} \qquad \beta_k + \gamma_m + (\alpha\beta)_{jk} + (\alpha\gamma)_{jm} \\ + (\beta\gamma)_{km} + (\alpha\beta\gamma)_{jkm} + \epsilon_{ijkm}$$

where

$\alpha_j = \mu_j - \mu$, the main effect of treatment A_j

$\beta_k = \mu_k - \mu$, the main effect of treatment B_k

$\gamma_m = \mu_m - \mu$, the main effect of treatment C_m

$(\alpha\beta)_{jk} = \mu_{jk} - \mu_j - \mu_k + \mu$, the interaction effect of A_j and B_k

$(\alpha\gamma)_{jm} = \mu_{jm} - \mu_j - \mu_m + \mu$, the interaction effect of A_j and C_m

$(\beta\gamma)_{km} = \mu_{km} - \mu_k - \mu_m + \mu$, the interaction effect of B_k and C_m

$(\alpha\beta\gamma)_{jkm} = \mu_{jkm} - \mu_{jk} - \mu_{jm} - \mu_{km} + \mu_j + \mu_k + \mu_m - \mu$, the interaction
effect of A_j, B_k, and C_m

$\epsilon_{ijkm} = Y_{ijkm} - [\mu + \alpha_j + \beta_k + \gamma_m + (\alpha\beta)_{jk} + (\alpha\gamma)_{jm} \\ + (\beta\gamma)_{km} + (\alpha\beta\gamma)_{jkm}]$

$- Y_{ijkm} - \mu_{jkm}$, the error component

If the levels of all three independent variables are arbitrarily chosen, then

$$\sum_j \alpha_j = 0 \qquad \sum_j \sum_k (\alpha\beta)_{jk} = 0$$

$$\sum_k \beta_k = 0 \qquad \sum_j \sum_m (\alpha\gamma)_{jm} = 0 \qquad \sum_j \sum_k \sum_m (\alpha\beta\gamma)_{jkm} = 0$$

$$\sum_m \gamma_m = 0 \qquad \sum_k \sum_m (\beta\gamma)_{km} = 0$$

The error component, ϵ_{ijkm}, is assumed to be independently and normally distributed, with zero mean and variance σ_e^2 within each of the abc treatment populations defined by the selected treatment combinations. As in the simpler designs already considered, the error component is that component of each score which is not accounted for by the contribution of the grand mean, μ, or by the systematic manipulation of the independent variables.

With one exception, the quantities defined above have all been encountered in the preceding sections of this chapter. The exception is $(\alpha\beta\gamma)_{jkm}$, which is designated the *second-order interaction effect* to distinguish it from the first-order interactions, which involve only two independent variables. Note that

$$\text{(5.50)} \quad (\alpha\beta\gamma)_{jkm} = (\mu_{jkm} - \mu) - [\alpha_j + \beta_k + \gamma_m + (\alpha\beta)_{jk} + (\alpha\gamma)_{jm} + (\beta\gamma)_{km}]$$

The interaction effect, $(\alpha\beta\gamma)_{jkm}$, is the combined effect of the jth level of A. the kth level of B, and the mth level of C adjusted for the independent contributions of the main and interaction effects which have been removed in Equation (5.50).

5.5 THE ANALYSIS OF VARIANCE FOR THE COMPLETELY RANDOMIZED THREE-FACTOR DESIGN

The relationship between any single score, Y_{ijkm}, and the single and joint effects of the variables A, B, and C is described in the identity of Equation (5.51).

$(\mu_{jkm} - \mu) - (\mu_j - \mu) - (\mu_k - \mu) - (\mu_m - \mu) - (\mu_{jk} - \mu_j - \mu_k + \mu)$ etc.

$$
\begin{aligned}
Y_{ijkm} - \overline{Y}_{\ldots\ldots} = & (Y_{ijkm} - \overline{Y}_{.jkm}) + (\overline{Y}_{.j..} - \overline{Y}_{\ldots\ldots}) \\
& + (\overline{Y}_{..k.} - \overline{Y}_{\ldots\ldots}) + (\overline{Y}_{...m} - \overline{Y}_{\ldots\ldots}) \\
& + (\overline{Y}_{.jk.} - \overline{Y}_{.j..} - \overline{Y}_{..k.} + \overline{Y}_{\ldots\ldots}) \\
& + (\overline{Y}_{.j.m} - \overline{Y}_{.j..} - \overline{Y}_{...m} + \overline{Y}_{\ldots\ldots}) \\
& + (\overline{Y}_{..km} - \overline{Y}_{..k.} - \overline{Y}_{...m} + \overline{Y}_{\ldots\ldots}) \\
& + (\overline{Y}_{.jkm} + \overline{Y}_{.j..} + \overline{Y}_{..k.} + \overline{Y}_{...m} - \overline{Y}_{.jk.} - \overline{Y}_{.j.m} \\
& \qquad\qquad\qquad\qquad\qquad\qquad - \overline{Y}_{..km} - \overline{Y}_{\ldots\ldots})
\end{aligned}
$$

(5.51)

Only one of the terms in the right-hand side of Equation (5.51) is new. The expression $(\overline{Y}_{.jkm} + \overline{Y}_{.j..} + \overline{Y}_{..k.} + \overline{Y}_{...m} - \overline{Y}_{.jk.} - \overline{Y}_{.j.m} - \overline{Y}_{..km} - \overline{Y}_{\ldots\ldots})$ is the least-squares estimate of $(\alpha\beta\gamma)_{jkm}$, the joint effect of the jth, kth, and mth levels of the variables A, B, and C adjusted for the main effects of these variables and for all first-order interaction effects of these variables. Equation (5.52) expresses this interpretation of the second-order, or three-variable, interaction effect more clearly.

$$
\begin{aligned}
(\overline{Y}_{.jkm} + \overline{Y}_{.j..} & + \overline{Y}_{..k.} + \overline{Y}_{...m} \\
& - \overline{Y}_{.jk.} - \overline{Y}_{.j.m} - \overline{Y}_{..km} - \overline{Y}_{\ldots\ldots}) = (\overline{Y}_{.jkm} - \overline{Y}_{\ldots\ldots}) - (\overline{Y}_{.j..} - \overline{Y}_{\ldots\ldots}) \\
& \qquad - (\overline{Y}_{..k.} - \overline{Y}_{\ldots\ldots}) - (\overline{Y}_{...m} - \overline{Y}_{\ldots\ldots}) \\
& \qquad - (\overline{Y}_{.jk.} - \overline{Y}_{.j..} - \overline{Y}_{..k.} + \overline{Y}_{\ldots\ldots}) \\
& \qquad - (\overline{Y}_{.j.m} - \overline{Y}_{.j..} - \overline{Y}_{...m} + \overline{Y}_{\ldots\ldots}) \\
& \qquad - (\overline{Y}_{..km} - \overline{Y}_{..k.} - \overline{Y}_{...m} + \overline{Y}_{\ldots\ldots})
\end{aligned}
$$

(5.52)

Squaring both sides of Equation (5.51) and summing over all indices as was done in the early part of this chapter and in Chapter 4, results in Equation (5.53) (note that the cross-product terms have again vanished).

$$
\sum_i^n \sum_j^a \sum_k^b \sum_m^c (Y_{ijkm} - \overline{Y}_{\ldots\ldots})^2 = nbc \sum_j^a (\overline{Y}_{.j..} - \overline{Y}_{\ldots\ldots})^2 + nac \sum_k^b (\overline{Y}_{..k.} - \overline{Y}_{\ldots\ldots})^2
$$

$$
[SS_{\text{tot}}] \qquad\qquad\qquad [SS_A] \qquad\qquad\qquad [SS_B]
$$

$$
+ nab \sum_m^c (\overline{Y}_{...m} - \overline{Y}_{\ldots\ldots})^2
$$

$$
[SS_C]
$$

$$
+ nc \sum_j^a \sum_k^b (\overline{Y}_{.jk.} - \overline{Y}_{.j..} - \overline{Y}_{..k.} + \overline{Y}_{\ldots\ldots})^2
$$

$$
[SS_{AB}]
$$

(5.53)

$$
+ nb \sum_j^a \sum_m^c (\overline{Y}_{.j.m} - \overline{Y}_{.j..} - \overline{Y}_{...m} + \overline{Y}_{\ldots\ldots})^2
$$

$$
[SS_{AC}]
$$

$$
+ na \sum_k^b \sum_m^c (\overline{Y}_{..km} - \overline{Y}_{..k.} - \overline{Y}_{...m} + \overline{Y}_{\ldots\ldots})^2
$$

$$
[SS_{BC}]
$$

$$\left(\begin{array}{c} 5.53 \\ \text{cont.} \end{array}\right)$$

$$+ n \sum_{j}^{a} \sum_{k}^{b} \sum_{m}^{c} (\overline{Y}_{.jkm} + \overline{Y}_{.j..} + \overline{Y}_{..k.}$$

$$+ \overline{Y}_{...m} - \overline{Y}_{.jk.} - \overline{Y}_{.j.m} - \overline{Y}_{..km} - \overline{Y}_{....})^2$$

$$[SS_{ABC}]$$

$$+ \sum_{i}^{n} \sum_{j}^{a} \sum_{k}^{b} \sum_{m}^{c} (\overline{Y}_{ijkm} - \overline{Y}_{....})^2$$

$$[SS_{S/ABC}]$$

We turn next to Table 5-13, which summarizes the analysis of variance for the three-dimensional case. The sources of variance follow immediately from Equation (5.53). The df are derived as before; for example, to obtain df_{ABC} we refer to Equation (5.52), which states that the second-order interaction effect is the cell effect (deviation of the cell mean from the grand mean) adjusted for first-order interaction effects and for main effects. This suggests

$$(5.54) \quad \begin{aligned} df_{ABC} &= (abc - 1) - (a - 1)(b - 1) - (a - 1)(c - 1) \\ &\quad - (b - 1)(c - 1) - (a - 1) - (b - 1) - (c - 1) \\ &= (a - 1)(b - 1)(c - 1) \end{aligned}$$

The various sums of squares can be obtained by appropriate substitution in, and expansion of, Equation (5.53). Since this is extremely laborious, it is preferable to utilize the isomorphism which is known to exist between df and squared quantities. For example, the $a - 1$ df for the A main effect suggests that the sum of squares expression consists of $a - 1$ squared quantities. We therefore have

$$\sum_{j}^{a} (\quad)^2 - C$$

where C is, as always, the squared sum of all scores, divided by the total number of scores, i.e.,

$$C = \frac{\left(\sum_{i}^{n} \sum_{j}^{a} \sum_{k}^{b} \sum_{m}^{c} Y_{ijkm}\right)^2}{nabc}$$

As before, any summations not represented outside the parentheses must be represented within the parentheses. We now have

$$\sum_{j}^{a} \left(\sum_{i}^{n} \sum_{k}^{b} \sum_{m}^{c} Y_{ijkm}\right)^2 - C$$

Finally, we divide by the number of scores within the parentheses, yielding

$$SS_A = \frac{\sum_{j}^{a} \left(\sum_{i}^{n} \sum_{k}^{b} \sum_{m}^{c} Y_{ijkm}\right)^2}{nbc} - C$$

The above operations may be stated verbally: all scores at a given level of A are summed, the sum is squared and divided by the number of scores which

TABLE 5-13

Analysis of variance for a three-factor design

SV	df	SS	EMS	F
A	$a-1$	$\dfrac{\sum\limits_j^a \left(\sum\limits_i^n \sum\limits_k^b \sum\limits_m^c Y\right)^2}{nbc} - C$	$\sigma_e^2 + nbc\theta_A^2$	$\dfrac{MS_A}{MS_{S/ABC}}$
B	$b-1$	$\dfrac{\sum\limits_k^b \left(\sum\limits_i^n \sum\limits_j^a \sum\limits_m^c Y\right)^2}{nac} - C$	$\sigma_e^2 + nac\theta_B^2$	$\dfrac{MS_B}{MS_{S/ABC}}$
C	$c-1$	$\dfrac{\sum\limits_m^c \left(\sum\limits_i^n \sum\limits_j^a \sum\limits_k^b Y\right)^2}{nab} - C$	$\sigma_e^2 + nab\theta_C^2$	$\dfrac{MS_C}{MS_{S/ABC}}$
AB	$(a-1)(b-1)$	$\dfrac{\sum\limits_j^a \sum\limits_k^b \left(\sum\limits_i^n \sum\limits_m^c Y\right)^2}{nc} - C - SS_A - SS_B$	$\sigma_e^2 + nc\theta_{AB}^2$	$\dfrac{MS_{AB}}{MS_{S/ABC}}$
AC	$(a-1)(c-1)$	$\dfrac{\sum\limits_j^a \sum\limits_m^c \left(\sum\limits_i^n \sum\limits_k^b Y\right)^2}{nb} - C - SS_A - SS_C$	$\sigma_e^2 + nb\theta_{AC}^2$	$\dfrac{MS_{AC}}{MS_{S/ABC}}$
BC	$(b-1)(c-1)$	$\dfrac{\sum\limits_k^b \sum\limits_m^c \left(\sum\limits_i^n \sum\limits_j^a Y\right)^2}{na} - C - SS_B - SS_C$	$\sigma_e^2 + na\theta_{BC}^2$	$\dfrac{MS_{BC}}{MS_{S/ABC}}$
ABC	$(a-1)(b-1)(c-1)$	$\dfrac{\sum\limits_j^a \sum\limits_k^b \sum\limits_m^c \left(\sum\limits_i^n Y\right)^2}{n} - C - SS_A - SS_B - SS_C - SS_{BC} - SS_{AB} - SS_{AC}$	$\sigma_e^2 + n\theta_{ABC}^2$	$\dfrac{MS_{ABC}}{MS_{S/ABC}}$
S/ABC	$abc(n-1)$	$\sum\limits_i^n \sum\limits_j^a \sum\limits_k^b \sum\limits_m^c Y^2 - \dfrac{\sum\limits_j^a \sum\limits_k^b \sum\limits_m^c \left(\sum\limits_i^n Y\right)^2}{n}$	σ_e^2	

have been summed, the process is repeated at the next level of A, and the next, until all levels of A have been exhausted, the a quantities are then added, and the correction term is subtracted from this total. The student should become so familiar with the notational language developed in Chapter 3 and used repeatedly in Chapters 4 and 5 that the much more succinct statement embodied in the computational formula becomes as meaningful to him as the lengthy verbal statement just completed. The SS_B and SS_C are obtained in a similar manner.

We next consider the sum of squares for the first-order interactions, taking for an example SS_{AB}. Expanding the df for AB, we obtain $ab - a - b + 1$. This suggests

$$\sum_j^a \sum_k^b (\quad)^2 - \sum_j^a (\quad)^2 - \sum_k^b (\quad)^2 + C$$

Remembering that all summation signs must be represented in each term, we have

$$\sum_j^a \sum_k^b \left(\sum_i^n \sum_m^c Y \right)^2 - \sum_j^a \left(\sum_i^n \sum_k^b \sum_m^c Y \right)^2 - \sum_k^b \left(\sum_i^n \sum_j^a \sum_m^c Y \right)^2 + C$$

The third step is division by the number of scores within each set of parentheses. We then have

$$
\begin{aligned}
SS_{AB} = {} & \frac{\sum_j^a \sum_k^b \left(\sum_i^n \sum_m^c Y \right)^2}{nc} - \frac{\sum_j^a \left(\sum_i^n \sum_k^b \sum_m^c Y \right)^2}{nbc} \\
& - \frac{\sum_k^b \left(\sum_i^n \sum_j^a \sum_m^c Y \right)^2}{nac} + C
\end{aligned}
$$

(5.55)

By subtracting and adding the correction term, C, the equation is fundamentally unchanged, but we may now write

$$
\begin{aligned}
SS_{AB} = {} & \left[\frac{\sum_j \sum_k \left(\sum_i \sum_m Y \right)^2}{nc} - C \right] - \left[\frac{\sum_j \left(\sum_i \sum_k \sum_m Y \right)^2}{nbc} - C \right] \\
& - \left[\frac{\sum_k \left(\sum_i \sum_j \sum_m Y \right)^2}{nac} - C \right]
\end{aligned}
$$

(5.56)

which is basically the form of the entry in Table 5-13. This form of the expression clearly demonstrates that the SS_{AB} is the variability among the means for the treatment combinations defined by A and B, adjusted for variability due to A and B effects. It is helpful to be able to think in terms of both Equation (5.55) and Equation (5.56). The approach underlying Equation (5.56) requires an understanding of the interpretation of interaction as a residual variability among cell means; that underlying Equation (5.55) is very general and readily provides computational formulas for even the most complex of designs.

The student who is still not comfortable with the notational language developed in Chapter 3 would do well to ponder the verbal translation of some of the expressions presented in this section. For example,

$$\frac{\sum\limits_{j}^{a}\sum\limits_{k}^{b}\left(\sum\limits_{i}^{n}\sum\limits_{m}^{c} Y\right)^2}{nc}$$

implies that we consider a single combination of levels of A and B (i.e., hold j and k constant), sum all scores at this combination of levels, square this sum, divide by the number of scores which have been summed, repeat this same process for all ab combinations of levels of A and B, and then sum the ab quantities which have been computed.

An expression for SS_{ABC} is no more difficult to arrive at than those previously considered; it is merely longer. Expanding the df results in $abc + a + b + c - ab - ac - bc - 1$, which suggests

$$\sum\limits_{j}^{a}\sum\limits_{k}^{b}\sum\limits_{m}^{c}(\ )^2 + \sum\limits_{j}^{a}(\ )^2 + \sum\limits_{k}^{b}(\ )^2 + \sum\limits_{m}^{c}(\ )^2 - \sum\limits_{j}^{a}\sum\limits_{k}^{b}(\ )^2$$

$$- \sum\limits_{j}^{a}\sum\limits_{m}^{c}(\ )^2 - \sum\limits_{k}^{b}\sum\limits_{m}^{c}(\ )^2 - C$$

Introducing the remaining summations within the parentheses, we obtain

$$\sum\limits_{j}^{a}\sum\limits_{k}^{b}\sum\limits_{m}^{c}\left(\sum\limits_{i}^{n} Y\right)^2 + \sum\limits_{j}^{a}\left(\sum\limits_{i}^{n}\sum\limits_{k}^{b}\sum\limits_{m}^{c} Y\right)^2 + \sum\limits_{k}^{b}\left(\sum\limits_{i}^{n}\sum\limits_{j}^{a}\sum\limits_{m}^{c} Y\right)^2$$

$$+ \sum\limits_{m}^{c}\left(\sum\limits_{i}^{n}\sum\limits_{j}^{a}\sum\limits_{k}^{b} Y\right)^2 - \sum\limits_{j}^{a}\sum\limits_{k}^{b}\left(\sum\limits_{i}^{n}\sum\limits_{m}^{c} Y\right)^2 - \sum\limits_{j}^{a}\sum\limits_{m}^{c}\left(\sum\limits_{i}^{n}\sum\limits_{k}^{b} Y\right)^2$$

$$- \sum\limits_{k}^{b}\sum\limits_{m}^{c}\left(\sum\limits_{i}^{n}\sum\limits_{j}^{a} Y\right)^2 - C$$

Finally, we divide by the number of scores within each set of parentheses, and obtain

$$SS_{ABC} = \frac{\sum\limits_{j}\sum\limits_{k}\sum\limits_{m}\left(\sum\limits_{i} Y\right)^2}{n} + \frac{\sum\limits_{j}\left(\sum\limits_{i}\sum\limits_{k}\sum\limits_{m} Y\right)^2}{nbc} + \frac{\sum\limits_{k}\left(\sum\limits_{i}\sum\limits_{j}\sum\limits_{m} Y\right)^2}{nac}$$

(5.57)
$$+ \frac{\sum\limits_{m}\left(\sum\limits_{i}\sum\limits_{j}\sum\limits_{k} Y\right)^2}{nab} - \frac{\sum\limits_{j}\sum\limits_{k}\left(\sum\limits_{i}\sum\limits_{m} Y\right)^2}{nc} - \frac{\sum\limits_{j}\sum\limits_{m}\left(\sum\limits_{i}\sum\limits_{k} Y\right)^2}{nb}$$

$$- \frac{\sum\limits_{k}\sum\limits_{m}\left(\sum\limits_{i}\sum\limits_{j} Y\right)^2}{na} - C$$

The right-hand side of Equation (5.56) is algebraically identical to the expression for SS_{ABC} in Table 5-13. That expression is of the form of Equation (5.54) for degrees of freedom, and it follows from the definition of interaction effect provided by Equation (5.52); i.e., the second-order interaction effect is the cell effect adjusted for the first-order interaction and main effects which contribute to the cell effect. If all main and first-order effects have been previously computed, the only new term to calculate is

$$\frac{\sum_j \sum_k \sum_m \left(\sum_i Y\right)^2}{n}$$

regardless of which expression for SS_{ABC} is used.

The $SS_{S/ABC}$ may again be computed as a residual term obtained by subtracting all main and interaction terms from the total. Alternatively, we note that $SS_{S/ABC}$ is the sum of the variability within the cells defined by the three independent variables. Consequently, it is the difference between the total variability and the variability among cell means. Therefore

$$SS_{S/ABC} = SS_{\text{tot}} - SS_{\overline{ABC}}$$

(5.58)
$$= \left(\sum_i \sum_j \sum_k \sum_m Y^2 - C\right) - \left[\frac{\sum_j \sum_k \sum_m \left(\sum_i Y\right)^2}{n} - C\right]$$

$$= \sum_i \sum_j \sum_k \sum_m Y^2 - \frac{\sum_j \sum_k \sum_m \left(\sum_i Y\right)^2}{n}$$

which is the expression in Table 5-13 and which is clearly on $nabc - abc = abc(n-1)$ degrees of freedom.

The mean square column has been omitted since it has been obtained, as previously, by dividing the entries in the SS column by the corresponding df. The entries in the EMS column are similar in form to those previously presented. With the exception of the entry for S/ABC they consist of two components, σ_e^2 and some term involving a θ^2 quantity. The subscript of the θ^2 term is always the entry in the SV column for that line of the analysis of variance table. The multiplier of the θ^2 term consists of the product of all dimensions of the design which are not included in the subscript. Thus, θ_{BC}^2 does not include S or A in the subscripts and is therefore multiplied by the levels of these, n and a. The definitions of the θ^2 term are similar to those encountered previously:

$$\theta_A^2 = \frac{\sum_j (\mu_j - \mu)^2}{a - 1}$$

$$\theta_B^2 = \frac{\sum_k (\mu_k - \mu)^2}{b - 1}$$

(5.59)

$$\theta_C^2 = \frac{\sum_m (\mu_m - \mu)^2}{c - 1}$$

$$\theta_{AB}^2 = \frac{\sum_j \sum_k (\mu_{jk} - \mu_j - \mu_k + \mu)^2}{(a - 1)(b - 1)}$$

$$\left(\begin{array}{c} 5.59 \\ \text{cont.} \end{array}\right)$$

$$\theta^2_{AC} = \frac{\sum_j \sum_m (\mu_{jm} - \mu_j - \mu_m + \mu)^2}{(a-1)(c-1)}$$

$$\theta^2_{BC} = \frac{\sum_k \sum_m (\mu_{km} - \mu_k - \mu_m + \mu)^2}{(b-1)(c-1)}$$

$$\theta^2_{ABC} = \frac{\sum_j \sum_k \sum_m (\mu_{jkm} + \mu_j + \mu_k + \mu_m - \mu_{jk} - \mu_{jm} - \mu_{km} - \mu)^2}{(a-1)(b-1)(c-1)}$$

Tests of null hypotheses about the various θ^2's are readily made by dividing the corresponding mean squares by $MS_{S/ABC}$. Since the EMS for this term differs from the expectations for all other terms only by the null hypothesis component, $MS_{S/ABC}$ is clearly the appropriate error term. We again note that this situation holds only when the levels of the independent variables have been arbitrarily selected; when one or more of the independent variables are random (in the sense defined in Chapter 1), different expectations will be encountered and, consequently, error terms other than the within-cells mean square may be required.

5.6 INTERACTION EFFECTS IN THE THREE-FACTOR DESIGN

The interpretation of first-order interactions follows that of the previous sections in which we dealt with two-factor designs. A significant AB interaction again indicates that the differences among the means of the populations defined by the levels of A change as a function of the level of B (or equivalently, that the differences among the means for the levels of B change as a function of the level of A). For example, assume that the entries in the $2 \times 2 \times 2$ (2^3) design of Table 5-14 are treatment population means. To investigate the AB interaction, we average over the levels of C, obtaining

$$\begin{array}{cc} & B_1 \quad B_2 \\ \begin{array}{c} A_1 \\ A_2 \end{array} & \left[\begin{array}{cc} 12 & 6 \\ 8 & 18 \end{array}\right] \end{array}$$

An AB interaction is clearly present, since

$$(\overline{Y}_{.11.} - \overline{Y}_{.21.}) - (\overline{Y}_{.12.} - \overline{Y}_{.22.}) = (12 - 8) - (6 - 18) = 16$$

TABLE 5-14

A set of treatment population means

		C_1		C_2	
	B_1	B_2	B_1	B_2
A_1	15	7	9	5
A_2	5	13	11	23

rather than zero, as would be the case if all AB interaction effects were absent. The AC and BC interactions also contribute to the variability among cell means; the relevant matrices are

$$
\begin{array}{cc}
 & \begin{array}{cc} C_1 & C_2 \end{array} \\
\begin{array}{c} A_1 \\ A_2 \end{array} & \begin{bmatrix} 11 & 7 \\ 9 & 17 \end{bmatrix}
\end{array}
\quad \text{and} \quad
\begin{array}{cc}
 & \begin{array}{cc} C_1 & C_2 \end{array} \\
\begin{array}{c} B_1 \\ B_2 \end{array} & \begin{bmatrix} 10 & 10 \\ 10 & 14 \end{bmatrix}
\end{array}
$$

A first-order interaction is significant when the differences among simple effects of one variable change significantly over the levels of the second variable. Similarly, a second-order interaction effect is significant when the simple interaction effects of two variables change as a function of the level of the third variable. This is easily investigated for the 2^3 design. For the data of Table 5-14, the measure of the simple AB interaction at C_1 is $(15 - 5) - (7 - 13) = 16$ and at C_2, $(9 - 11) - (5 - 23) = 16$. According to the definition just given, the ABC interaction does not contribute to the variability among cell means, since the measure of the AB interaction is the same at both levels of the third variable, C. It is important to realize that the same conclusion follows if the AC interaction is considered at each level of B, or the BC interaction at each level of A. These are all equivalent approaches, yielding identical information.

The approach just exemplified may be extended to any three-factor design, regardless of the number of treatment levels involved. Assuming that no error variance exists, if there is no second-order interaction

$$
(5.60) \quad [(\overline{Y}_{.jkm} - \overline{Y}_{.j'km}) - (\overline{Y}_{.jk'm} - \overline{Y}_{.j'k'm})]
$$
$$
- [(\overline{Y}_{.jkm'} - \overline{Y}_{.j'km'}) - (\overline{Y}_{.jk'm'} - \overline{Y}_{.j'k'm'})] = 0
$$

for all values of j, j', k, k', m, and m'. Suppose a third level of A is added to the data of Table 5-14, yielding

$$
\begin{array}{cc}
\begin{array}{cc} C_1 \end{array} & \begin{array}{cc} C_2 \end{array} \\
\begin{array}{cc} B_1 & B_2 \end{array} & \begin{array}{cc} B_1 & B_2 \end{array} \\
\begin{array}{c} A_1 \\ A_2 \\ A_3 \end{array}
\begin{bmatrix} 15 & 7 \\ 5 & 13 \\ 8 & 3 \end{bmatrix}
&
\begin{bmatrix} 9 & 5 \\ 11 & 23 \\ 10 & 9 \end{bmatrix}
\end{array}
$$

Applying Equation (5.60), when $j = 1$, $j' = 2$, $k = 1$, $k' = 2$, $m = 1$, and $m' = 2$,

$$
[(15 - 5) - (7 - 13)] - [(9 - 11) - (5 - 23)] = 16 - 16 = 0
$$

and when $j = 1$, $j' = 3$, $k = 1$, $k' = 2$, $m = 1$, and $m' = 2$,

$$
[(15 - 8) - (7 - 3)] - [(9 - 10) - (5 - 9)] = 3 - 3 = 0
$$

and when $j = 2$, $j' = 3$, $k = 1$, $k' = 2$, $m = 1$, and $m' = 2$,

$$
[(5 - 8) - (13 - 3)] - [(11 - 10) - (23 - 9)] = -13 - (-13) = 0
$$

One can again conclude that there is no ABC interaction.

An alternative method of investigating the *ABC* interaction is suggested by Tables 5-3, 5-4, and 5-5, which are the result of direct application of the analysis of variance model to first-order interaction effects. For second-order effects, Equation (5.50) could be applied, removing all main and first-order interaction effects from the three-dimensional matrix of means. If the *ABC* interaction is not significant, the variance among the adjusted cell means would be insignificant.

To further promote understanding of interaction effects in three-factor designs, we next consider graphs of several sets of means for various combinations of effects. Assuming that no error variance is present, the data of Figure 5-6 clearly reflect the presence of *A*, *B*, and *C* main effects. Averaging over the combinations of *B* and *C*, we have

$$A_1 \quad A_2 \quad A_3$$
$$[25 \quad 20 \quad 18]$$

averaging over the combinations of *A* and *C*, we have

$$B_1 \quad B_2 \quad B_3$$
$$[27 \quad 17 \quad 19]$$

and averaging over the combinations of *A* and *B*, we have

$$C_1 \quad C_2 \quad C_3$$
$$[16 \quad 24 \quad 23]$$

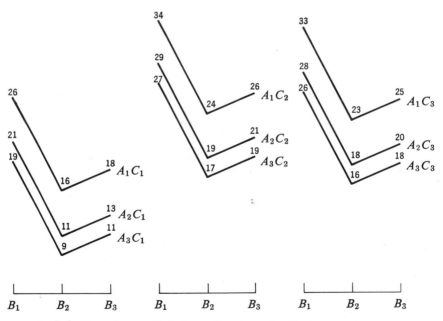

FIGURE 5-6 Data from a 3^3 design with only main effects present

We next note that at each level of C the three curves are parallel; there are no simple AB interaction effects at any of the levels of C. This absence of simple interaction effects is a *sufficient* condition for the absence of an overall AB interaction, since the overall effect is merely an average of the simple effects at the different C levels and the average of a set of zeros is just zero. The absence of simple effects is also a sufficient condition for the conclusion that there is no ABC interaction. The existence of the ABC interaction requires that the simple interaction effects of two variables change as a function of the level of the third variable. This condition is not met, since the AB interaction effects are zero at all levels of C. Using other sets of data, we will soon illustrate the fact that the absence of simple interaction effects is not a *necessary* condition for overall zero AB or ABC interactions.

The status of the AC and BC interactions is not as clear as that of the AB. Upon shifting the curves in Figure 5-6 so that the three curves in each set are similar with respect to the level of A, it becomes clearer that no BC interaction exists. Alternatively, we can average over the levels of A to obtain the matrix

$$\begin{array}{c c c c} & C_1 & C_2 & C_3 \\ B_1 & \begin{bmatrix} 22 & 30 & 29 \\ B_2 & 12 & 20 & 19 \\ B_3 & 14 & 22 & 21 \end{bmatrix} \end{array}$$

A plot of this set of means will result in three parallel lines. This is also true of

$$\begin{array}{c c c c} & A_1 & A_2 & A_3 \\ C_1 & \begin{bmatrix} 20 & 15 & 13 \\ C_2 & 28 & 23 & 21 \\ C_3 & 27 & 22 & 20 \end{bmatrix} \end{array}$$

the matrix of means for the AC combinations.

Two plots of the same data set are presented in the upper and lower halves of Figure 5-7. It is again assumed that the means are population means, that there is no error variance in the data set. Considering first the upper half of the figure, we find that an A main effect exists (the means are lower under the A_3 conditions than under the A_1 and A_2 conditions at all combinations of levels of B and C); that a B main effect exists (the B_1 means are highest, B_2 next, and B_3 lowest at combinations of A and C levels); and that a C main effect exists (the means generally increase as the level of C does). The status of interaction effects is more difficult to determine than it was for the data of Figure 5-6. The added complication is the presence of simple interaction effects; there is definitely an AB interaction at each level of C. The replot of the data in the bottom half of Figure 5-7 provides some illumination in this case. Shifting curves so that each set of three is at a single level of A, we find that there are no simple BC interaction effects.

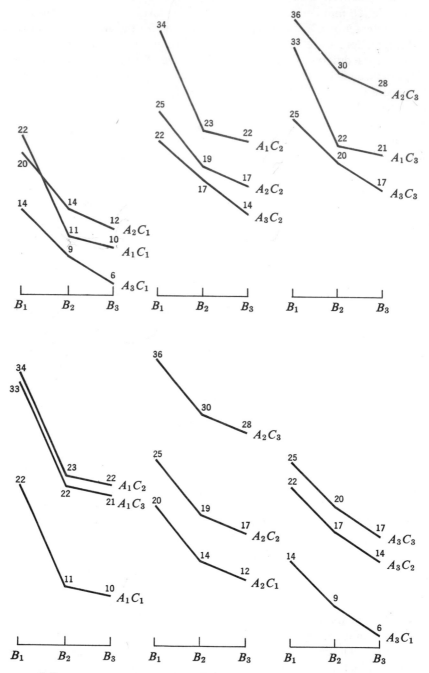

FIGURE 5-7 Two plots of a set of data with A, B, C, AB, and AC effects present

At each level of A, the spread among the curves does not change as a function of the level of B.   As in our discussion of the data of Figure 5-6, we may draw two conclusions from the absence of BC effects at the levels of A: (a) there is no overall BC interaction, and (b) there is no overall ABC interaction.   A plot of the means for the BC combinations, averaging over levels of A, will further verify (a), and the truth of (b) may be tested by investigating the validity of Equation (5.60) for the data of Figure 5-7.   The appropriate data plots will also verify that AC and AB interactions do exist.

It has been seen that the absence of simple first-order interaction effects means that the overall first-order interaction, as well as the second-order interaction, cannot be a source of variance.   The next question is whether it is possible to have simple interaction effects, but no overall interaction, and what the implications of such results are for the second-order interaction. The relevant data are plotted in Figure 5-8.   At each level of C, AB inter-

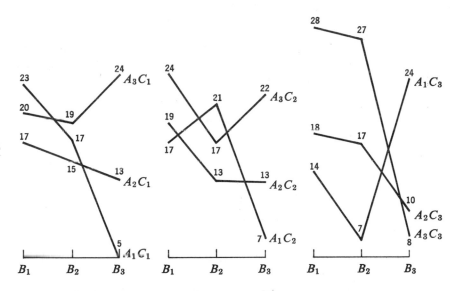

FIGURE 5-8   Data from a 3^3 design with A, B, and ABC effects present

action effects are present.   Alternative plots of the data will verify that simple AC and BC interaction effects also exist.   However, when we table the means for the AB combinations, first averaging over levels of C, we obtain

$$
\begin{array}{c}
\begin{array}{ccc} B_1 & B_2 & B_3 \end{array} \\
\begin{array}{c} A_1 \\ A_2 \\ A_3 \end{array}
\begin{bmatrix}
18 & 15 & 12 \\
18 & 15 & 12 \\
24 & 21 & 18
\end{bmatrix}
\end{array}
$$

which, when plotted, results in a set of parallel curves.   Similarly, we obtain

$$\begin{array}{c} & C_1 & C_2 & C_3 \\ A_1 & \begin{bmatrix} 15 & 15 & 15 \\ A_2 & 15 & 15 & 15 \\ A_3 & 21 & 21 & 21 \end{bmatrix} \end{array}$$

demonstrating the absence of an AC interaction. A third tabulation demonstrates that no BC interaction exists:

$$\begin{array}{c} & B_1 & B_2 & B_3 \\ C_1 & \begin{bmatrix} 20 & 17 & 14 \\ C_2 & 20 & 17 & 14 \\ C_3 & 20 & 17 & 14 \end{bmatrix} \end{array}$$

Thus it is possible that simple two-variable interaction effects may exist at each level of the third variable, but vary in such a way over levels of the third variable as to cancel each other out. The result is that there is no overall first-order interaction. An additional consequence of the situation just described is that a second-order, or three-variable, interaction must exist, since by definition if the interaction effects of two variables change over the levels of the third variable, there is a second-order interaction. Independent verification of the hypothesis of an ABC interaction may be obtained by applying Equation (5.60) to the data of Figure 5-8. For example, let

$$\begin{array}{cc} j = 1 & j' = 3 \\ k = 1 & k' = 2 \\ m = 1 & m' = 3 \end{array}$$

Then,

$$[(\overline{Y}_{jkm} - \overline{Y}_{j'km}) - (\overline{Y}_{jk'm} - \overline{Y}_{j'k'm})]$$
$$- [(\overline{Y}_{jkm'} - \overline{Y}_{j'km'}) - (\overline{Y}_{jk'm'} - \overline{Y}_{j'k'm'})] = [(23 - 20) - (17 - 19)]$$
$$- [(14 - 28) - (7 - 27)]$$
$$= 5 - 6 = -1$$

Since the above result is not equal to zero, the ABC interaction contributes to the variability among cell means.

Still assuming errorless data (or equivalently, that we are dealing with population means), the preceding results may be summarized in a very general way. Let X be any source of variance (e.g., A, AB, ABC) and Y be some variable not involved in the effect. Then it is possible to speak of the simple X effects at the levels of Y; the overall X effects obtained by averaging over the levels of Y; and the interaction of X and Y:

(a) If the X effects are zero at all levels of Y, the overall X effects will be zero. Thus, if there is no effect due to A at any level of B, there will be no A main effect; if there are no AB interactions at any level of C, there will be no overall AB effects.

(b) If the X effects at all levels of Y are zero, the overall interaction of X and Y will be zero. Thus, if the simple effects due to A are zero at all

If there are no simple effects of A at any level of B there will be no A main effect

levels of B, the overall AB effects will be zero; if the effects due to AB are zero at all levels of C, the overall effects due to ABC will be zero.

(c) If the overall effects due to X are zero but some of the simple effects of X at the levels of Y are not zero, effects due to the interaction XY will not be zero. Thus, if the main effects due to A are zero but simple effects at various levels of B are not, the AB interaction effects will not be zero; if the overall AB interaction effects are zero and if the simple AB effects at levels of C are not, the ABC interaction effects will be non-zero.

(d) If the interaction effects of X and Y are zero and if the overall effects of X are zero, then the simple effects of X at each level of Y will be zero. Thus, if the overall A main effects and the overall AB interaction effects are zero, the simple effects of A at each level of B will be zero; if the overall AB and ABC effects are zero, the AB simple interaction effects at each level of C will all be zero.

The preceding discussion has dealt solely with relationships among population means. With actual data, apparent violations of our conclusions will occasionally occur. For example, overall tests of A and AB effects may yield nonsignificant results, but tests of simple effects of A may prove significant at one or more levels of B. This set of statistical outcomes is inconsistent with statement (d), which is a true statement about population means. Such inconsistencies between the results of the analysis and our conclusions about relationships in the population serve as a warning to view our inferences with more than the usual skepticism. In the present example either a Type II error has occurred in testing the overall effects or a Type I error has occurred in testing the simple effects.

5.7 • A NUMERICAL EXAMPLE FOR THE THREE-FACTOR DESIGN

Assume that 120 subjects are each given 45 trials on a discrimination problem. The subjects are equally divided with respect to age (A: 6, 8, 10 years), amount of reward (R: 1¢, 5¢), and delay of reward (D: 0 sec., 10 sec.). The data have been summarized in Table 5-15 in a manner most convenient for the analysis of variance. The indices of notation are to be interpreted as follows:

i indexes the scores in each cell: $i = 1, 2, \cdots, 10$
j indexes the age levels: $j = 1$ (6 years), 2 (8 years), 3 (10 years)
k indexes the reward levels: $k = 1$ (1¢), 2 (5¢)
m indexes the delay levels: $m = 1$ (0 sec.), 2 (10 sec.)

We have the sum of scores and squared scores for each combination of A, R, and D ($\sum_i Y$, $\sum_i Y^2$); the sum of scores for each combination of R and D ($\sum_i \sum_j Y$), for each combination of A and D ($\sum_i \sum_k Y$), for each combination of A and R ($\sum_i \sum_m Y$), for each level of A ($\sum_i \sum_k \sum_m Y$), for each level of R ($\sum_i \sum_j \sum_m Y$), for each level of D ($\sum_i \sum_j \sum_k Y$); and the sum of all scores and of all squared scores ($\sum_i \sum_j \sum_k \sum_m Y$; $\sum_i \sum_j \sum_k \sum_m Y^2$). With

TABLE 5-15

Data from a three-factor experiment

			6 Years	8 Years	10 Years	
0 sec.	1¢	$\sum_i Y =$	258	329	368	$\sum_j \sum_i Y = 955$
		$\sum_i Y^2 =$	6,864	11,209	13,704	
	5¢	$\sum_i Y =$	262	351	383	$\sum_j \sum_i Y = 996$
		$\sum_i Y^2 =$	7,306	12,585	14,789	
		$\sum_k \sum_i Y =$	520	680	751	$\sum_k \sum_j \sum_i Y = 1,951$
		$\sum_k \sum_i Y^2 =$	14,166	23,794	28,493	
10 sec.	1¢	$\sum_i Y =$	217	238	308	$\sum_j \sum_i Y = 763$
		$\sum_i Y^2 =$	4,887	5,928	9,696	
	5¢	$\sum_i Y =$	220	263	381	$\sum_j \sum_i Y = 864$
		$\sum_i Y^2 =$	5,220	7,221	14,625	
		$\sum_k \sum_i Y =$	437	501	689	$\sum_k \sum_j \sum_i Y = 1,627$
		$\sum_k \sum_i Y^2 =$	10,107	13,149	24,321	
		$\sum_m \sum_k \sum_i Y =$	957	1,181	1,440	$\sum_m \sum_k \sum_j \sum_i Y = 3,578$
	1¢	$\sum_m \sum_i Y =$	675	567	676	$\sum_m \sum_j \sum_i Y = 1,718$
	5¢	$\sum_m \sum_i Y =$	482	614	764	$\sum_m \sum_j \sum_i Y = 1,860$
		$\sum_m \sum_k \sum_i Y =$	957	1,181	1,440	$\sum_m \sum_k \sum_j \sum_i Y = 3,578$
						$\sum_m \sum_k \sum_j \sum_i Y^2 = 114,030$

these quantities calculated, it is only necessary to substitute in the formulas of Table 5-13 to complete the analysis of variance. These totals will also be useful in subsequent tests which will be described in Chapters 13 and 14 and in tests of simple effects. (The sum of squared scores for each cell may be used to compute cell variances and to test for heterogeneity of variance. These calculations were performed and the cell variances were reasonably homogeneous; the actual calculations are the same as those of Section 5.3.4 and have therefore been omitted.)

The correction term, C, is again the sum of all scores, squared, and divided by the total number of scores.

$$C = \frac{\left(\sum_i \sum_j \sum_k \sum_m Y\right)^2}{120}$$

$$= \frac{(3,578)^2}{120}$$

$$= 106,684.03$$

The SS_{tot} is again

$$SS_{tot} = \sum_i \sum_j \sum_k \sum_m Y^2 - C$$

$$= 114,030 - 106,684.03$$

$$= 7,345.97$$

To obtain the sum of squares for *any* main effect:

(a) square the sum for each level of the variable,
(b) sum the squared quantities,
(c) divide by the number of scores at each level,
(d) subtract C.

Thus,

$$SS_A = \frac{\sum_j \left(\sum_i \sum_k \sum_m Y\right)^2}{40} - C$$

$$= \frac{(957)^2 + (1,181)^2 + (1,440)^2}{40} - \frac{(3,578)^2}{120}$$

$$= 109,605.25 - 106,684.03$$

$$= 2,921.22$$

$$SS_R = \frac{\sum_k \left(\sum_i \sum_j \sum_m Y\right)^2}{60} - C$$

$$= \frac{(1,718)^2 + (1,860)^2}{60} - \frac{(3,578)^2}{120}$$

$$= 106,852.06 - 106,684.03$$

$$= 168.03$$

$$SS_D = \frac{\sum_m \left(\sum_i \sum_j \sum_k Y\right)^2}{40} - C$$

$$= \frac{(1,951)^2 + (1,627)^2}{60} - \frac{(3,578)^2}{120}$$

$$= 107,558.83 - 106,684.03$$

$$= 874.80$$

To obtain the sums of squares for *any* interaction:

(a) square the sum for each combination of levels of the variables involved in the interaction,

(b) sum the squared quantities,

(c) divide by the number of scores in each combination of levels,

(d) subtract C,

(e) subtract the sums of squares for all effects contributing to the variability among the means for the treatment combinations involved in the interaction; e.g., to obtain the ARD interaction sum of squares, we remove the sums of squares for A, R, D, AR, AD, and DR.

Thus,

$$SS_{AR} = \frac{\sum_j \sum_k \left(\sum_i \sum_m Y \right)^2}{20} - C - SS_A - SS_R$$

$$= \frac{(675)^2 + \cdots + (764)^2}{20} - \frac{(3,578)^2}{120} - 2,921.22 - 168.03$$

$$= 109,855.30 - 106,684.03 - 2,921.22 - 168.03$$

$$= 82.02$$

$$SS_{AD} = \frac{\sum_j \sum_m \left(\sum_i \sum_k Y \right)^2}{20} - C - SS_A - SS_D$$

$$= \frac{(520)^2 + \cdots + (689)^2}{20} - \frac{(3,578)^2}{120} - 2,921.22 - 874.80$$

$$= 110,674.60 - 106,684.03 - 2,921.22 - 874.80$$

$$= 194.55$$

$$SS_{RD} = \frac{\sum_k \sum_m \left(\sum_i \sum_j Y \right)^2}{30} - C - SS_R - SS_D$$

$$= \frac{(955)^2 + \cdots + (864)^2}{30} - \frac{(3,578)^2}{120} - 168.03 - 874.80$$

$$= 107,756.86 - 106,684.03 - 168.03 - 874.80$$

$$= 30.00$$

$$SS_{ARD} = \frac{\sum_j \sum_k \sum_m \left(\sum_i Y \right)^2}{10} - C - SS_A - SS_R - SS_D - SS_{AR}$$
$$- SS_{AD} - SS_{RD}$$

$$= \frac{(258)^2 + \cdots + (381)^2}{10} - \frac{(3,578)^2}{120} - 2,921.22 - 168.03$$
$$- 874.80 - 82.02 - 194.55 - 30.00$$

$$= 111,009.00 - 106,684.03 - 2,921.22 - 168.03 - 874.80$$
$$- 82.02 - 194.55 - 30.00$$

$$= 54.35$$

The sum of squares for *subjects-within-ARD treatment combinations* may be most simply computed as

$$SS_{S/ARD} = SS_{tot} - SS_{\overline{ARD}}$$
$$= 7,345.97 - (111,009.00 - 106.684.03)$$
$$= 3,021.00$$

The results of the complete analysis of variance are summarized in Table 5-16. It is clear that performance improves with age and deteriorates

TABLE 5-16

Analysis of variance for data from a three-factor experiment

SV	df	SS	MS	F
A	2	2,921.22	1,460.61	52.33 *
R	1	168.03	168.03	6.02
D	1	874.80	874.80	31.34 *
AR	2	82.02	41.01	1.47
AD	2	194.55	97.28	3.49
RD	1	30.00	30.00	1.07
ARD	2	54.35	27.18	.97
S/ARD	108	3,021.00	27.91	
				* $p < .01$

when reinforcement is delayed. The main effect of reward is less clearly established, but the F ratio is almost significant at the .01 level, and the effects are in the direction which theory and experimental data would suggest (i.e., performance is better under the higher reward). It appears reasonable to conclude that the levels of reward used in this study do differ in their effects. The failure to obtain any significant interactions suggests that the effects of any one variable do not change markedly over levels of the other two variables.

5.8 MORE THAN THREE INDEPENDENT VARIABLES

The analysis and interpretation of data for completely randomized designs involving four or more independent variables are in all respects straightforward generalizations of the material previously presented in this chapter. Each variable and each of all possible combinations of variables is a potential contributor to the total variability, as is the variability among subjects within each combination of variables.

The *df* for main effects are again the number of levels of the variable minus one; those for an interaction are the product of the *df* for the variables entering into the interaction. For example, assume a design involving six independent variables labeled $A, B, \cdots, F$. Then the df for the $ABDE$ inter-action are $(a - 1)(b - 1)(d - 1)(e - 1)$, where $a, b, d,$ and e are the numbers of levels of $A, B, D,$ and E, respectively, following our previous notational usage.

The rules for computing SS for main (p. 129) and for interaction (p. 130) effects apply in all designs.   Thus, to obtain the SS for the $ABDE$ interaction:

(a) square the sum of scores for each of the $abde$ combinations of levels of the four variables,

(b) sum the $abde$ squared quantities,

(c) divide by the number of scores obtained in each of the $abde$ combi-nations,

(d) subtract C,

(e) subtract the sums of squares for all main and interaction effects im-bedded in the $ABDE$ combination.

The above steps may be summarized by

$$(5.61) \quad SS_{ABDE} = \frac{\overset{a}{\sum} \overset{b}{\sum} \overset{d}{\sum} \overset{e}{\sum} \left(\overset{n}{\sum} \overset{c}{\sum} \overset{f}{\sum} Y \right)^2}{ncf} - C - SS_A - SS_B - SS_D$$
$$- SS_E - SS_{AB} - SS_{AD} - SS_{AE} - SS_{BD} - SS_{BE}$$
$$- SS_{DE} - SS_{ABD} - SS_{ABE} - SS_{ADE} - SS_{BDE}$$

Note that if each term in Equation (5.61) is replaced by the corresponding df, the result is

$$(abde - 1) - 1 - (a - 1) - (b - 1) - \cdots - (b - 1)(d - 1)(e - 1)$$
$$= (a - 1)(b - 1)(d - 1)(e - 1)$$

The computations which are illustrated above are applicable when all cells contain equal numbers of subjects.   Alternative analyses have been pre-viously presented for the two-factor case for unequal but proportionate n's and for disproportionate n's.   These analyses are easily extended to data from designs involving more than two factors, and the details are therefore omitted.

In all designs, regardless of the number of variables, mean squares are ratios of sums of squares to degrees of freedom.   Still assuming completely randomized designs in which the levels of all variables have been arbitrarily chosen, the EMS will consist of σ_e^2 plus some quantity, θ^2, with a subscript which denotes the source of variance being referred to and which is multi-plied by n (where n is the number of subjects in each cell) and by the numbers of levels of those variables in the design which are not in the subscript.   For example, the EMS for the $ABDE$ interaction in the six-variable experiment referred to before is $\sigma_e^2 + cfn\theta_{ABDE}^2$, where n is the number of subjects in each of the $abcdef$ cells.   It follows from this discussion that the mean square for subjects within cells will be the error term (i.e., the denominator) for all F tests to be made in completely randomized designs.   The assumptions underlying the F test for multi-factor designs parallel those discussed previously for the two- and three-factor designs. Specifically, we assume that the error components of the scores are independently and normally distributed, with mean of zero and variance σ_e^2 within each population defined by the total number of treatment combinations.

5.9 COMPUTATIONS FOR SINGLE *df* EFFECTS

Consider an experimental design in which there are two levels of the variables, A and B. We then have four treatment combinations: A_1B_1, A_1B_2, A_2B_1, and A_2B_2. Designate the sum of n scores in each cell as T_{11}, T_{12}, T_{21}, and T_{22}, respectively. The usual computational formula for the SS_A is then

$$(5.62) \qquad SS_A = \frac{(T_{11} + T_{12})^2}{2n} + \frac{(T_{21} + T_{22})^2}{2n} - \frac{(T_{11} + T_{12} + T_{21} + T_{22})^2}{4n}$$

Let

$$(5.63) \qquad \begin{aligned} T_{1.} &= T_{11} + T_{12} = \sum_{i=1}^{n} \sum_{k=1}^{2} Y_{i1k} \\ T_{2.} &= T_{21} + T_{22} = \sum_{i=1}^{n} \sum_{k=1}^{2} Y_{i2k} \end{aligned}$$

Substituting Equation (5.63) into Equation (5.62) and expanding,

$$(5.64) \qquad \begin{aligned} SS_A &= \frac{T_{1.}^2 + T_{2.}^2}{2n} - \frac{T_{1.}^2 + T_{2.}^2 + 2T_{1.}T_{2.}}{4n} \\ &= \frac{T_{1.}^2 + T_{2.}^2 - 2T_{1.}T_{2.}}{4n} \\ &= \frac{(T_{1.} - T_{2.})^2}{4n} \end{aligned}$$

Equation (5.64) provides a much faster way of calculating SS_A than does Equation (5.62). The reduction in computational effort is even more marked when we consider the shortcut formula for SS_{AB}:

$$(5.65) \qquad SS_{AB} = \frac{(T_{11} + T_{22} - T_{12} - T_{21})^2}{4n}$$

Note that there is no need to subtract sums of squares for main effects or to remove a correction term. Equation (5.65) may be derived from the general interaction formula presented earlier, as was done for Equation (5.63). A quick and very general method for arriving at sum of squares formulas for any single *df* term is available if we redesignate the treatment combinations:

$$\begin{aligned} A_1B_1 &= ab \\ A_1B_2 &= a \\ A_2B_1 &= b \\ A_2B_2 &= (1) \end{aligned}$$

The subscript 1 indicates the presence of the lower-case letter, and the subscript 2 indicates the absence of the letter. If all subscripts are 2's, the new designation is (1). This notation can be extended to any number of variables, all of which are tested at two levels. Thus, the cell $A_1B_2C_2D_1$ in a 2^4 design is relabeled ad. Given these new labels, we may readily state the appropriate shortcut formula. The following steps are involved:

(a) List the new designations for all cells. For a 2^3 design, these would be

$$abc \ (= A_1B_1C_1) \qquad a \ (= A_1B_2C_2)$$
$$ab \ (= A_1B_1C_2) \qquad b \ (= A_2B_1C_2)$$
$$ac \ (= A_1B_2C_1) \qquad c \ (= A_2B_2C_1)$$
$$bc \ (= A_2B_1C_1) \qquad (1) \ (= A_2B_2C_2)$$

(b) Divide the cells into two classes, those that have an even number of letters in common with the effect and those that have an odd number of letters in common with the effect. For the AC interaction, the two classes are

1	2
abc	a
ac	c
b	ab
(1)	bc

Each of the designations in class 1 contains either two or zero of the letters a and c. All designations in class 2 contain one of the letters a and c.

(c) Obtain the sum of scores for classes 1 and 2 above and then square the difference in the sums. Divide this quantity by the total number of scores.

In the preceding 2^3 example, we might represent the operation of subtracting class 2 totals from class 1 totals by

$$[abc + ac + b + (1)] - [a + c + ab + bc]$$

which equals

$$[(abc + ac) - (ab + a)] - \{(bc + c) - [b + (1)]\}$$

This last quantity is the difference between C_1 and C_2 totals at A_1 minus the difference between C_1 and C_2 totals at A_2, which we have previously defined (Section 5.3.2) as a measure of first-order interaction. To further exemplify the development of single df formulas and their relationship to the meaning of interaction, we next consider the ABC interaction for a 2^3 design. According to the developments of Section 5.6 [in particular, see Equation (5.60)], the ABC interaction is a measure of the variation in the interaction of two variables which occurs over the levels of the third variable. In our new notation the appropriate contrast is

$$[(abc - ac) - (bc - c)] - \{(ab - a) - [b - (1)]\}$$

which equals

$$[abc + a + b + c] - [ab + ac + bc + (1)]$$

exactly the contrast which the odd-even rule, rule (b) above, demands. All designations to the left of the minus sign have one or three letters in common with ABC. To obtain SS_{ABC} we therefore insert the appropriate cell totals in the preceding formula for the contrast, square the result, and divide by $8n$, the total number of measurements.

As an alternative to the odd-even rule, consider this algebraic technique for generating contrasts. If the SS_{AC} is required, expand the quantity $(a - 1)(b + 1)(c - 1)$. We then have

$$(abc + ac + b + 1) - (a + c + ab + bc)$$

the contrast previously arrived at by the odd-even rule. For the SS_A, expand $(a - 1)(b + 1)(c + 1)$ and obtain

$$(a + ab + ac + abc) - (b + c + bc + 1)$$

The approach is simply to insert a minus sign only within those parentheses containing the letters appearing in the designation of the effect of interest.

In Section 5.7 sums of squares for a $2 \times 2 \times 3$ design were computed. The D, R, and DR effects are all on one df. Applying our single df approach to the cell totals of Table 5-15, we obtain

$$SS_D = \frac{(1,951 - 1,627)^2}{120}$$

$$= 874.80$$

$$SS_R = \frac{(1,718 - 1,860)^2}{120}$$

$$= 168.03$$

$$SS_{DR} = \frac{(955 + 864 - 996 - 763)^2}{120}$$

$$= 30.00$$

These are exactly the results obtained in Section 5.7.

5.10 CONCLUDING REMARKS

The completely randomized designs discussed in Chapters 4 and 5 have several advantages. The analysis of the data is simpler than for most other designs. For any given number of measurements, the error df will be larger for these designs than for comparable designs. The requirements of the underlying model are most easily met by completely randomized designs, and violations of the assumptions embedded in the model are least likely to affect inferences derived from the F ratio. These designs share one main deficit.

Since the within-cells variability which forms the error term is a function of individual differences, the efficiency of this design is relatively low. Other designs which allow the experimenter to remove from the error term variability due to individual differences will generally yield a more precise estimate of population effects. A completely randomized approach should be considered whenever subjects are reasonably homogeneous with regard to the variable being measured; whenever a large n is available, compensating to some extent for the variability of measurements; or whenever the available n is so small that the loss in degrees of freedom which always accompanies more efficient designs yields a considerable loss in power. It should also be noted that there are many experimental situations in which it is impossible to do anything other than assign different subjects to different levels of the variables. This is self-evident in the case where the independent variable is personality type or training technique. It may also be true where much time is needed to obtain a measure from the subject and it is therefore preferable to obtain only one measure from each subject.

EXERCISES

5.1 Plot *all* main and interaction effects. Assuming errorless data, which effects are significant?

	A_1			A_2			A_3		
	B_1	B_2	B_3	B_1	B_2	B_3	B_1	B_2	B_3
C_1	22	12	14	19	6	8	16	5	6
C_2	18	8	10	21	8	10	18	7	8
C_3	14	4	6	20	7	9	23	12	13

5.2 Prove that

$$n \sum_j \sum_k (\bar{Y}_{.jk} - \bar{Y}_{.j.} - \bar{Y}_{..k} + \bar{Y}_{...})^2 = SS_{AB}$$

as defined by Equation (5.15).

5.3 Suppose that in the design of Exercise 5.1, we have the following cell frequencies:

	A_1			A_2			A_3		
	B_1	B_2	B_3	B_1	B_2	B_3	B_1	B_2	B_3
C_1	10	10	10	5	5	5	15	15	15
C_2	10	10	10	5	5	5	15	15	15
C_3	4	4	4	2	2	2	6	6	6

Assuming that the entries in Exercise 5.1 are cell totals, compute sums of squares for all main and interaction effects.

5.4 Prove that $\sum_j n_j.(\bar{Y}_{.j.} - \bar{Y}_{...}) = 0$.

5.5 Suppose the cell frequencies for Table 5-3 are as follows:

$$\begin{bmatrix} 2 & 4 & 4 \\ 4 & 8 & 8 \\ 4 & 8 & 8 \end{bmatrix}$$

Remove the variability among row means. Do the column means change? Suppose the cell frequencies for Table 5-3 are

$$\begin{bmatrix} 2 & 3 & 5 \\ 2 & 5 & 3 \\ 6 & 2 & 2 \end{bmatrix}$$

Now what happens when the row main effects are adjusted?

5.6 In the experiment on age, amount of reward, and delay of reward, the experimenter had formed the following hypotheses:

(1) Performance should improve with age and amount of reward, and deteriorate with increased delays.

(2) The effect of delay should become more pronounced as age increases. Graph a set of data which would be consistent with the above hypotheses. Is a second-order interaction present?

5.7 *abcen* children are divided into *abce* groups according to age (A), level of B, level of C, and experimenter (E). Only the main and interaction effects of B and C are of interest. To save computational time it is decided to pull out one SV containing all terms which include A, E, or both. The SV's are therefore

$$B$$
$$C$$
$$BC$$
Pooled A, E effects
Within-cells error

(a) Give the SS and df formulas for the pooled term.
(b) Suppose we analyzed the data as having the following SV's:

$$B$$
$$C$$
$$BC$$
Residual

What are the residual df? Why might the first analysis be preferred?

DESIGNS USING A

CONCOMITANT VARIABLE

6

6.1 TREATMENTS X BLOCKS: INTRODUCTION

It was noted in preceding chapters that the major disadvantage of completely randomized designs is their relative inefficiency. The variability among subjects within groups, the error term against which the variability among treatment means is tested, is generally large. Much of this error variance can be attributed to individual differences in factors which contribute to performance. Even people treated alike will differ in their scores because of differences in such factors as attitude, previous experience, and intelligence. If the contribution of such individual difference variables could somehow be removed from the data matrix, the error variance would be reduced and it would be easier to detect the effects of the independent variable. In this chapter we consider one procedure for doing this, for removing some of the error variance attributable to individual differences.

In the design under consideration, subjects are divided into b blocks on the basis of their scores on a concomitant variable, a measure thought to be highly correlated with the dependent variable. For example, in a study in which some measure of paired-associate learning is of interest, the available population of subjects might be divided into blocks on the basis of intelligence test scores or even on the basis of scores in a paired-associate task other than the one to be used in the experiment. The simplest way to accomplish the distribution of subjects among blocks is to rank order them on the basis of the concomitant score. Assume that we have abn subjects. Then the highest scoring an subjects will be assigned to one block (e.g., B_1), the next an subjects will be assigned to B_2, and so on. The an subjects within each block are then randomly assigned to the levels of A, with the sole restriction that there be an equal number at each level. The result of the procedure that we have described is a two-factor (A, B) design with n subjects in each of the ab cells. The an subjects in each block are considered to be a random sample from an infinitely large population defined by the range of concomitant scores for that block. The members of this population have been randomly assigned to the a levels of A.

The treatments × blocks design has several advantages over the completely randomized, one-factor design. First, treatment groups are roughly matched for at least one measure which should affect performance. Second, since the design is essentially a two-factor design, the treatments × blocks interaction effects may be investigated. This means that we may consider such a question as, Are differences in the effects of different training methods greater at one level of intelligence than at another? Third, and most important, the treatments × blocks design will generally be much more efficient than a one-factor design involving the same total number of dependent measures at each treatment level. To see why this is so, we next turn to a detailed analysis of the efficiency of the treatments × blocks design relative to that of the completely randomized design.

6.2 RELATIVE EFFICIENCY

This section has several purposes. It is desired to prove the contention that the treatments × blocks design is usually more efficient than the completely randomized design. As a by-product of the proof, an estimate of the ratios of error variances will be obtained for the two designs. If it is known how much more efficient the treatments × blocks design has been than the completely randomized design would have been, there is a basis for judging whether it would be worthwhile to establish blocks in subsequent related experiments. Finally, it should be noted that although a specific derivation will be given for the relative efficiency of the treatments × blocks and the completely randomized one-factor designs, the procedure to be presented can be readily generalized for investigation of relative efficiencies of various other designs.

Table 6-1 contains the information necessary for a statement of the relative efficiency of the completely randomized and treatments × blocks designs. Instead of the usual σ_e^2, $\sigma_{e,r}^2$ and $\sigma_{e_{bd}}^2$ are used to distinguish between the error variances. Sums of squares formulas have been omitted, since those for the one-factor case were previously presented in Chapter 4 and those for the treatments × blocks design are the same as those for the two-factor design of Chapter 5. For the completely randomized design, bn scores are assumed at each level of A so that both designs are based on a total of abn scores.

TABLE 6-1

Expectations for two designs

	Completely Randomized	
SV	*df*	*EMS*
A	$a - 1$	$\sigma^2_{e_{c.r.}} + bn\theta^2_A$
S/A	$a(bn - 1)$	$\sigma^2_{e_{c.r.}}$
	Treatments × Blocks	
SV	*df*	*EMS*
A	$a - 1$	$\sigma^2_{e_{txb}} + bn\theta^2_A$
B	$b - 1$	$\sigma^2_{e_{txb}} + an\theta^2_B$
AB	$(a - 1)(b - 1)$	$\sigma^2_{e_{txb}} + n\theta^2_{AB}$
S/AB	$ab(n - 1)$	$\sigma^2_{e_{txb}}$

The expected total sum of squares for the completely randomized design is

$$(6.1) \qquad ESS_{\text{tot}_{e.r.}} = (a - 1)(\sigma^2_{e_{c.r.}} + bn\theta^2_A) + a(bn - 1)\sigma^2_{e_{c.r.}}$$

and the expected total sum of squares for the treatments × blocks design is

$$(6.2) \qquad \begin{aligned} ESS_{\text{tot}_{txb}} &= (a - 1)(\sigma^2_{e_{txb}} + bn\theta^2_A) + (b - 1)(\sigma^2_{e_{txb}} + an\theta^2_B) \\ &+ (a - 1)(b - 1)(\sigma^2_{e_{txb}} + n\theta^2_{AB}) + ab(n - 1)\sigma^2_{e_{txb}} \end{aligned}$$

Since both designs involve a groups of bn subjects, it is reasonable to assume that $ESS_{\text{tot}_{e.r.}} = ESS_{\text{tot}_{txb}}$. Then, setting the right-hand side of Equation (6.1) equal to the right-hand side of Equation (6.2), canceling $bn(a - 1)\theta^2_A$, and simplifying, we have

$$(6.3) \qquad \begin{aligned} (abn - 1)\sigma^2_{e_{c.r.}} &= (abn - ab + a - 1)\sigma^2_{e_{txb}} + (b - 1)(\sigma^2_{e_{txb}} + an\theta^2_B) \\ &\quad + (a - 1)(b - 1)(\sigma^2_{e_{txb}} + n\theta^2_{AB}) \\ &= (abn - ab + a - 1)\sigma^2_{e_{txb}} + ESS_B + ESS_{AB} \end{aligned}$$

and

$$(6.4) \qquad \sigma^2_{e_{c.r.}} = \left[1 - \frac{a(b - 1)}{abn - 1}\right]\sigma^2_{e_{txb}} + \frac{ESS_B + ESS_{AB}}{abn - 1}$$

We now have the population error variance for the completely randomized design as a function of population parameters estimated from data obtained with the treatments × blocks design. But relative efficiency involves comparisons of mean squares rather than expected mean squares. Therefore, Equation (6.4) is replaced by a similar statement in which sample statistics are substituted for population parameters:

$$(6.5) \qquad MS_{S/A} = \left[1 - \frac{a(b - 1)}{abn - 1}\right]MS_{S/AB} + \frac{SS_B + SS_{AB}}{abn - 1}$$

By Equation (6.5), the data from a treatments × blocks design may be used to estimate what the error variance would have been if the completely randomized design had been used. Such information should aid in selecting designs for future experiments in an area.

The efficiency of the treatments × blocks design relative to that of the completely randomized design is defined as

$$\text{R.E.} = \frac{MS_{S/A}}{MS_{S/AB}}$$

$MS_{S/A}$ is therefore replaced by the right side of Equation (6.5), resulting in

(6.6)
$$\text{R.E.} = \frac{[1 - a(b - 1)/(abn - 1)]MS_{S/AB} + (SS_B + SS_{AB})/(abn - 1)}{MS_{S/AB}}$$

$$= 1 - \frac{a(b - 1)}{abn - 1} + \frac{SS_B + SS_{AB}}{(abn - 1)MS_{S/AB}}$$

From Equation (6.6) it is seen that R.E. will be greater than 100 per cent (the treatments × blocks design will be more efficient than the completely randomized) whenever

$$\frac{SS_B + SS_{AB}}{(abn - 1)MS_{S/AB}} > \frac{a(b - 1)}{abn - 1}$$

or, multiplying both sides by

$$\frac{(abn - 1)}{a(b - 1)}$$

whenever

$$\frac{(SS_B + SS_{AB})/a(b - 1)}{MS_{S/AB}} > 1$$

The quantity $SS_B + SS_{AB}$ is distributed on

$$(b - 1) + (a - 1)(b - 1) = a(b - 1)$$

df. Therefore

$$\frac{SS_B + SS_{AB}}{a(b - 1)}$$

is a mean square and

$$\frac{(SS_B + SS_{AB})/a(b - 1)}{MS_{S/AB}}$$

is essentially an *F* ratio. Thus, R.E. will be greater than 1 whenever an *F* test of the combined *B* and *AB* effects is greater than 1 (not necessarily significant, merely greater than 1) and will increase as the variability due to either *B* or *AB* increases. The condition that this *F* be greater than 1 will have high probability whenever the concomitant and dependent variables are correlated in the population. For example, if intelligence and paired-associate scores are correlated, high intelligence subjects should have higher paired-associate scores than low intelligence subjects. This implies differences among the blocks based on level of intelligence and will generally be reflected in large values of SS_B and result in high relative efficiency.

While $MS_{S/A}$ will generally be larger than $MS_{S/AB}$, the former is distributed on $abn - a$ df while the latter is distributed on $abn - ab$ df (assuming abn measures for both designs). Thus, the completely randomized design is less efficient than the treatments $\times$ blocks, but its greater number of error df may result in a more powerful F ratio. Fisher* has proposed an adjustment to account for the discrepancies in df. He suggests that relative efficiency may be defined as

$$(6.7) \qquad \text{R.E.} = \frac{(df_{S/AB} + 1)(df_{S/A} + 3)}{(df_{S/AB} + 3)(df_{S/A} + 1)} \cdot \frac{MS_{S/A}}{MS_{S/AB}}$$

For example, if $a = 2$ and N (the total number of observations) $= 8$, for the completely randomized design $df_{S/A} = 2(4 - 1) = 6$, and for the treatments $\times$ blocks design with $b = 2$, $df_{S/AB} = 2[2(2 - 1)] = 4$. Then the adjusted relative efficiency is

$$\text{R.E.} = \left(\frac{5}{7}\right)\left(\frac{9}{7}\right)\frac{MS_{S/A}}{MS_{S/AB}}$$

$$= (.92)\frac{MS_{S/A}}{MS_{S/AB}}$$

6.3 SELECTING THE OPTIMAL NUMBER OF BLOCKS

The number of blocks, b, influences experimental results in two ways. On the one hand, as b increases, the number of error df decreases (assuming that the total number of observations is held constant), resulting in reduced power of the F test. On the other hand, increasing the number of blocks results in a reduction of error variance. The variability within a block $\times$ treatment combination should be smaller when there are three blocks (e.g., high, medium, and low intelligence) than when there are two blocks (high and low intelligence). Because of these opposed effects of increased block number, an optimal block number exists. There is some level of b such that lesser and greater values result in less precise tests of treatment effects. This optimal value of b changes as a function of a (number of treatment levels), n, and ρ (the correlation coefficient for the population of concomitant and dependent measures). In this section we will attempt to clarify the relationships among these factors. In doing so, we will provide information of practical value in designing treatments $\times$ blocks experiments, as well as the basis for a better understanding of the way in which the design operates.

Some measure of the adequacy of the design is required in order to decide upon the value of b for various experiments. Such a measure should also clearly reflect the influences of a, n, and ρ. Since the influence of ρ is

* R. A. Fisher, *Statistical Methods for Research Workers*, 12th ed. (London: Oliver & Boyd, 1952).

not clear in the R.E. formula, and since R.E. must be computed relative to another design, we seek some other index of error variability for the present purpose. The most generally accepted measure is I_a, the *apparent imprecision* of the design, the formula for which is

$$I_a = \frac{df_{S/AB} + 3}{df_{S/AB} + 1} I_t$$

(6.8)

$$= \left[\frac{ab(n-1) + 3}{ab(n-1) + 1}\right] \left\{\frac{1 - \rho^2[1 - (\bar{\sigma}_x^2/\sigma_X^2)]}{1 - \rho^2}\right\}$$

where σ_X^2 is the variance of concomitant measures for the jth treatment population, and $\bar{\sigma}_x^2$ is computed by obtaining the variance of concomitant measures for each block in the jth treatment population and then averaging over the b blocks; ρ is the correlation between X and Y measures in the jth treatment population. I_t is referred to as the true imprecision. I_a is the preferred measure, since Fisher's correction, $(df_{S/AB} + 3)/(df_{S/AB} + 1)$, adjusts for the loss of df (and therefore power) due to estimation of B and AB effects. To provide some idea of how we arrive at Equation (6.8), as well as a better feeling for the meaning of imprecision, we consider the sample-to-sample fluctuation in the difference between two treatment group means. We denote this variance of the difference between the means as $\sigma_{\bar{Y}_j - \bar{Y}_{j'}}^2$. An expression for aver $\sigma_{\bar{Y}_j - \bar{Y}_{j'}}^2$ ("aver" refers to the average variance over the b blocks) can be derived if it is assumed that

(a) within the population from which each block is sampled, Y (the dependent measure) is a linear function of X (the concomitant measure) and the slope of this function is the same for all b populations

(b) the population variability of the Y's about the best fitting straight line is the same for all b populations.

The appropriate expression is

(6.9) $$\text{aver } \sigma_{\bar{Y}_j - \bar{Y}_{j'}}^2 = \frac{2\sigma_Y^2}{n}\left[1 - \rho^2\left(1 - \frac{\bar{\sigma}_x^2}{\sigma_X^2}\right)\right]$$

where σ_Y^2 is the variance of dependent measures for the jth treatment population; σ_X^2, $\bar{\sigma}_x^2$, and ρ have been defined above. It is assumed that these population values are the same for all a treatment populations.

It is evident from Equation (6.9) that as the number of observations (n) is increased, the average sampling error decreases. The same relationship holds for ρ and sampling error. Note that when ρ is zero,

$$\text{aver } \sigma_{\bar{Y}_j - \bar{Y}_{j'}}^2 = \frac{2\sigma_Y^2}{n}$$

When ρ is 1,

$$\text{aver } \sigma_{\bar{Y}_j - \bar{Y}_{j'}}^2 = \left(\frac{2\sigma_Y^2}{n}\right)\left(\frac{\bar{\sigma}_x^2}{\sigma_X^2}\right)$$

Since the average variability over the blocks in a population will be less than the total variability in the population, $\bar{\sigma}_x^2 / \sigma_X^2 < 1$, and the sampling error when ρ is 1 will be some fraction of the sampling error when ρ is zero.

While the number of blocks, b, does not explicitly appear in Equation (6.9), its influence can be understood by considering $\bar{\sigma}_x^2$. If there is only one block, we actually have a completely randomized design, $\bar{\sigma}_x^2$ is identical to σ_X^2, and

$$\text{aver } \sigma_{\bar{Y}_i - \bar{Y}_{i'}}^2 = \frac{2\sigma_Y^2}{n}$$

As the number of blocks increases, the range of concomitant scores within each block must necessarily decrease, and $\bar{\sigma}_x^2$ becomes progressively smaller. Therefore, when the number of blocks is very large, $\bar{\sigma}_x^2$ is near zero and the average error is approximately

(6.10)
$$\min \sigma_{\bar{Y}_i - \bar{Y}_{i'}}^2 = \frac{2\sigma_Y^2}{n}(1 - \rho^2)$$

Cox* has proposed that the ratio of the average to the theoretically minimum sampling error (i.e., $\min \sigma_{\bar{Y}_i - \bar{Y}_{i'}}^2$) be utilized as an index of the precision of the design. Specifically, for the treatments $\times$ blocks design we have the *true imprecision*, I_t, where

(6.11)
$$I_t = \frac{\text{aver } \sigma_{\bar{Y}_i - \bar{Y}_{i'}}^2}{\min \sigma_{\bar{Y}_i - \bar{Y}_{i'}}^2}$$
$$= \frac{1 - \rho^2[1 - (\bar{\sigma}_x^2 / \sigma_X^2)]}{1 - \rho^2}$$

Multiplying by Fisher's adjustment, we have Equation (6.8), which defines I_a.

Feldt† has used I_a as the basis for determining the optimal number of blocks to be included in an experiment. That number of blocks which results in a lower value of I_a than any other number of blocks is considered the optimal number. Table 6-2 has been reproduced from Feldt's article. Data available from previous research or from pilot studies may be used to estimate ρ. With this estimate and knowledge of a and N (the total number of scores), the experimenter has a sound basis for deciding upon the number of blocks to be included in the experiment.‡

The relationships among the optimal value of b and the values of a, ρ, and N may be summarized as follows:

(a) As ρ increases, the optimal value of b also increases. The increased loss in error df due to increase in b is more than compensated for by the improvement in precision due to increase in ρ.

---

* D. R. Cox, "The Use of a Concomitant Variable in Selecting an Experimental Design," *Biometrika*, 44:150–158 (1957).

† L. S. Feldt, "A Comparison of the Precision of Three Experimental Designs Employing a Concomitant Variable," *Psychometrika*, 23:335–354 (1958).

‡ The entries in Table 6-2 have been rounded to the nearest integer.

TABLE 6-2

Optimal values of b for selected experimental conditions, assuming levels defined by equal proportions of the population

ρ	a	20	30	50	70	100	150
.2	2	2	3	4	5	7	9
	5	1	2	2	3	4	6
.4	2	3	4	6	9	13	17
	5	2	3	4	5	7	10
.6	2	4	6	9	13	17	25 **
	5	2	3	5	7	9	14
.8	2	5 *	7 *	12 *	17	23	25 **
	5	2 *	3 *	5 *	7 *	10 *	15 *

N header spans columns 20–150.

* Limit imposed by the requirement $N \geq ab$
** Slight improvement possible with more than 25 levels

This table is reproduced from L. S. Feldt, "A Comparison of the Precision of Three Experimental Designs Employing a Concomitant Variable," *Psychometrika*, 23:335–354 (1958), by permission of the author and editor.

(b) As N increases, the optimal value of b increases. The increased loss in error df due to increases in b has less effect on precision as the total number of observations increases.

(c) As a decreases, the optimal value of b increases. The increased loss in error df due to increases in b is compensated for by the reduced loss due to df_{AB} as a decreases.

The imprecision for a completely randomized design is easily obtained if we note that this is actually a treatments × blocks design with only one block. Consequently $\bar{\sigma}_{\bar{x}}^2 = \sigma_X^2$, and substituting in Equation (6.8),

$$(6.12) \qquad I_a = \left[\frac{df_{S/A} + 3}{df_{S/A} + 1}\right] \frac{1}{1 - \rho^2}$$

On the basis of Equations (6.8) and (6.12), Table 6-3 was derived; this presents the ratio of values of I_a for the completely randomized design to values of I_a for the treatments × blocks design (assuming that the optimal value of b is used). The tabled values are consistently greater than 1, indicating that the completely randomized design is more imprecise, or less precise. The advantage of the treatments × blocks design increases as ρ and N increase and as a decreases. To put it another way, the effort involved in assigning subjects to blocks is most worthwhile when the optimal number of blocks is large.

In using Table 6-2 to design experiments, it is helpful to note that the experimenter can readily use values of ρ, N and a other than those in the table. For example, suppose $\rho = .6$, $N = 30$, and $a = 4$. The value of optimal b

TABLE 6-3

Ratio of I_a for completely randomized design to I_a for treatments $\times$ blocks design

				N			
ρ	a	20	30	50	70	100	150
.2	2	1.015	1.023	1.029	1.034	1.036	1.038
	5	1.000	1.009	1.021	1.027	1.031	1.035
.4	2	1.117	1.141	1.161	1.170	1.176	1.181
	5	1.060	1.097	1.136	1,153	1.165	1.174
.6	2	1.388	1.443	1.494	1.516	1.531	1.541
	5	1.235	1.340	1.431	1.470	1.500	1.523
.8	2	2.196	2.378	2.543	2.615	2.666	2.699
	5	1.608	1.943	2.276	2.427	2.543	2.629

Based on Table 4 from L. S. Feldt, "A Comparison of the Precision of Three Experimental Designs Employing a Concomitant Variable," *Psychometrika*, 23:335–354 (1958), by permission of the author and editor.

for $a = 4$ is not tabled, but can be approximated by linear interpolation. When $\rho = .6$, $N = 30$, and $a = 5$, the value of b is 3. When $a = 2$, $b = 6$. Since $a = 4$ is $\frac{1}{3}$ the distance between $a = 5$ and $a = 2$, we take as the required value of b the number falling $\frac{1}{3}$ of the distance between 3 and 6. The optimal value chosen for the experiment is therefore 4. We may interpolate among various values of N in exactly the same manner.

If the value of ρ which has been estimated for an experiment does not appear in Table 6-2, we may linearly interpolate between values of ρ^2. For example, suppose that $N = 150$, $\rho = .3$, and $a = 2$. The square of ρ is .09, which falls $\frac{5}{12}$ of the distance between $.2^2$ ($= .04$) and $.4^2$ ($= .16$). When $N = 150$, $\rho = .2$, and $a = 2$, the optimal value of b is 9; when $\rho = .4$, $b = 17$. The level of b for our example should therefore fall at the value $\frac{5}{12}$ of the distance between 9 and 17. To the nearest integer, the result is 12.

6.4 EXTENSIONS OF THE TREATMENTS X BLOCKS DESIGN

The discussion has thus far been limited to the case in which only one treatment variable is under investigation. Extension to experiments in which several treatment variables are of interest is straightforward. For example, if one wants to test hypotheses about the single and joint effects of two variables, A and C, the model and the analysis is the same as that for the three-factor design of Chapter 5, blocks (B) being the third factor. Subjects are divided into blocks on the basis of the control variable; within each block, there is random assignment of subjects to the ac treatment combinations. The derivation of relative efficiency follows directly from that of Section 6.2.

I_t, the true imprecision, will not be influenced by the number of treatment variables. However, apparent imprecision will be increased if additional treatments are investigated and N is held constant. To see why this is so, note that the adjustment factor which transforms I_t into I_a is $(df_{error} + 3)/(df_{error} + 1)$. If, for example, $N = 80$, $a = 2$, and $b = 4$,

$$df_{error} = 80 - 1 - (2 - 1) - (4 - 1) - (2 - 1)(4 - 1)$$
$$= 72$$

and

$$I_a = \frac{75}{73} I_t$$

$$= 1.03 I_t$$

If five levels of a variable, C, are added to the design, we would then have

$$df_{error} = 72 - (5 - 1) - (2 - 1)(5 - 1) - (4 - 1)(5 - 1)$$
$$- (2 - 1)(4 - 1)(5 - 1)$$
$$= 40$$

In this case,

$$I_a = \frac{43}{41} I_t$$

$$= 1.09 I_t$$

When the error df are considered, the design involving more treatment variables is slightly less precise.

Tables similar to Table 6-2 have not been designed for the multivariable cases. However, because of the reduction in precision just noted, values of b smaller than those presented in Table 6-2 should be used whenever there is more than one treatment variable. As N becomes larger, the loss of error df, occasioned by the inclusion of additional variables, has a correspondingly smaller effect on I_a. Therefore, the tabled values become better approximations to optimal b.

6.5 THE EXTREME GROUPS DESIGN

A design related to the treatments × blocks design is one in which only two extreme blocks of subjects are used. For example, the eyelid conditioning rates of subjects who score high on the Taylor Manifest Anxiety Scale are compared with those for low scoring subjects, or the gambling behavior of subjects scoring high on the MMPI Psychopathic Deviant Scale is compared with the gambling behavior of subjects who score low on the scale. At the outset the distinction between this design and the treatments × blocks should be made clear. In the treatments × blocks design, subjects are divided into blocks on the assumption that the block, or concomitant, variable is correlated with the dependent variable. The purpose of the design is to improve the precision of the test of some treatment effect.   In the extreme groups design, the blocks variable is the variable whose effect is of interest.   Rather than assume a correlation between concomitant and dependent variable, the experimenter investigates whether such a correlation exists.   Do high anxious subjects give more conditioned responses than low anxious subjects?   Do those subjects who score high on a psychopathic deviant scale take more risks in a laboratory gambling task than those who score low on the scale?

There are two major questions to be resolved in relation to the extreme groups design.   First, what percentage of the available population should define the extreme groups?   Should the number of conditioned responses be compared for the top and bottom 10 per cent on the anxiety scale?   The top and bottom 25 per cent?   The top and bottom halves?   Second, when should the extreme groups approach be discarded in favor of sampling from all levels of the concomitant measure?   To clarify this second question, consider the following example.   Anxiety measures are available on 200 subjects. It is not feasible to obtain eyelid conditioning scores from more than 100 of the original group.   These 100 could be the highest and the lowest 50 on the anxiety scale, in which case a t test comparing their mean conditioning scores would be used to assess the relationship between anxiety and conditioning. Alternatively, the 100 subjects to be conditioned could be randomly sampled from the original group of 200, with an equal probability of representation for all anxiety scores.   In this instance a correlation coefficient would be computed and its deviation from zero tested by a t statistic.   Which test of relationship is more powerful?

We first consider the question of the optimal size of the extreme groups. The criterion of optimality is the power of the t test comparing the means of the two groups.   Feldt* has shown that when ρ is .10, the power of the t test is greatest if each extreme group consists of 27 per cent of the population tested on the concomitant measure.   As the correlation between the concomitant and dependent measures increases, the optimal percentage decreases, but not markedly.   When ρ is .80, power is greatest if each extreme group contains 23.3 per cent of the population.   Obviously, we never know ρ; the purpose of the experiment is to determine whether ρ is different from zero.   However, it seems reasonable to conclude that if we use the top and bottom fourths of concomitant measures, we will not depart far from optimality, regardless of the true value of ρ.   For example, the Taylor Manifest Anxiety Scale might be administered to a class of 100 elementary psychology students.   Fifty of these, the 25 scoring highest and the 25 scoring lowest, would then be asked to serve as subjects in an eyelid conditioning experiment. Mean number of conditioned responses would be compared for the two extreme groups.

* L. S. Feldt, "The Use of Extreme Groups to Test for the Presence of a Relationship," *Psychometrika*, 26:307–316 (1961).

We next consider the question of whether it is better to use the extreme groups approach, or to sample randomly from the population of test takers. The answer to this depends on two factors: the percentage of the original test takers who are available for the experimental session and the correlation between the two measures. Before attempting to answer the question we need some ground rules. Suppose that 100 students have been tested on the Taylor scale and we can run some maximum percentage on the eyelid conditioning apparatus. If the percentage is above 50, the rule will be that for purposes of comparing the extreme groups and random sampling approaches, only 50 per cent will be used for the extreme groups approach. For example, it may be undesirable in terms of the expenditure of time and effort to run more than 60 of our population of 100 in the conditioning phases. Since, for the extreme groups approach, two groups, each consisting of 25 subjects, are optimal, this is all we will use. The power of the t test between means for this optimal grouping will be compared with a t test of the correlation coefficient for a random sample of 60 subjects. If less than 50 per cent of the population is available for the conditioning phase, the available percentage is divided in half to determine the size of the extreme groups.

We may briefly summarize Feldt's findings with regard to this comparison of two approaches. If both concomitant and dependent measures are available on 80 per cent or more of the population, the random sampling–correlational approach is more powerful. If the dependent measure can be obtained from only 75 per cent of the subjects originally tested, the extreme groups approach should be used if $\rho < .492$; otherwise 75 per cent should be sampled at random from the population, tested in the second phase of the experiment, and a correlation coefficient then computed. As the percentage of subjects for whom both measures are available decreases, a higher value of ρ is required if the correlational approach is to be used. Thus, if no more than 50 per cent of the subjects given the Taylor scale are to be tested in the conditioning phase, the extreme groups approach should be used whenever $\rho < .847$.

Let us attempt to reduce this discussion to some simple recommendations. We again note that the value of ρ is never known; the purpose of the experiment is to get some information about it. However, we may be able to obtain a rough estimate from other research. In the case of the Taylor scale and conditioned eyelid responding, correlations between other anxiety measures and other forms of conditioning may be found in the literature. Such correlations tend to be low, rarely exceeding .2. In general, correlations greater than .6 are rarely observed in the psychological literature. Therefore, unless both concomitant and dependent measures are obtainable from at least 80 per cent of the population, the extreme groups approach should generally be used. There will be some rare occasions when the value of ρ is surprisingly high, and the correlational approach would therefore have proved more powerful. However, if ρ is very large, even a less powerful

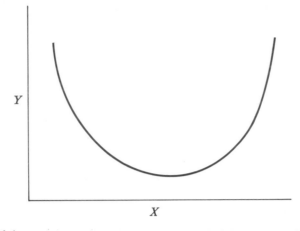

FIGURE 6-1   Example of a nonlinear relationship between Y and X

approach should be sufficiently sensitive.   If more than 80 per cent of the population is available for both phases of the experiment, then the total available proportion should be randomly sampled from the population and a correlation coefficient computed.

Feldt points out that his results depend upon the assumptions that the distribution of the concomitant and dependent measures is bivariate normal and that the relationship between the two variables is linear.   If the latter assumption is incorrect, the extreme groups approach is at worst misleading, at best relatively uninformative.   Consider Figure 6-1 to understand why the extreme groups approach might be misleading.   If the extreme groups are tested, we will surely conclude that they do not differ with respect to Y, the concomitant measure.   This is true, but completely misses the important fact that there is a relationship between X and Y, that the extreme groups differ from a middle group.   Even if the relationship between X and Y is monotonic (i.e., Y consistently increases or consistently decreases as X increases), if it is not linear, the extreme groups approach results in a loss of information.   Whenever there is reason to suspect a nonlinear relationship, it is better to sample the available proportion randomly, regardless of its size, from the total population from which the concomitant measure was taken.   In this way, information about the shape of the function relating X and Y can be obtained.

EXERCISES

6.1   Assume that we are interested in the main and joint effects of two variables, A and B.   Derive the efficiency of an $A \times B \times$ blocks design relative to that of a two-factor (A, B) completely randomized design.

6.2 Analyze the following set of data obtained with an $A \times$ blocks design

	A_1	A_2	A_3
B_1	1	11	3
	2	5	1
B_2	4	8	3
	3	7	3
B_3	6	2	9
	8	5	5
B_4	10	2	5
	8	2	12

Estimate the efficiency relative to a completely randomized design. What is the primary reason that the $A \times$ blocks design is more efficient?

6.3 Several previous studies have yielded estimates of the correlation between an intelligence test and paired-associate learning which range from .25 to .35. Given four levels of A and a total of 80 available subjects, what value of b would yield optimal precision?

REPEATED MEASUREMENTS DESIGNS

7

7.1 INTRODUCTION

In Chapters 4 and 5 error variance was separated from the variance among treatment effects. Within the completely randomized designs, error variance was a large complex contributed to by individual differences and errors of measurement. In Chapter 6 one way of reducing the error variance was considered. It was shown that some of the variability due to individual differences could be removed if subjects were divided into blocks on the basis of a concomitant variable correlated with the dependent variable. In this chapter consideration will be given to designs in which error variability due to individual differences is further reduced, in fact completely removed.

The one-factor repeated measurements design entails a test of each subject under each of the a levels of the treatment variable A. The order of presentation of the A_j is randomized independently for each subject. The design may be laid out as a two-factor design where subjects constitute the second factor, as has been done in Table 7-1. The important point is that

TABLE 7-1

Data matrix for a one-factor repeated measurements design

	A_1	$\cdots$	A_2	$\cdots$	A_j	$\cdots$	A_a
S_1	Y_{11}		Y_{12}		Y_{1j}		Y_{1a}
S_2	Y_{21}		Y_{22}		Y_{2j}		Y_{2a}
$\vdots$							
S_i	Y_{i1}		Y_{i2}		Y_{ij}		Y_{ia}
$\vdots$							
S_n	Y_{n1}		Y_{n2}		Y_{nj}		Y_{na}

subjects may be treated like any main effect in a two-factor design, the variability associated with the effect can be isolated, and as a consequence the error variance in this design is not inflated by variability due to individual differences. The design will generally be more efficient than even the treatments ✕ blocks design, since variability due to individual differences will be more effectively separated from error variance.

Increased precision is not the sole reason for the use of the repeated measurements design. Both the completely randomized and treatments ✕ blocks designs require more subjects than does the repeated measurements design to achieve the same power of the F test. Therefore, the use of the repeated measurements design should be considered whenever a limited number of subjects are available for long periods of time. This will frequently be the case in small clinics, military research installations, and industrial settings. It will less often be a factor in the choice of a design in large universities.

The repeated measurements design is the natural one to select when one is concerned with performance trends over time. For example, if one wants to measure the course of dark adaptation over time, the most efficient use of subjects requires that each subject be tested at all points in time that are of interest. In this instance, time is the treatment variable A.

Although the repeated measurements design does not involve any new computational problems, two other issues arise which have not been considered in the context of previous designs. For the first time, the levels of one of our variables, S (subjects), may be considered a random sample from a population of levels. In Section 7.2 some implications of random, as opposed to fixed, effects will be considered. There is also the strong possibility that scores for two treatments will be correlated, since both sets of scores are obtained from the same individuals. The implication of this violation of the usual independence assumption will also be dealt with in Section 7.2.

7.2 MODELS FOR THE ONE-FACTOR REPEATED MEASUREMENTS DESIGN

7.2.1 The additive model

Consider a group of n subjects, each of whom is tested once under each level of A, the treatment variable. The order of exposure of the subject to the treatment levels is random, and the randomization is carried out independently for each subject. In order to develop a model for this experiment, it is assumed that the n subjects are a random sample from an infinite population of subjects. Furthermore, the observed score for the ith subject under treatment A_j is viewed as being randomly sampled from an infinite population of independent measurements on the ith subject under A_j. We first consider the additive model:

$$(7.1) \qquad\qquad Y_{ij} = \mu + \eta_i + \alpha_j + \epsilon_{ij}$$

where Y_{ij} is the score of subject i under A_j; $\eta_i = \mu_i - \mu$ (μ_i is the population mean of the a scores for the ith subject); $\alpha_j = \mu_j - \mu$ (μ_j is the mean of the scores of an infinite population of subjects tested under A_j); and ϵ_{ij} is the deviation of Y_{ij} from μ which is not accounted for by the treatment effect (α_j) or by individual differences (η_i).

Ordinarily, the a levels of the treatment variable are arbitrarily selected by the experimenter. It is as if there were only a levels in the population and they were all represented in the study. If this is the case, $\sum_{j=1}^{a} \alpha_j = 0$, since the sum of all deviations of treatment means about their mean, μ, must be zero. As was seen in Chapter 4, this fact is used in deriving the expected mean squares. A second implication of the fact that the effects of A are fixed (i.e., its levels are arbitrarily sampled) is that inferences about treatment effects should be limited to those treatment levels that are included in the experiment. To put it another way, $\theta_A^2 \ [= \sum_j (\mu_j - \mu)^2/(a-1)]$ is a measure of the variability of only those a treatment effects included in the population, and strictly speaking, our null hypothesis is that θ_A^2 equals zero.

When subjects are considered, the situation is somewhat different. The most reasonable assumption about the subjects is that they are a random sample from an infinite population. Admittedly, it would be hard to defend the usual procedures of subject selection as truly random, and it is sometimes difficult to characterize precisely the population sampled. However, it is clear that the n subjects have not been arbitrarily selected because of a desire to compare n qualitatively or quantitatively differing characteristics. The random sampling assumption seems to describe the true state of affairs best.

It is further assumed that the η_i are distributed normally in the population sampled and that this population has mean zero and variance σ_S^2, i.e., $E(\eta_i) = 0$ and var $(\eta_i) = \sigma_S^2$. Note that $\sum_{i=1}^{n} \eta_i \neq 0$, since the η_i sampled in any one experiment do not exhaust the population of such deviation scores. In further contrast to fixed effect variables, conclusions about the variability of the η_i are conclusions about the variance of the population from which the n η_i have been sampled; the conclusions are not restricted to the particular sample of subjects in the experiment.

As usual, the ϵ_{ij} are assumed to be random samples from a normally distributed treatment populations, each with mean zero and variance σ_e^2. The η, α, and ϵ are assumed to be uncorrelated.

Table 7-2, which summarizes the analysis of variance for the repeated measurements design, is a consequence of Equation (7.1) and the sampling and distributional assumptions that have been presented.

We consider the SV first. Equation (7.1) suggests that the total variance should have three components: A, S, and error. The error source has been

TABLE 7-2
Analysis of variance for the additive model

SV	df	SS	MS	EMS	F
S	$n-1$	$\dfrac{\sum_i \left(\sum_j Y_{ij}\right)^2}{a} - C$	$\dfrac{SS_S}{n-1}$	$\sigma_e^2 + a\sigma_S^2$	$\dfrac{MS_S}{MS_{SA}}$
A	$a-1$	$\dfrac{\sum_j \left(\sum_i Y_{ij}\right)^2}{n} - C$	$\dfrac{SS_A}{a-1}$	$\sigma_e^2 + n\theta_A^2$	$\dfrac{MS_A}{MS_{SA}}$
SA	$(n-1)(a-1)$	$\sum_i \sum_j Y_{ij}^2 - C - SS_S - SS_A$	$\dfrac{SS_{SA}}{(n-1)(a-1)}$	σ_e^2	

prove →

TABLE 7-3
Analysis of variance for the nonadditive model

SV	df	SS	MS	EMS	F
S	$n-1$	$\dfrac{\sum_i \left(\sum_j Y_{ij}\right)^2}{a} - C$	$\dfrac{SS_S}{n-1}$	$\sigma_e^2 + a\sigma_S^2$	
A	$a-1$	$\dfrac{\sum_j \left(\sum_i Y_{ij}\right)^2}{n} - C$	$\dfrac{SS_A}{a-1}$	$\sigma_e^2 + \sigma_{SA}^2 + n\theta_A^2$	$\dfrac{MS_A}{MS_{SA}}$
SA	$(n-1)(a-1)$	$\sum_i \sum_j Y_{ij}^2 - C - SS_S - SS_A$	$\dfrac{SS_{SA}}{(n-1)(a-1)}$	$\sigma_e^2 + \sigma_{SA}^2$	

labeled SA as a reminder that the computations involved are those for an interaction. To obtain the error sums of squares, the variability among cell means (in this design the mean is based on one score) is adjusted for the contributions of A and S variability. Despite the form of the computations, it is important to note that under the additive model, MS_{SA} estimates the population error variance and nothing more; no interaction is assumed to exist in the population.

The computations for both SS_A and SS_S follow directly from those for the two-factor designs of Chapter 5. There is one index of summation less in the present case because there is only one score in each cell of this "two-factor" design. The df are also straightforward; nothing new need be added to the discussions of Chapters 4 and 5.

The F tests for both A and S follow the usual rule: a denominator is required such that, under H_0, $E(F) = 1$. Clearly, MS_{SA} will be appropriate for both F tests.

7.2.2   The nonadditive model

The assumption that η_i and α_j contribute in an additive manner to the "true" (errorless) score of the ith subject in treatment A_j permits the simple analysis just presented in the preceding section. Unfortunately, data are rarely so obliging as to conform to Equation (7.1). More often than not, the variability among subjects' scores will be a function of the particular treatment under observation. This means that an interaction of subject and treatment level contributes to the score. Such a state of affairs requires a revision of our model to include an interaction term in the population as a contribution to the score, Y_{ij}. The equation which expresses this nonadditive model is

$$(7.2) \qquad Y_{ij} = \mu + \eta_i + \alpha_j + (\eta\alpha)_{ij} + \epsilon_{ij}$$

where $(\eta\alpha)_{ij}$ is the interaction effect of the ith subject and the jth level of A and is assumed to be a random variable sampled from a normally distributed population with mean zero and variance σ_{SA}^2. Turning to Table 7-3, we see that sources of variance, df, and sums of squares are the same under the nonadditive model as they were under the additive model; merely assuming separate interaction and error components in the population does not enable us to compute them separately. To put it another way, regardless of the model, SS_A, SS_S, and SS_{SA} add to SS_{tot}. However, the EMS have changed. The interaction variance, σ_{SA}^2, now contributes to the expectations for A and SA. Of particular interest is the $E(MS_A)$, which is the first instance that we have encountered of an EMS which contains a component other than σ_e^2 and the null hypothesis term. In view of this development, it would seem worthwhile to derive the EMS for the nonadditive model.

We first consider $E(MS_S)$. Summing over j for both sides of Equation (7.2) and dividing by a, we obtain

$$(7.3) \qquad \overline{Y}_{i.} = \mu + \frac{\sum_j \eta_i}{a} + \frac{\sum_j \alpha_j}{a} + \frac{\sum_j (\eta\alpha)_{ij}}{a} + \frac{\sum_j \epsilon_{ij}}{a}$$

Since A is a fixed variable, $\sum_j \alpha_j = 0$. Furthermore, the sum of all interaction effects for a subject will also be zero. Therefore, we may replace Equation (7.3) by

$$(7.4) \qquad \overline{Y}_{i.} = \mu + \eta_i + \frac{\sum_j \epsilon_{ij}}{a}$$

Note that the interaction effect does not appear in Equation (7.4). If we now sum over i on both sides of Equation (7.4) and divide by n, we obtain

$$(7.5) \qquad \overline{Y}_{..} = \mu + \frac{\sum_i \eta_i}{n} + \frac{\sum_i \sum_j \epsilon_{ij}}{na}$$

Subtracting Equation (7.5) from Equation (7.4), we have

$$(7.6) \qquad \overline{Y}_{i.} - \overline{Y}_{..} = \left(\eta_i - \frac{\sum_i \eta_i}{n} \right) + \left(\frac{\sum_j \epsilon_{ij}}{a} - \frac{\sum_i \sum_j \epsilon_{ij}}{na} \right)$$

The remainder of the derivation parallels that for the one-factor completely randomized design. Squaring both sides of Equation (7.6) and summing over i and j, we have the following expression for SS_S:

$$\sum_j \sum_i (\overline{Y}_{i.} - \overline{Y}_{..})^2 = a \sum_i \eta_i^2 + na \frac{\left(\sum_i \eta_i \right)^2}{n^2} - 2a \frac{\left(\sum_i \eta_i \right)^2}{n} + a \sum_i \frac{\left(\sum_j \epsilon_{ij} \right)^2}{a^2}$$

$$(7.7) \qquad + na \frac{\left(\sum_i \sum_j \epsilon_{ij} \right)^2}{n^2 a^2} - 2a \frac{\left(\sum_i \sum_j \epsilon_{ij} \right)^2}{na^2}$$

$$+ 2 \sum_i \sum_j \left(\eta_i - \frac{\sum_i \eta_i}{n} \right) \left(\frac{\sum_j \epsilon_{ij}}{a} - \frac{\sum_i \sum_j \epsilon_{ij}}{na} \right)$$

We next take the expectation over an infinite number of replications of the experiment. When this is done, the right-hand side of Equation (7.7) is considerably simplified. First, since η_i and ϵ_{ij} are independent of each other, $E(\eta_i)(\epsilon_{ij}) = 0$, and the last term on the right side of Equation (7.7) therefore vanishes. Secondly, since the η_i and the ϵ_{ij} are both independently distributed, $E(\eta_i)(\eta_{i'})$ and $E(\epsilon_{ij})(\epsilon_{i'j'})$ both equal zero. Consequently,

$$E \left(\sum_i \eta_i \right)^2 = E(\eta_1^2 + \eta_2^2 + \cdots + \eta_n^2 + 2\eta_1\eta_2 + \cdots + 2\eta_i\eta_{i'} + \cdots 2\eta_{n-1}\eta_n)$$

$$= E(\eta_1^2 + \eta_2^2 + \cdots + \eta_n^2)$$

$$= E \left(\sum_i \eta_i^2 \right)$$

and similarly,

$$E \left(\sum_i \sum_j \epsilon_{ij} \right)^2 = E \left(\sum_i \sum_j \epsilon_{ij}^2 \right)$$

Applying these independence results and combining terms in Equation (7.7), we have

$$(7.8) \quad E(SS_S) = a \sum_i E(\eta_i)^2 - \frac{a}{n} \sum_i E(\eta_i)^2 + \frac{1}{a} \sum_i \sum_j E(\epsilon_{ij})^2 - \frac{1}{an} \sum_i \sum_j E(\epsilon_{ij})^2$$

It was previously assumed that η_i is distributed with variance σ_S^2, and that ϵ_{ij} is distributed with variance σ_e^2. This is equivalent to stating that $E(\eta_i^2) = \sigma_S^2$ and $E(\epsilon_{ij}^2) = \sigma_e^2$. Then, making the appropriate substitution for the expectations, replacing $\sum_i$ by n and $\sum_j$ by a (since we are now summing over a constant), and combining terms, we obtain the final result:

$$(7.9) \qquad\qquad E(SS_S) = a(n - 1)\sigma_S^2 + (n - 1)\sigma_e^2$$

The expression for the $E(MS_A)$ is derived in the same way as that for $E(MS_S)$. First the mean of the jth treatment level is related to the population parameters. Returning to Equation (7.2) and summing over i and dividing by n, we have

$$(7.10) \qquad\qquad \overline{Y}_{.j} = \mu + \alpha_j + \frac{\sum_i \eta_i}{n} + \frac{\sum_i (\eta\alpha)_{ij}}{n} + \frac{\sum_i \epsilon_{ij}}{n}$$

As was previously pointed out, η is a random, rather than a fixed, variable. Only n of the infinite population of possible values of η_i are sampled in any one experiment, and therefore $\sum_i \eta_i \neq 0$. For the same reason, $\sum_i (\eta\alpha)_{ij} \neq 0$, i.e., all of the possible interaction effects at A_j are not summed, only those n sampled in the experiment. This point is critical, for this is the fundamental reason why σ_{SA}^2 contributes to $E(MS_A)$ but not to $E(MS_S)$. When we consider the variability among subjects' means, the mean for each subject in the experiment is based on *all* possible levels of A, but when we consider the variability among treatment level means, each mean is computed over only those n subjects in the sample. The mean of all interaction effects for a subject is zero, but the mean of n (sampled from many) interaction effects for a level of A will generally not be zero. Furthermore, the mean interaction effect will differ at the various levels of A and therefore variability among the $\overline{Y}_{.j}$ will be in part due to variability among interaction effects.

Returning to our derivation, the next step is to subtract Equation (7.5) from Equation (7.10), obtaining

$$(7.11) \qquad\qquad \overline{Y}_{.j} - \overline{Y}_{..} = \alpha_j + \frac{\sum_i (\eta\alpha)_{ij}}{n} + \frac{\sum_i \epsilon_{ij}}{n} - \frac{\sum_i \sum_j \epsilon_{ij}}{na}$$

Squaring, summing, and taking the expectation gives the appropriate *EMS*, provided that the assumptions of independence and homogeneity of variance are applied as in the previous derivation.

This discussion of the nonadditive model will be concluded with a numerical example to illustrate the points that have been previously covered through algebraic manipulations. Table 7-4 contains data for a population

TABLE 7-4

Data for a population of four subjects

	A_1		A_2		A_3			
	Y_{i1}	$(\eta\alpha)_{i1}$	Y_{i2}	$(\eta\alpha)_{i2}$	Y_{i3}	$(\eta\alpha)_{i3}$	μ_i	η_i
S_1	2	-1	6	1	10	0	6	$-.5$
S_2	4	3	5	2	3	-5	4	-2.5
S_3	5	-1	8	0	14	1	9	2.5
S_4	3	-1	3	-3	15	4	7	.5
μ_j	3.5		5.5		10.5		$\mu = 6.5$	
α_j	-3		-1		4			

consisting of four subjects. Assume that two subjects, S_1 and S_2, are sampled for an "experiment." We "test" both subjects at all three levels of A. Thus, "subjects" is a random effects variable, while A is a fixed effects variable. Check the calculations for S (η_i), A (α_j), and SA $[(\eta\alpha)_{ij}]$ effects. Note that the mean interaction effect is zero for each subject, and therefore interaction variability does not contribute to the variability among subject means. On the other hand, calculate the mean interaction effect for each level of A, limiting the calculations to the two subjects included in the experiment. We have

$$(\eta\alpha)_{.1} = \frac{1}{2}(-1 + 3) = 1$$

$$(\eta\alpha)_{.2} = \frac{1}{2}(1 + 2) = 1.5$$

$$(\eta\alpha)_{.3} = \frac{1}{2}(0 - 5) = -2.5$$

Clearly, the variability among treatment means is partly based upon variability among interaction effects.

7.2.3 The test of the subject effect

In the preceding sections two alternative models for the analysis of variance were presented for the repeated measurements design. Though neither the partitioning of the total variability nor the computations for the various sums of squares differ under the two models, the choice of models does have implications for our inferences. The most obvious implication is that nonadditivity permits only a negatively biased test of the subject effect. By negatively biased, we mean that $E(F) < 1$ when H_0 is true. Returning to Table 7-3, we find that

$$E(F) = \frac{\sigma_e^2 + a\sigma_S^2}{\sigma_e^2 + \sigma_{SA}^2}$$

and if H_0 is true ($\sigma_S^2 = 0$), $E(F)$ is clearly less than 1.   This tendency for too many Type II errors to result is not a particularly important consequence of nonadditivity, since subject variability is usually large enough to be detected by even the most conservative test.   In fact, if there were not strong a priori evidence for significant subject variability, the use of the design would be of questionable value since there would be no basis for expecting precision to be better than with any other design.

7.2.4   Additivity, nonadditivity, and covariances

A more important reason for distinguishing between the additive and non-additive models is the problem of heterogeneity of covariance.   The covariance of two groups of scores is the average cross-product of deviations about the group mean; in the repeated measurements design, the covariance for treatments j and j' is

$$(7.12) \qquad \text{cov } Y_{ij}Y_{ij'} = \frac{\sum_i (Y_{ij} - \overline{Y}_{.j})(Y_{ij'} - \overline{Y}_{.j'})}{n - 1}$$

Note that this is the numerator of the correlation coefficient for the two sets of scores; we could also express the covariance by

$$(7.13) \qquad \text{cov } Y_{ij}Y_{ij'} = r_{j,\,j'}S_jS_{j'}$$

where $r_{j,\,j'}$ is the correlation of scores for A_j and $A_{j'}$ and S_j is the standard deviation of scores at A_j.

The importance of the covariance lies in the fact that homogeneity of the treatment population covariances is required for the ratio MS_A/MS_{SA} to be distributed as F.   By homogeneity of the treatment population covariances we mean that $E(Y_{ij} - \mu_{.j})(Y_{ij'} - \mu_{.j'})$ is constant for all values of j and j' ($j \neq j'$).   This condition will always be met when the additive model holds, that is, whenever all population interaction effects are zero.   We can see this by considering a "population" of scores in which the interaction effects are zero, as in Table 7-5.   The covariance is always the same for any two treatment levels.   A closer look indicates that the covariances are not only all equal to each other, but equal to the variance at any level of j as

TABLE 7-5

A population of scores with all interaction effects zero

	A_1	A_2	A_3
S_1	3	6	5
S_2	8	11	10
S_3	6	9	8
S_4	9	12	11

well. A little algebraic manipulation indicates why this is so. If there are no interaction effects, then the scores at one treatment level differ only by a constant, C, from the scores at any other treatment level. Then

$$\text{cov } Y_{ij} Y_{ij'} = \frac{\sum_i (Y_{ij} - \mu_j)(Y_{ij'} - \mu_{j'})}{N}$$

$$= \frac{\sum_i (Y_{ij} - \mu_j)[(Y_{ij} + C) - (\mu_j + C)]}{N}$$

$$= \frac{\sum_i (Y_{ij} - \mu_j)^2}{N}$$

which is the variance for the jth treatment population.

If the nonadditive model is correct, heterogeneity of covariance may occur. Table 7-6 presents an example of such a situation. Without any

TABLE 7-6

A nonadditive population of scores

	A_1	A_2	A_3
S_1	3	12	5
S_2	8	11	8
S_3	6	9	10
S_4	9	6	11

calculations, it is clear that the covariances for the first and second, and for the second and third, columns are negative while that for the first and third columns is positive.

Assuming that the appropriate model for our data is the nonadditive model, we are faced with two questions. What is the direction of the bias in the F test of treatments? What can be done about the bias? In answer to the first question, Box* (1953) has shown that the bias is generally positive and that too many Type I errors are made in testing treatment effects when the covariances are heterogeneous. The consequences of heterogeneity of covariance are greater than those for heterogeneity of variance.

We could approach the problem of bias by first testing for homogeneity of covariances and variances. Such a test is extremely tedious. It involves the calculation of $[a(a - 1)]/2$ correlation coefficients and the inversion of an $a \times a$ matrix containing the sample covariances and variances; the last operation is unfamiliar to most psychologists. For those who are interested,

* G. E. P. Box, "Non-normality and Tests on Variance," *Biometrika*, 40:318–335 (1953).

the test is available in a 1950 paper by Box.* The present author prefers an alternative which stems from Box's 1953 paper. Box has shown that the statistic MS_A/MS_{SA} is distributed as F but on $(a - 1)\lambda$ and $(a - 1)(n - 1)\lambda$ df. If the homogeneity of variance and the homogeneity of covariance assumptions are met by the data, $\lambda = 1$ and we have the usual F test. As heterogeneity of variances and covariances increases, λ approaches a lower bound of $1/(a - 1)$. Therefore, for an extreme violation of the homogeneity assumptions, F would be distributed on 1 and $n - 1$ df. In view of these comments upon the F distribution, it is suggested that the F statistics be first assessed against the F required for significance on 1 and $n - 1$ df. In other words, first assume the worst possible degree of heterogeneity of variances and covariances and consequently set λ equal to $1/(a - 1)$. If λ is actually larger than this value, that is, if the variances and covariances are more homogeneous than has been assumed, we have thrown away df and are using a negatively biased F test. Thus, if the obtained F is significant with this generally conservative approach, we can have reasonable faith in our rejection of the null hypothesis.

What if the conservative F test just outlined is not significant? It may mean that the null hypothesis is true. On the other hand, nonsignificance may merely indicate that our homogeneity assumptions are not as badly violated as the conservative test implies. To check this last possibility, now assess the obtained F against that required for significance on $a - 1$ and $(n - 1)(a - 1)$ df. In other words, assume homogeneity of variances and covariances and consequently set λ equal to 1. If this positively biased F test is not significant, it is reasonably sure that the null hypothesis should be accepted.

It is possible for the two F tests to yield contradictory results. The F assessed on 1 and $n - 1$ df might not be significant, while that assessed on $a - 1$ and $(n - 1)(a - 1)$ df might be significant. Since the first F may be negatively biased and the second F may be positively biased, a clear-cut decision about the null hypothesis is difficult to achieve. However, a statement about the approximate level of significance may generally be made. For example, the negatively biased F may not be significant at the 5 per cent level but may be significant at the 10 per cent level, while the positively biased F is significant at the 5 per cent level, leading to the conclusion that the true significance level is somewhere between 5 per cent and 10 per cent. If this sort of approximation is not sufficient, an exact F test can be computed. This test, Hotelling's T^2, involves the computation of all treatment variances and covariances, and some matrix manipulations. It is described in Anderson's† text on multivariate analysis.

* G. E. P. Box, "Problems in the Analysis of Growth and Wear Curves," *Biometrics*, 6:362–389 (1950).

† T. W. Anderson, *Introduction to Multivariate Statistical Analysis* (New York: Wiley, 1958).

7.2.5 Additivity, nonadditivity, and efficiency

Even if the covariance problem does not exist, an efficiency problem may. If the data are best described by a nonadditive model, efficiency will be less than in the additive case, and the resulting F test will be less powerful. In other words, if the null hypothesis is false, $E(F)$ under the additive model where

$$E(F) = \frac{\sigma_e^2 + n\theta_A^2}{\sigma_e^2}$$

will be greater than $E(F)$ under the nonadditive model where

$$E(F) = \frac{\sigma_e^2 + \sigma_{SA}^2 + n\theta_A^2}{\sigma_e^2 + \sigma_{SA}^2}$$

To see why this is so, consider the following illustrative ratios:

$$\frac{15}{5}, \quad \frac{20}{10}, \quad \frac{50}{40}, \quad \frac{100}{90}$$

As we add the same constant to the numerator and denominator of any one ratio, we obtain a smaller ratio. Thus,

$$\frac{15+5}{5+5} < \frac{15}{5} \quad \text{and} \quad \frac{50+50}{40+50} < \frac{50}{40}$$

Values of $E(F)$ for the two models are like any two of the illustrative ratios. If the nonadditive model is correct, the constant σ_{SA}^2 has essentially been added to both numerator and denominator of the value of $E(F)$ for additive data; thus the size of the expected F ratio has been decreased.

We will next provide a numerical example which should further make our point about efficiency and at the same time illustrate the calculations involved in analyzing data from the one-factor repeated measurements design.

TABLE 7-7

Response time data

	A_1	A_2	A_3	$\sum_j Y_{ij}$
S_1	1.7	1.9	2.0	5.6
S_2	4.4	4.5	5.7	14.6
S_3	6.6	7.4	10.5	24.5
$\sum_i Y_{ij} = 12.7$		13.8	18.2	$\sum_i \sum_j Y_{ij} = 44.7$

Table 7-7 contains response time scores to which we will apply the analysis of variance. Since the *df* for *subjects* are $n - 1$,

$$SS_S = \frac{\sum\limits_{i=1}^{3} \left(\sum\limits_{j=1}^{3} Y_{ij} \right)^2}{3} - C$$

$$= \frac{(5.6)^2 + (14.6)^2 + (24.5)^2}{3} - \frac{(44.7)^2}{9}$$

$$= 59.58$$

For the treatment effects, we have

$$SS_A = \frac{\sum\limits_{j=1}^{3} \left(\sum\limits_{i=1}^{3} Y_{ij} \right)^2}{3} - C$$

$$= \frac{(12.7)^2 + (13.8)^2 + (18.2)^2}{3} - \frac{(44.7)^2}{9}$$

$$= 5.65$$

For the error variability, we have

$$SS_{SA} = \sum_i \sum_j Y_{ij}^2 - C - SS_S - SS_A$$

$$= 291.17 - \frac{(44.7)^2}{9} - 59.58 - 5.65$$

$$= 3.93$$

To test the treatment effects, we compute

$$F = \frac{5.65/2}{3.93/4}$$

$$= 2.87$$

which is not significant at the 5 per cent level.

Most investigators would agree that response speed, the reciprocal of response time, is a perfectly meaningful measure. Instead of considering the time per response, the number of responses per unit of time is noted. Speed measures have been obtained by taking the reciprocals of the data in Table 7-7, and the results are presented in Table 7-8. The analysis of variance is

TABLE 7-8

Response speed data obtained by taking reciprocals of the scores in Table 7-7

	A_1	A_2	A_3	$\sum\limits_{j} Y_{ij}$
S_1	.589	.526	.500	1.615
S_2	.227	.222	.175	.624
S_3	.152	.135	.095	.382
$\sum\limits_{i} Y_{ij} =$	.968	.883	.770	$\sum\limits_{i} \sum\limits_{j} Y_{ij} = 2.621$

executed as before, but to help prevent misplaced decimal points the pre-caution was taken of multiplying all the entries of Table 7-8 by 1,000. (Note that this will not affect the F ratios.) Then,

$$SS_S = \frac{(1{,}615)^2 + (624)^2 + (382)^2}{3} - \frac{(2{,}621)^2}{9}$$
$$= 284{,}548.3$$

and

$$SS_A = \frac{(968)^2 + (883)^2 + (770)^2}{3} - \frac{(2{,}621)^2}{9}$$
$$= 6{,}577.6$$

and

$$SS_{SA} = 1{,}055{,}389 - \frac{(2{,}621)^2}{9} - 284{,}548.3 - 6{,}577.6$$
$$= 969.7$$

The test of treatment effects yields

$$F = \frac{6{,}577.6/2}{969.7/4}$$
$$= 13.56$$

a result significant at the .01 level.

Why do such diverse inferences result from the two sets of data which, after all, are merely transforms of each other? The answer lies in a closer examination of the data in the two tables. Returning to Table 7-7, we note that the spread among scores at A_3 is considerably greater than that at A_1. In Table 7-8, the variability among subjects seems less affected by the level of A. The point is more clearly made in Figure 7-1, in which both data sets

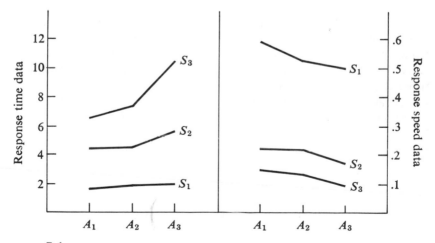

FIGURE 7-1   A plot of the data in Tables 7-7 and 7-8

are plotted, that of Table 7-7 against the left-hand axis and that of Table 7-8 against the right-hand axis. The response time data more clearly contain interaction effects. As a result of this nonadditivity, efficiency is lower and the F test is less powerful.

7.2.6 A test for nonadditivity

Several implications of the distinction between the additive and nonadditive models for repeated measurements designs have been indicated. At best, data that conform to the nonadditive model may result in a less efficient F test of the treatment effect; at worst, the F test may actually be biased. There is another, a nonstatistical, consideration. Additive data may be more parsimoniously described than nonadditive data. For example, again consider the data of Figure 7-1. The experimenter who presents a mathematical model of response time as a function of level of A must estimate a different regression coefficient for each subject; each curve has a different slope. On the other hand, looking at the response speed data, only the slope-intercepts differ among subjects. One regression coefficient describes the inclination of all three curves.

In view of the potential advantages of working with additive data, two questions arise. How can one determine which model is appropriate for any given data set? Assuming that the nonadditive model is appropriate, how should the experimenter handle his data? The answers to these questions generally involve computational labor beyond the usual analysis of variance and are not always satisfactory. Nevertheless, they seem to merit consideration.

The choice between data models reduces to a test of the null hypothesis that σ_{SA}^2 is zero. If the null hypothesis is rejected, the nonadditive model is appropriate; otherwise, the additive model applies. Tukey* has proposed a single df test which involves the further analysis of the interaction sum of squares into two components. One of these represents nonadditivity and is distributed on one df. The remaining interaction variability provides the error term for the nonadditivity test and is distributed on $(n - 1)(a - 1) - 1\ df$.

As an example of the calculations, the Tukey test will be carried out on the response time data originally presented in Table 7-7 and reproduced in Table 7-9. Note that the deviations of each column and row mean from the grand mean have also been tabled. This is the first step in calculating the F statistic for additivity. Next obtain the cross-product terms, $\sum_j Y_{ij}(\overline{Y}_{.j} - \overline{Y}_{..})$. These are

* J. W. Tukey, "One Degree of Freedom for Nonadditivity," *Biometrics*, 5:232–242 (1949)

$$(-.7)(1.7) + (-.4)(1.9) + (1.1)(2.0) = .25$$
$$(-.7)(4.4) + (-.4)(4.5) + (1.1)(5.7) = 1.39$$
$$(-.7)(6.6) + (-.4)(7.4) + (1.1)(10.5) = 3.97$$

TABLE 7-9

Data for Tukey's single df test

	A_1	A_2	A_3	$\bar{Y}_{i.}$	$\bar{Y}_{i.} - \bar{Y}_{..}$	$\sum_j Y_{ij}(\bar{Y}_{.j} - \bar{Y}_{..})$
S_1	1.7	1.9	2.0	1.9	-3.1	.25
S_2	4.4	4.5	5.7	4.9	$-.1$	1.39
S_3	6.6	7.4	10.5	8.2	3.2	3.97
$\bar{Y}_{.j}$	4.3	4.6	6.1	$\bar{Y}_{..} = 5.0$		
$\bar{Y}_{.j} - \bar{Y}_{..}$	$-.7$	$-.4$	1.1			

These are in turn multiplied by the row deviations:

$$\sum_i \sum_j Y_{ij}(\bar{Y}_{.j} - \bar{Y}_{..})(\bar{Y}_{i.} - \bar{Y}_{..}) = (.25)(-3.1) + (1.39)(-.1) + (3.97)(3.2)$$
$$= 11.8$$

The formula for Tukey's single df sum of squares is

(7.14)
$$SS_{\text{nonadd}} = \frac{\left[\sum_i \sum_j Y_{ij}(\bar{Y}_{.j} - \bar{Y}_{..})(\bar{Y}_{i.} - \bar{Y}_{..})\right]^2}{\sum_j (\bar{Y}_{.j} - \bar{Y}_{..})^2 \sum_i (\bar{Y}_{i.} - \bar{Y}_{..})^2}$$

For our example, we have

$$SS_{\text{nonadd}} = \frac{(11.8)^2}{(1.8)(19.9)}$$
$$= 3.89$$

Subtracting the above from the SS_{SA} for this data computed previously, we obtain the balance,

$$SS_{\text{bal}} = 3.93 - 3.89$$
$$= .04$$

The F ratio is

$$F = \frac{MS_{\text{nonadd}}}{MS_{\text{bal}}}$$
$$= \frac{3.89}{.04/3}$$
$$= 292$$

a result which, even on one and three df, is clearly significant.

To provide some feeling for the basis of Tukey's test, look at the cross-products column in Table 7-9. Note that the cross-products (.25, 1.39, 3.97) increase as a function of the row means (1.9, 4.9, 8.2). The nonadditivity sum of squares depends upon the slope of the function relating the cross-products and the means. In contrast, consider the perfectly additive data set of Table 7-10. Note that there is no change in the cross-products as a

TABLE 7-10

An additive data set

	A_1	A_2	A_3	$\bar{Y}_{i.}$	$\bar{Y}_{i.} - \bar{Y}_{..}$	$\sum_j Y_{ij}(\bar{Y}_{.j} - \bar{Y}_{..})$
S_1	3	5	1	3	-2	8
S_2	4	6	2	4	-1	8
S_3	8	10	6	8	3	8
$\bar{Y}_{.j}$	5	7	3	$\bar{Y}_{..} = 5$		
$\bar{Y}_{.j} - \bar{Y}_{..}$	0	2	-2			

function of changes in the row mean. The SS_{nonadd} will be zero for this data set.

Tukey's test will not be sensitive to all interactions. There are clearly interaction effects in Table 7-11, but the SS_{nonadd} equals zero since

TABLE 7-11

Nonadditive data not sensitive to Tukey's F test

	A_1	A_2	A_3	$\bar{Y}_{i.}$	$\bar{Y}_{i.} - \bar{Y}_{..}$	$\sum_j Y_{ij}(\bar{Y}_{.j} - \bar{Y}_{..})$
S_1	4	7	4	5	1	4
S_2	4	4	4	4	0	0
S_3	2	5	2	3	-1	4
$\bar{Y}_{.j}$	10/3	16/3	10/3	$\bar{Y}_{..} = 4$		
$\bar{Y}_{.j} - \bar{Y}_{..}$	$-2/3$	4/3	$-2/3$			

$[(1)(4) + (0)(0) + (-1)(4)]^2$ equals zero. Why doesn't the Tukey test work here? The answer lies in the cross-products column. Note that the entries decrease and then increase as the row means increase. In other words, the slope of the straight line which best relates cross-products to row means is zero. Figure 7-2 contains the plot of cross-products against row means for the data sets of Tables 7-9 to 7-11. It is the slope of the dashed line, the best fitting straight line, which is of interest. If Tukey's test is to be sensitive

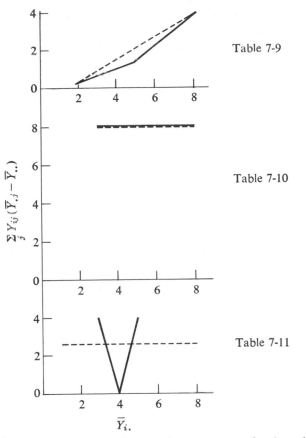

FIGURE 7-2   A plot of cross-products against row means for three data sets

to interaction effects, the slope of the dashed line must deviate from a slope of zero; the greater the departure from a horizontal line, the greater will be the SS_{nonadd}.   Fortunately, the nature of most interaction effects is such that the cross-product–row mean relationship will have a linear component and Tukey's test will therefore be serviceable.

7.2.7   Transformations of the data

We turn next to the problem of dealing with data when the evidence suggests that the nonadditive model is appropriate.   The example of Tables 7-7 and 7-8 suggest one solution.   It was possible to transform the original data to a data set which appears to be well described by an additive model.   The choice of an appropriate transformation is not always this simple.   Generally, one might first try the transformations recommended in Chapter 4 for heterogeneity of variance; however, the additive transformation is not necessarily the transformation which stabilizes the variances. As a further rough guide, Tukey indicates that when the sign of the sum of cross-products (11.8, in our example) is positive, a square root transform may be appropriate; when the sign is negative, raising each score to a power (e.g., squaring or cubing) or taking the logarithm of each score may work.

7.3 MORE THAN ONE TREATMENT VARIABLE

Although the discussion has thus far been limited to two-dimensional designs involving subjects and a single treatment variable, there is no reason why several treatment variables cannot be investigated. As before, n subjects would be randomly sampled, and each one would be tested under all combinations of all treatment variables. Thus, if there were the variables A and B, each subject would be tested ab times, once under each treatment combination, the order of the ab presentations being independently randomized for each subject. Our previous comments about the choice between models and the implications of this choice still hold. The computations are straightforward. For a $S \times A \times B$ design, proceed as with a three-factor design (see Chapter 5) with one score in each cell. The analysis for this case is presented in Table 7-12. A nonadditive model, with A and B having fixed effects and subjects having random effects, has been assumed. The composition of each EMS can be summarized by noting that it contains σ_e^2 plus a null hypothesis term. If the effect does not involve S (i.e., if A, B, or AB is being considered), the EMS will also contain the interaction of the effect with S. Thus, for the AB effect, we immediately have $\sigma_e^2 + n\theta_{AB}^2$. Since S is not part of the effect, σ_{ABS}^2 is also included in the EMS. Coefficients, such as the n by which θ_{AB}^2 is multiplied, are determined as in the past. If a factor (including S) does not appear in the subscript, then the number of levels of the factor appear in the coefficient. More general rules will be developed in Chapter 8. However, those just stated will suffice for any simple repeated measurements design involving S and any number of fixed effect variables.

7.4 CONCLUDING REMARKS

The psychological literature abounds with examples of designs involving repeated measurements—both the relatively simple designs of this chapter and the more complex variations which will be considered in subsequent chapters. The reasons for this are not difficult to discern. The precision of the design is potentially far better than that of the designs considered before. Furthermore, the design is natural when the supply of subjects is limited relative to the number of treatment combinations to be studied, or when the experimenter's goal is to collect data on some performance measure plotted as a

TABLE 7-12

Analysis of variance for a two-factor repeated measurements design

SV	df	SS	EMS	F
Total	$abn - 1$	$\displaystyle\sum_i \sum_j \sum_k Y_{ijk}^2 - C$		
A	$a - 1$	$\displaystyle\frac{\sum_j \left(\sum_i \sum_k Y_{ijk}\right)^2}{nb} - C$	$\sigma_e^2 + b\sigma_{AS}^2 + bn\theta_A^2$	$\dfrac{MS_A}{MS_{AS}}$
B	$b - 1$	$\displaystyle\frac{\sum_k \left(\sum_i \sum_j Y_{ijk}\right)^2}{na} - C$	$\sigma_e^2 + a\sigma_{BS}^2 + an\theta_B^2$	$\dfrac{MS_B}{MS_{BS}}$
S	$n - 1$	$\displaystyle\frac{\sum_i \left(\sum_j \sum_k Y_{ijk}\right)^2}{ab} - C$	$\sigma_e^2 + ab\sigma_S^2$	
AB	$(a-1)(b-1)$	$\displaystyle\frac{\sum_j \sum_k \left(\sum_i Y_{ijk}\right)^2}{n} - C - SS_A - SS_B$	$\sigma_e^2 + \sigma_{ABS}^2 + n\theta_{AB}^2$	$\dfrac{MS_{AB}}{MS_{ABS}}$
AS	$(a-1)(n-1)$	$\displaystyle\frac{\sum_j \sum_i \left(\sum_k Y_{ijk}\right)^2}{b} - C - SS_A - SS_S$	$\sigma_e^2 + b\sigma_{AS}^2$	
BS	$(b-1)(n-1)$	$\displaystyle\frac{\sum_k \sum_i \left(\sum_j Y_{ijk}\right)^2}{a} - C - SS_B - SS_S$	$\sigma_e^2 + a\sigma_{BS}^2$	
ABS	$(a-1)(b-1)(n-1)$	$\displaystyle\sum_i \sum_j \sum_k Y_{ijk}^2 - C - SS_A - \cdots - SS_{BS}$	$\sigma_e^2 + \sigma_{ABS}^2$	

function of time.   However, in using these designs the experimenter must be aware of the potential problems.   In particular, we have been concerned with the possible consequences of population interactions between subjects and treatments.   We have suggested alternative F tests when heterogeneity of covariance is suspected, an F test to detect nonadditivity, and possible ways of transforming the data to an additive scale.   We have also indicated that these techniques will not always suffice; adjusting df when heterogeneity is suspected may still not permit a clear inference about the null hypothesis, Tukey's test will not detect all departures from additivity, and appropriate transformations will not always be found.   Nevertheless, these techniques do provide a starting point for coping with some of the problems which may result from the use of the repeated measurements design.   More important, awareness of the potential problems is the first requirement for deciding whether to use the design and for an intelligent evaluation of summary statistics such as the F ratio.

Where the independent variable is something other than time or trial number, it is important that great care be taken to randomize the order of presentation of treatments independently for each subject.   In part, this is done to guard against confounding of time and treatments.   What inference can be drawn in the extreme case in which A_1 is always presented first, A_2 always is presented second, and so on?   In part, proper randomization of the order of presentation is important because it should serve to minimize heterogeneity of covariance.   Scores for treatments close together in time should be more highly correlated than those for treatments further apart in time.   By randomizing the treatment presentations independently for each subject, each pair of treatments is given an equal opportunity to appear any given distance apart in time.   It is also helpful to provide sufficient time between presentations of treatments to minimize "carry-over" effects.   For example, if rats are being tested in a Skinner box under each of several drugs, time between testings should be sufficient to allow the effects of the last drug to wear off.   Even if the different orders of presentation balance out so that treatments and trials are not confounded, carry-over effects, if present, will result in increased variability among orders of presentation and will thus reduce the efficiency of the design.

The design considered in this chapter is the simplest possible design involving repeated measurements.   In subsequent chapters complications will be introduced, such as having subjects randomly distributed over levels of a second treatment variable and systematically counterbalancing the orders of presentation of treatments.   The importance of this chapter lies in the fact that it provides a relatively simple context in which to consider a number of problems peculiar to all repeated measurements designs—*EMS* under non-additivity, implications of nonadditivity, the use of transformations, the implications of heterogeneity of covariance.   With some understanding of these aspects of repeated measurements designs, it will be possible to concentrate more on the actual data analysis in subsequent chapters.

EXERCISES

7.1 Prove that the two expressions, Equation (7.12) and Equation (7.13), for covariance are algebraically identical.

7.2 Compute the covariances for Table 7-5 as well as the variance among subjects at any level of A_j.

7.3 In the analysis of the data in Table 7-8, we multiplied each score by 1,000. Prove that the F test of A in an SA design is generally not influenced when a constant multiplier is introduced. What happens when a constant is added to each score? Prove your answer.

7.4 Apply Tukey's single df test to the data of Table 7-8. How do the results compare with those for Table 7-7?

7.5 Consider the following summary statistics for three sets of data. Which data sets should be sensitive to the Tukey test?

		$\bar{Y}_{i.} - \bar{Y}_{..}$	$\sum_{j} Y_{ij}(\bar{Y}_{.j} - \bar{Y}_{.1})$
Set 1	S_1	-3	2
	S_2	-1	4
	S_3	1	4
	S_4	3	2
Set 2	S_1	-3	2
	S_2	-1	6
	S_3	1	2
	S_4	3	6
Set 3	S_1	-3	2
	S_2	-1	5
	S_3	1	4
	S_4	3	7

7.6 Prove that $\sum_{i} (\eta\alpha)_{ij} = 0$ where α is a fixed effects variable.

MIXED DESIGNS: BETWEEN- AND

WITHIN-SUBJECTS VARIABILITY

8

8.1 INTRODUCTION

Thus far two types of designs have been discussed, those in which different treatments involve different subjects and those in which all subjects are tested under each treatment. The most prevalent design in the psychological literature is a combination of these two approaches. For example, n subjects might be tested at A_1, n other subjects tested at A_2, and so on, until an subjects have been accounted for. The subjects will have been randomly assigned to the a treatments, and thus the design appears to be a completely randomized one-factor design. However, each of the an subjects are also tested at each of the b levels of the independent variable, B, the order of presentation of the b treatments being randomized independently for each subject, as in the repeated measurements design. We will generally refer to A as a *between-subjects* variable and B as a *within-subjects* variable. The data matrix for this mixed design is presented in Table 8-1.

It is not difficult to determine why the mixed designs are so frequently used in psychological research. One reason is that psychologists are often interested in comparing group performances over time or trials. For example, in a free operant situation, different subjects may be tested at different percentages of reinforcement for several successive minutes. Percentage is the A variable and blocks of time is the B variable. As another example, one might measure the signal brightness required for detection at various times after entering a darkened room, different groups of subjects having been exposed to different illuminations prior to the dark-adaptation test. In experiments such as these, the interest lies in comparing the average performance over time for the various levels of A (the A main effect); in deter-

TABLE 8-1

Data matrix for a mixed design, one between- and one within-subjects variable

		B_1	B_2	$\cdots$	B_k	$\cdots$	B_b
	S_{11}	Y_{111}	Y_{112}		Y_{11k}		Y_{11b}
	S_{21}	Y_{211}	Y_{212}		Y_{21k}		Y_{21b}
A_1	$\vdots$						
	S_{i1}	Y_{i11}	Y_{i12}		Y_{i1k}		Y_{i1b}
	$\vdots$						
	S_{n1}	Y_{n11}	Y_{n12}		Y_{n1k}		Y_{n1b}
$\vdots$							
	S_{1j}	Y_{1j1}	Y_{1j2}		Y_{1jk}		Y_{1jb}
	S_{2j}	Y_{2j1}	Y_{2j2}		Y_{2jk}		Y_{2jb}
A_j	$\vdots$						
	S_{ij}	Y_{ij1}	Y_{ij2}		Y_{ijk}		Y_{ijb}
	$\vdots$						
	S_{nj}	Y_{nj1}	Y_{nj2}		Y_{njk}		Y_{njb}
$\vdots$							
	S_{1a}	Y_{1a1}	Y_{1a2}		Y_{1ak}		Y_{1ab}
	S_{2a}	Y_{2a1}	Y_{2a2}		Y_{2ak}		Y_{2ab}
A_a	$\vdots$						
	S_{ia}	Y_{ia1}	Y_{ia2}		Y_{iak}		Y_{iab}
	$\vdots$						
	S_{na}	Y_{na1}	Y_{na2}		Y_{nak}		Y_{nab}

mining whether, averaging over all subjects, performance is modified over time (the B main effect); and in determining whether the shapes and slopes of the performance curves are similar for the a groups (the AB interaction effect).

A second frequent use of the mixed design is in psychometric research. Arts and Science, Engineering, and Education majors might be tested on each of several measures in some standard battery of tests. One usually wants to know whether the average performance over tests is the same for all groups and whether the group profiles are of the same shape. By profiles are meant the bar graphs showing group performance on each measure. Thus, if Arts and Science majors perform better on a verbal aptitude measure and engineers perform better on a quantitative aptitude measure, the profiles will not be parallel. This variability in the simple effects for each measure will be reflected in the magnitude of the AB interaction. At this point it might also be noted that unless the b measures are on the same scale, the profile analysis (test of interaction) is difficult to interpret. Generally, people working with these measures have used Z or T scores; data from different levels of B are then comparable in the sense that the b populations may be considered to have been drawn from the same parent population.

The mixed designs are also appropriate whenever B and AB effects are of greater interest than A effects, since the B and AB effects will usually be tested against a smaller error term with more df than will the A effects. There will also be instances in which the mixed design is required by the nature of the independent variables: one variable is clearly a between-subjects variable while the second seems to meet the requirements of the repeated measurements model. Variables which will generally be between-subjects variables are those which will entail carry-over effects (e.g., method of training) and individual characteristics (e.g., age, personality characteristic as evidenced by position on some scale). On the other hand, stage of practice is naturally a within-subjects variable.

8.2 ONE BETWEEN- AND ONE WITHIN-SUBJECTS VARIABLE

8.2.1 The analysis of variance model

The simplest mixed design is that represented in Table 8-1. Consider Y_{ijk}, the score at the kth level of B for the ith subject in the jth level of A. The immediate problem is to arrive at an equation relating Y_{ijk} to the parameters of the population from which it has been sampled. One way to begin is to structure the design so that it looks somewhat more familiar. For example, one might ignore the variable A, in which case one would have the simple repeated measurements design ($S \times B$) of Chapter 7, with an subjects and b levels of the treatment variable. By analogy to Equation (7.2),

$$(8.1) \qquad Y_{ijk} = \mu + \eta_{ij} + \beta_k + (\eta\beta)_{ijk} + \epsilon_{ijk}$$

where $\eta_{ij} = \mu_{ij} - \mu$, $\beta_k = \mu_k - \mu$, and

$$(\eta\beta)_{ijk} = (\mu_{ijk} - \mu) - (\mu_{ij} - \mu) - (\mu_k - \mu)$$
$$= \mu_{ijk} - \mu_{ij} - \mu_k + \mu$$

Thus, ignoring A effects, each score is viewed as a combination of subject effect, B effect, $S \times B$ interaction effect, and error, just as in the nonadditive case in Chapter 7. At this point, reality intrudes. We have more than a passing interest in the variable A, and we must therefore modify our model to include the A main and interaction effects. To do this, we first note that the an subjects may differ not only because they are different individuals, but also because some are at one level of A, while others are at a different level. A more precise statement of this is

$$(8.2) \qquad \mu_{ij} - \mu = (\mu_{ij} - \mu_j) + (\mu_j - \mu)$$

or

(8.2′)
$$\eta_{ij} = \eta_{i/j} + \alpha_j$$

The deviation of the mean score for an individual from the grand mean of the population has two components: a deviation of his score from the mean of those individuals who receive the same treatment ($\eta_{i/j}$, the effect of the ith subject within the jth level of A) and a deviation of the treatment mean from the grand mean (α_j, the effect of the jth treatment level of A). In other words, the main effect of the ijth subject consists of his simple effect at A_j and the main effect of A_j. Given Equation (8.2′), we may now rewrite Equation (8.1).

(8.3)
$$Y_{ijk} = \mu + \eta_{i/j} + \alpha_j + \beta_k + (\eta\beta)_{ijk} + \epsilon_{ijk}$$

Equation (8.3) still ignores the possibility of an AB source of variance. Since this seems unreasonable, we further modify the model. Note that

(8.4) $\mu_{ijk} - \mu_{ij} - \mu_k + \mu = (\mu_{ijk} - \mu_{ij} - \mu_{jk} + \mu_j) + (\mu_{jk} - \mu_j - \mu_k + \mu)$

or

(8.4′)
$$(\eta\beta)_{ijk} = (\eta\beta)_{ik/j} + (\alpha\beta)_{jk}$$

The quantity $(\eta\beta)_{ijk}$ is the overall interaction effect of the ijth subject and the kth level of B. It consists of two components: the simple interaction effect of the ith subject and the kth level of B at A_j, and the overall AB interaction effect. Equation (8.4′) prepares the way for the final statement of our model:

(8.5) $Y_{ijk} = \mu + \alpha_j + \eta_{i/j} + \beta_k + (\alpha\beta)_{jk} + (\eta\beta)_{ik/j} + \epsilon_{ijk}$

Assuming that A and B are variables having fixed effects and that subjects are randomly sampled from a large population of subjects, several statements about the population parameters follow. With regard to fixed effects, $\sum \alpha_j = 0$, $\sum \beta_k = 0$, and $\sum (\alpha\beta)_{jk} = 0$. It is further assumed that the $\eta_{i/j}$, $(\eta\beta)_{ik/j}$, and ϵ_{ijk} are all randomly sampled from normally distributed populations with mean zero and variances $\sigma_{S/A}^2$, $\sigma_{SB/A}^2$, and σ_e^2, respectively.

In order to clarify the discussion leading to Equation (8.5), and in particular the relationship between η_{ij} and its components and $(\eta\beta)_{ijk}$ and its components, we consider the numerical example of Table 8-2. The data are assumed to be errorless, i.e., each value in the matrix is some μ_{ijk}. According to Equation (8.2′), each η_{ij} has two components, $\eta_{i/j}$ and α_j. To calculate the $\eta_{i/j}$, we have

$$\eta_{1/1} = \mu_{11.} - \mu_{.1.} = (4.00 - 5.00) = -1.00$$
$$\eta_{2/1} = \mu_{21.} - \mu_{.1.} = (6.00 - 5.00) = 1.00$$
$$\eta_{1/2} = \mu_{12.} - \mu_{.2.} = (2.00 - 4.50) = -2.50$$
$$\eta_{2/2} = \mu_{22.} - \mu_{.2.} = (7.00 - 4.50) = 2.50$$

For the α_j, we have

$$\alpha_1 = \mu_{.1.} - \mu = (5.00 - 4.75) = .25$$
$$\alpha_2 = \mu_{.2.} - \mu = (4.50 - 4.75) = -.25$$

TABLE 8-2

Mixed design: a population of scores

		B_1	B_2	B_3	
A_1	S_{11}	4	1	7	$\mu_{11.} = 4.0$
	S_{21}	6	2	10	$\mu_{21.} = 6.0$
	$\mu_{.11} = 5$		$\mu_{.12} = 1.5$	$\mu_{.13} = 8.5$	$\mu_{.1.} = 5.0$
A_2	S_{12}	3	1	2	$\mu_{12.} = 2.0$
	S_{22}	8	9	4	$\mu_{22.} = 7.0$
	$\mu_{.21} = 5.5$		$\mu_{.22} = 5.0$	$\mu_{.23} = 3.0$	$\mu_{.2.} = 4.5$
	$\mu_{..1} = 5.25$		$\mu_{..2} = 3.25$	$\mu_{..3} = 5.75$	
			$\mu = 4.75$		

Combining $\eta_{i/j}$ and α_j, as Equation (8.2′) suggests, we arrive at values of η_{ij}:

$$\eta_{11} = -1.00 + .25 = -.75$$
$$\eta_{21} = 1.00 + .25 = 1.25$$
$$\eta_{12} = -2.50 - .25 = -2.75$$
$$\eta_{22} = 2.50 - .25 = 2.25$$

Note that the η_{ij} can also be computed from the definition $\eta_{ij} = \mu_{ij} - \mu$:

$$\eta_{11} = \mu_{11.} - \mu = (4.00 - 4.75) = -.75$$
$$\eta_{21} = \mu_{21.} - \mu = (6.00 - 4.75) = 1.25$$
$$\eta_{12} = \mu_{12.} - \mu = (2.00 - 4.75) = -2.75$$
$$\eta_{22} = \mu_{22.} - \mu = (7.00 - 4.75) = 2.25$$

In part, each μ_{ijk} differs from μ (and therefore from every other μ_{ijk}) because of the variability among subjects, i.e., the variability in η_{ij}. However, η_{ij} variability does not account for all the variability in the data matrix of Table 8-2. Note that $(\mu_{ijk} - \mu) - \eta_{ij} = \mu_{ijk} - \mu_{ij.}$. The portion of each score's deviation from the grand mean which is not accounted for by η_{ij} is the deviation of the score (μ_{ijk}) from the mean of scores $(\mu_{ij.})$ for the subject in question. We next attempt to show that this "within-subjects" deviation consists of β_k and $(\eta\beta)_{ijk}$; the quantity $(\eta\beta)_{ijk}$ in turn can be partitioned into the components of Equation (8.4′). We first compute the effect of each level of the independent variable, B:

$$\beta_1 = (\mu_{..1} - \mu) = (5.25 - 4.75) = .50$$
$$\beta_2 = (\mu_{..2} - \mu) = (3.25 - 4.75) = -1.50$$
$$\beta_3 = (\mu_{..3} - \mu) = (5.75 - 4.75) = 1.00$$

Next, we compute the component effects of $(\eta\beta)_{ijk}$. The first of these is

$$(\alpha\beta)_{jk} = (\mu_{.jk} - \mu) - (\mu_{.j.} - \mu) - (\mu_{..k} - \mu)$$
$$= (\mu_{.jk} - \mu) - \alpha_j - \beta_k$$
$$= \mu_{.jk} - \mu_{.j.} - \mu_{..k} + \mu$$

Since α_j and β_k have already been calculated, the second of the three forms is most convenient. For example,

$$(\alpha\beta)_{13} = (\mu_{13} - \mu) - \alpha_1 - \beta_3$$
$$= 3.75 - .25 - 1.00$$
$$= 2.50$$

Similar computations for the other cells yield Table 8-3. Still assuming

TABLE 8-3

The values of $(\alpha\beta)_{jk}$ for the data of Table 8-2

	B_1	B_2	B_3
A_1	$-.5$	-2.0	2.5
A_2	$.5$	2.0	-2.5

errorless data, we conclude that there is an AB interaction since the $(\alpha\beta)_{jk}$ are not all zero.

We next compute the $(\eta\beta)_{ik/j}$. Basically, this is a two-variable (S, B) interaction computed at one level of the third variable (A), as if the design consisted only of the n subjects at that level of A. Consistent with this definition, we have

$$(\eta\beta)_{ik/j} = (\mu_{ijk} - \mu_j) - (\mu_{ij} - \mu_j) - (\mu_{jk} - \mu_j)$$
$$= \mu_{ijk} - \mu_{ij} - \mu_{jk} + \mu_j$$

For example,

$$(\eta\beta)_{22/1} = \mu_{212} - \mu_{21.} - \mu_{.12} + \mu_{.1.}$$
$$= 2.0 - 6.0 - 1.5 + 5.0$$
$$= -.5$$

Similar calculations result in Table 8-4. Note that subjects and B do interact at each level of A, and that the shape of the interaction differs at the two levels of A.

The values of $(\alpha\beta)_{jk}$ and $(\eta\beta)_{ik/j}$ may be combined to give the $(\eta\beta)_{ijk}$. As a check, the $(\eta\beta)_{ijk}$ may also be calculated directly:

$$(\eta\beta)_{ijk} = (\mu_{ijk} - \mu) - (\mu_{ij.} - \mu) - (\mu_{..k} - \mu)$$

The $(\eta\beta)_{ijk}$ and β_k should sum to $\mu_{ijk} - \mu_{ij.}$ if the calculations have been correctly carried out.

To summarize, our development of the model began by viewing the design as a simple repeated measurements design. It was then noted that the presence of the variable A suggests a further analysis of the usual subject

TABLE 8-4

The values of $(\eta\beta)_{ik/j}$ for the data of Table 8-2

		B_1	B_2	B_3
A_1	S_{11}	0	.5	−.5
	S_{21}	0	−.5	.5
A_2	S_{12}	0	−1.5	1.5
	S_{22}	0	1.5	−1.5

(S) and subjects $\times$ B (SB) effects. The form of this further analysis having been shown algebraically, the effects postulated in the model were computed for a "population" of scores. The reason for this emphasis on the development of the model should be clear from previous chapters. It was seen that the sources of variance in the data analysis follow directly from the model and that the *EMS*, which dictate our choice of error terms, are derived on the basis of the assumed relationship between Y_{ijk} and the population parameters. The development of Equation (8.5) seems a necessary prerequisite to the actual data analysis.

8.2.2 The analysis of variance

Table 8-5 presents the *SV, df, SS, EMS*, and *F* (*MS* have been omitted; as usual, they are simply ratios of *SS* to *df*). The *SV* follow directly from Equation (8.5), with one source for each term in the equation except ϵ_{ijk}. The omission of an independent error term is consistent with the analyses of Chapter 7. Since there is only a single score in each combination of *S, A,* and *B*, no within-cells variability exists, and the sources of Table 8-5 therefore account for the total variability in the data matrix. For convenience, we have grouped the sources into two sets, those which account for the variability between subjects and those which account for the variability within subjects. The first set corresponds to η_{ij} effects in our model, while the second set corresponds to the quantity $\mu_{ijk} - \mu_{ij}$. Within the first set, we have *A* and *S/A*, corresponding to α_j and $\eta_{i/j}$ effects. Within the second set of terms, we have *B, AB,* and *SB/A*, corresponding to β_k, $(\alpha\beta)_{jk}$, and $(\eta\beta)_{ik/j}$. The nature of the correspondence will shortly become clearer when we turn to the *EMS*.

Scanning the *SV*, the reader may wonder why there is no *SA* term present. The answer lies in the distinction between *crossing* and *nesting*. When data are obtained for all combinations of two variables, the variables are said to cross. In this case, an interaction sum of squares may be computed for the two variables, since the question, Is the difference in the effects

TABLE 8-5

Analysis of variance for the mixed design, one between- and one within-subjects variable

SV	df	SS	EMS	F
Total	$anb - 1$	$\displaystyle\sum_i^n \sum_j^a \sum_k^b Y_{ijk}^2 - C$		
Between S	$an - 1$	$\displaystyle\frac{\sum_i^a \sum_j^n \left(\sum_k^b Y_{ijk}\right)^2}{b} - C$		
A	$a - 1$	$\displaystyle\frac{\sum_j^a \left(\sum_i^n \sum_k^b Y_{ijk}\right)^2}{nb} - C$	$\sigma_e^2 + b\sigma_{S/A}^2 + nb\theta_A^2$	$\dfrac{MS_A}{MS_{S/A}}$
S/A	$a(n - 1)$	$SS_{\text{B.S}} - SS_A$	$\sigma_e^2 + b\sigma_{S/A}^2$	
Within S	$an(b - 1)$	$SS_{\text{tot}} - SS_{\text{B.S}}$		
B	$b - 1$	$\displaystyle\frac{\sum_k^b \left(\sum_i^n \sum_j^a Y_{ijk}\right)^2}{na} - C$	$\sigma_e^2 + \sigma_{SB/A}^2 + na\theta_B^2$	$\dfrac{MS_B}{MS_{SB/A}}$
AB	$(a - 1)(b - 1)$	$\displaystyle\frac{\sum_j^a \sum_k^b \left(\sum_i^n Y_{ijk}\right)^2}{n} - C - SS_A - SS_B$	$\sigma_e^2 + \sigma_{SB/A}^2 + n\theta_{AB}^2$	$\dfrac{MS_{AB}}{MS_{SB/A}}$
SB/A	$a(n - 1)(b - 1)$	$SS_{\text{W.S}} - SS_B - SS_{AB}$	$\sigma_e^2 + \sigma_{SB/A}^2$	

of A a function of the level of B? is a meaningful one. Subjects and B, and A and B, cross in the design under discussion.

Scores cannot be obtained for all combinations of subjects and levels of A, since any given subject appears in combination with only one level of A. The question of interaction is meaningless. Consider asking whether the difference between Subject 1 and Subject 2 is greater at A_1 than at A_2. In our design, either both subjects appear only at A_1, or both appear only at A_2, or one appears only at A_1 while the other appears only at A_2. In any of these cases, the question posed above has no answer. What we have instead of crossing is the nesting of subjects within levels of A; i.e., there are n subjects at A_1, n others at A_2, and so on.

How do we interpret the nested terms? Simply enough, the variability associated with S/A is the variability among subjects at A_1 added to the variability among subjects at A_2, and so on until all levels of A have been accounted for. In a sense, this is a measure of the "pure" variability among subjects, the variability which remains after the variability due to A treatment effects has been subtracted from the total variability among subjects. In a similar manner, SB/A represents the pooling over levels of A of the variability due to the SB interaction at each level of A. An SB source corresponding to $(\eta\beta)_{ijk}$ would be "impure," inflated by the presence of the AB interaction. The term in Table 8-5 is the interaction variability of subjects and levels of B which remains after the total interaction variability has been adjusted for the contribution of the AB interaction. These interpretive remarks about the nested terms are essential not only to an understanding of the meaning of each term in the SV column, but because the df and SS follow naturally if one understands just what each source represents.

Next turn to the df column of Table 8-5. No discussion of the entries for A, B, or AB seems necessary; their rationale has been previously considered. The df for the *between-subjects* source reflect the variability of *an* means about the grand mean. The $df_{S/A}$ may be calculated as a residual:

$$df_{S/A} = df_{\text{B S}} - df_A$$

$$a(n - 1) = (an - 1) - (a - 1)$$

or we may note that, at each level of A, the variability of subject means about their mean is based on $n - 1$ df. Pooling over levels of A gives the appropriate result.

The *within-subjects* variability is obtained by computing for each subject the variability of his b measures about their mean and then pooling over subjects. Therefore, we have $b - 1$ df for each subject, and since there *an* subjects, pooling results in $an(b - 1)$ df. Alternatively,

$$df_{\text{w.s}} = df_{\text{tot}} - df_{\text{B.s}}$$

$$an(b - 1) = (abn - 1) - (an - 1)$$

The $df_{SB/A}$ may be computed in several ways. It is a residual from the *within-subjects* variability:

$$df_{SB/A} = df_{w.s} - df_B - df_{AB}$$
$$= an(b - 1) - (b - 1) - (a - 1)(b - 1)$$
$$= a(n - 1)(b - 1)$$

The $df_{SB/A}$ reflects the difference between the overall interaction of subjects and levels of B (disregarding the presence of the variable A) and the AB interaction:

$$df_{SB/A} = df_{SB} - df_{AB}$$
$$= (an - 1)(b - 1) - (a - 1)(b - 1)$$
$$= a(n - 1)(b - 1)$$

The $df_{SB/A}$ reflects the SB variability at each level of A, pooled over levels of A:

$$df_{SB/A} = (n - 1)(b - 1) + \cdots + (n - 1)(b - 1)$$
$$= a(n - 1)(b - 1)$$

The computational formulas for sums of squares present no difficulties. They follow the same logic just developed for df. In those cases in which several approaches to the calculation of df (e.g., SB/A) have been presented, the simplest one has been used as a basis for computing sums of squares. An alternative calculation for $SS_{SB/A}$ will be suggested to prepare the reader for subsequent designs in which similar nested terms cannot always be calculated as simple residual quantities. The alternative approach rests upon the expansion of df proposed earlier in this book. We begin with

$$df_{SB/A} = a(n - 1)(b - 1)$$
$$= anb - an - ab + a$$

We require a squared quantity for each df; therefore, we have

$$\sum_i^n \sum_j^a \sum_k^b (\quad)^2 - \sum_i^n \sum_j^a (\quad)^2 - \sum_j^a \sum_k^b (\quad)^2 + \sum_j^a (\quad)^2$$

Since all indices of summation must be represented, we now have

$$\sum_i^n \sum_j^a \sum_k^b (Y_{ijk})^2 - \sum_i^n \sum_j^a \left(\sum_k^b Y_{ijk}\right)^2 - \sum_j^a \sum_k^b \left(\sum_i^n Y_{ijk}\right)^2 + \sum_j^a \left(\sum_i^n \sum_k^b Y_{ijk}\right)^2$$

Since each squared quantity must be divided by the number of scores summed prior to squaring, the final result is

$$(8.6) \quad SS_{SB/A} = \sum_i^n \sum_j^a \sum_k^b Y_{ijk}^2 - \frac{\sum_i^n \sum_j^a \left(\sum_k^b Y_{ijk}\right)^2}{b} - \frac{\sum_j^a \sum_k^b \left(\sum_i^n Y_{ijk}\right)^2}{n} + \frac{\sum_j^a \left(\sum_i^n \sum_k^b Y_{ijk}\right)^2}{nb}$$

Note that each of the four component terms has been computed previously as part of some other sum of squares quantity. For example, $\sum_i^n \sum_j^a (\sum_k^b Y_{ijk})^2/b$ is calculated in obtaining $SS_{\text{B.s.}}$. Where do the other three terms appear among other sum of squares entries?

The rationale for the *EMS* is essentially that of Section 7.2.2 for the nonadditive repeated measurements model. However, the designs are now becoming sufficiently complex so that some rules for generating *EMS* would seem helpful. The following will apply to designs involving fixed effects, random effects, or both. The major stipulation in the use of these rules is that an infinite number of levels are assumed in populations from which a random sample is obtained. This assumption will be approximately correct in most psychological research.

RULES OF THUMB FOR GENERATING *EMS*

RULE 1. Decide for each independent variable *(including subjects)* whether it is fixed or random. Assign a letter to designate each variable. Assign another letter to be used as a coefficient which represents the number of levels of each variable. In the example of Table 8-5, the variables are designated A, B, and S; the coefficients are a, b, and n.

RULE 2. List σ_e^2 as part of each *EMS*.

RULE 3. For each *EMS* list the null hypothesis component, i.e., the component corresponding directly to the *SV* under consideration. Thus we add $nb\theta_A^2$ to the *EMS* for the A line, $b\sigma_{S/A}^2$ to the *EMS* for the S/A line. Note that a component consists of three parts:

(1) a coefficient representing the number of scores at each level of the effect (e.g., nb scores at each level of A, or b scores for each subject),

(2) a σ^2 or θ^2 depending upon whether the effect is assumed to be random or fixed [σ^2 is the variance of the population of effects, e.g., $\sigma_{S/A}^2 = E(\eta_{i/j}^2)$; $\theta_A^2 = \sum_j \alpha_j^2/(a-1)$], and

(3) as subscripts, those letters which designate the effect under consideration.

RULE 4. Now add to each *EMS* all components whose subscripts contain *all* of the letters designating the *SV* in question. For example, since the subscript SB/A contains the letters S and A, add $\sigma_{SB/A}^2$ to the *EMS* for the S/A line (this is later deleted according to Rule 6).

RULE 5. Next, examine the gathered components. If a slash appears in the subscript, define only the letters to the left of the slash as "essential." If there are several slashes (as in the next chapter), only the letters prior to the first slash are essential. If there is no slash in the subscript, all letters are considered essential.

RULE 6. Among the essential letters, ignore any which are necessary to designate the *SV*. For example, if the source is A, when considering $n\theta_{AB}^2$ ignore the A. If *any* of the remaining essential letters

te fixed variables, delete the entire component from the
nus, in the preceding example, since B represents a fixed
e, $n\theta^2_{AB}$ does not contribute to the EMS for A.

8-6 are listed the EMS as they would appear following the

TABLE 8-6

EMS for the mixed design, one between- and one within-subjects variable

SV		EMS	
A	$\sigma^2_e + nb\theta^2_A$	$+ n\theta^2_{AB} + b\sigma^2_{S/A} + \sigma^2_{SB/A}$	
S/A	σ^2_e	$+ b\sigma^2_{S/A} + \sigma^2_{SB/A}$	
B	σ^2_e	$+ na\theta^2_B + n\theta^2_{AB}$	$+ \sigma^2_{SB/A}$
AB	σ^2_e	$+ n\theta^2_{AB}$	$+ \sigma^2_{SB/A}$
SB/A	σ^2_e		$+ \sigma^2_{SB/A}$

execution of Rules 1 to 4. The underlined components are those which are
deleted on the basis of Rule 6. If the underlined components are erased, we
have the results in the EMS column of Table 8-5.

With the EMS available, the F tests readily follow. As always, error
terms are required such that $E(F)$ equals 1 when the null hypothesis is true.
Such error terms are possible for tests of A, B, and AB effects. One word
of caution is in order with regard to the tests of B and AB effects; heterogeneity of covariance can positively bias the test, as in the simpler repeated
measurements designs of Chapter 7. We will consider this problem in more
detail in Section 8.4 after presenting several more mixed designs.

8.2.3 A numerical example

An illustrative set of data is presented in Table 8-7. Running only two subjects at each level of A is not generally recommended; it is hoped that the
reader will use this example as a model for computations rather than as a
model for experimentation.

Prior to the actual analysis of variance, sub-totals are obtained for each
subject, for each level of A, for each level of B, and for each AB combination.
Since all of these quantities are eventually used in the analysis, it is wise to
have them available from the start.

We first calculate the correction term. As usual, this is the squared
total of all scores divided by the total number of observations. In this case,

$$C = \frac{(99)^2}{12}$$

$$= 816.75$$

TABLE 8-7

Data for a numerical example, one between- and one within-subjects variable

		B_1	B_2	B_3	$\sum_k Y_{ijk}$
A_1	S_{11}	7	1	7	15
	S_{21}	9	2	10	21
	$\sum_i Y_{i1k} = 16$		3	17	$\sum_i \sum_k Y_{i1k} = 36$
A_2	S_{12}	11	6	7	24
	S_{22}	16	14	9	39
	$\sum_i Y_{i2k} = 27$		20	16	$\sum_i \sum_k Y_{i2k} = 63$
	$\sum_i \sum_j Y_{ijk} = 43$		23	33	$\sum_i \sum_j \sum_k Y_{ijk} = 99$

The SS_{tot} is obtained by squaring each score, summing the squared scores, and subtracting C. Thus, we have

$$SS_{tot} = \sum_i^n \sum_j^a \sum_k^b Y_{ijk}^2 - C$$

$$= (7)^2 + (1)^2 + \cdots + (14)^2 + (9)^2 - C$$

$$= 1{,}023.00 - 816.75$$

$$= 206.25$$

We turn next to the first major component of the SS_{tot}, the $SS_{B.s}$:

$$SS_{B.s} = \frac{\sum_i^n \sum_j^a \left(\sum_k^b Y_{ijk} \right)^2}{b} - C$$

$$= \frac{(15)^2 + (21)^2 + (24)^2 + (39)^2}{3} - C$$

$$= \frac{2{,}763}{3} - 816.75$$

$$= 104.25$$

The $SS_{B.s}$ are then partitioned:

$$SS_A = \frac{\sum\limits_j^a \left(\sum\limits_i^n \sum\limits_k^b Y_{ijk} \right)^2}{nb} - C$$

$$= \frac{(36)^2 + (63)^2}{6} - C$$

$$= \frac{5,265}{6} - 816.75$$

$$= 60.75$$

and

$$SS_{S/A} = SS_{\text{B.s}} - SS_A$$

$$= 104.25 - 60.75$$

$$= 43.50$$

The second major component of the SS_{tot} is the $SS_{\text{w.s}}$. This is simply the difference between the SS_{tot} and $SS_{\text{B.s}}$. Therefore,

$$SS_{\text{w.s}} = SS_{\text{tot}} - SS_{\text{B.s}}$$

$$= 206.25 - 104.25$$

$$= 102.00$$

The within-subjects variability is now analyzed into its components:

$$SS_B = \frac{\sum\limits_k^b \left(\sum\limits_i^n \sum\limits_j^a Y_{ijk} \right)^2}{na} - C$$

$$= \frac{(43)^2 + (23)^2 + (33)^2}{4} - C$$

$$= \frac{3,467}{4} - 816.75$$

$$= 50.00$$

and

$$SS_{AB} = \frac{\sum\limits_j^a \sum\limits_k^b \left(\sum\limits_i^n Y_{ijk} \right)^2}{n} - C - SS_A - SS_B$$

$$= \frac{(16)^2 + (3)^2 + \cdots + (16)^2}{2} - C - SS_A - SS_B$$

$$= \frac{1,939}{2} - 816.75 - 60.75 - 50.00$$

$$= 42.00$$

and

$$SS_{SB/A} = SS_{W.S} - SS_B - SS_{AB}$$
$$= 102.00 - 50.00 - 42.00$$
$$= 10.00$$

Table 8-8 summarizes the analysis. Assuming that our α level is .05, both the B and AB effects are significant. To instill some meaning into this last statement, we turn to Figure 8-1, which contains a plot of the six cell means. In addition, the dashed line represents the main effect of B. The

TABLE 8-8

Analysis of variance for the data of Table 8-7

SV	df	SS	MS	F
Total	11	206.25		
Between S	3	104.25		
A	1	60.75	60.75	2.79
S/A	2	43.50	21.75	
Within S	8	102.00		
B	2	50.00	25.00	10.00 *
AB	2	42.00	21.00	8.40 *
SB/A	4	10.00	2.50	

$*p < .05$

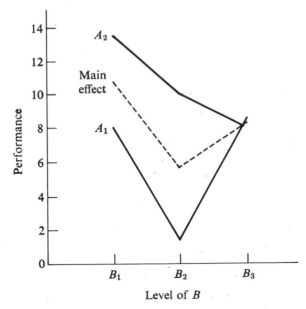

FIGURE 8-1   A plot of cell means of Table 8-7

source of the significant B effect is due to the roughly V-shaped function obtained when the average performance is plotted against the levels of B. If high scores are desirable, it would seem that B_1 is the preferred treatment. It is tempting to go somewhat further and more precisely conclude that B_1 is better than both B_2 and B_3, and that B_3 is better than B_2; however, our F test only permits the inference that at least one of these three contrasts involves a difference in the population. Presumably, it is safe to assume that B_1 and B_2 differ in their effects, since the difference in their means is greatest. In Chapter 13 the set of three contrasts will be evaluated, as well as others which are not quite as obvious.

It has just been noted that inferences about the population effects of B are limited until further comparisons can be made within pairs of means. Our conclusions about B are now further qualified by noting that the AB interaction is significant. The simple effects of B at each level of A are not identical to the main effect. The source of the AB interaction is not difficult to detect in Figure 8-1. The B means, when plotted at A_1, form a symmetric V-shaped function; when the means are plotted for the A_2 data, the function decreases monotonically as the level of B increases.

8.3 ADDITIONAL MIXED DESIGNS

Countless variations of the design of the preceding section have appeared in the experimental journals. They should present no insurmountable difficulties. The development of the model follows that of Section 8.2.1, and the model in turn generates SV and df. The df are sufficient to lead to the proper computational formulas for sums of squares. Finally, the rules of thumb of Section 8.2.2 may be applied without modification. To illustrate how the developments of Section 8.2 extend to more complex designs, two additional mixed designs will be dealt with in the present section.

8.3.1 Two between- and one within-subjects variables

Table 8-9 presents the data matrix for the design to be considered next. A random sample from a large population of subjects has been randomly distributed among the ab combinations of levels of the variables A and B, with the restriction that there be n subjects in each combination. Each subject is tested at c levels of the variable C, the order of presentation of the c treatments being independently randomized for each subject. The notation used in Table 8-9, and throughout this section, will be as follows:

$$i = 1, 2, \cdots, n$$
$$j = 1, 2, \cdots, a$$
$$k = 1, 2, \cdots, b$$
$$m = 1, 2, \cdots, c$$

TABLE 8-9

Data matrix for a mixed design, two between- and one within-subjects variables

			C_1	$\cdots$	C_m	$\cdots$	C_c
		S_{111}	Y_{1111}		Y_{111m}		Y_{111c}
	A_1	S_{i11}	Y_{i111}		Y_{i11m}		Y_{i11c}
		S_{n11}	Y_{n111}		Y_{n11m}		Y_{n11c}
B_1	A_j	S_{ij1}	Y_{ij11}		Y_{ij1m}		Y_{ij1c}
	A_a	S_{ia1}	Y_{ia11}		Y_{ia1m}		Y_{ia1c}
B_k	A_j	S_{ijk}	Y_{ijk1}		Y_{ijkm}		Y_{ijkc}
B_b	A_j	S_{ijb}	Y_{ijb1}		Y_{ijbm}		Y_{ijbc}

The Model. The first approximation to the model is achieved as in Section 8.2.1; the variables A and B are ignored, in which case we have a simple repeated measurements design ($S \times C$) with abn subjects and c levels of the treatment variable. By analogy to Equation (7.2)

(8.7) $$Y_{ijkm} = \mu + \eta_{ijk} + \gamma_m + (\eta\gamma)_{ijkm} + \epsilon_{ijkm}$$

where $\eta_{ijk} = \mu_{ijk} - \mu$, $\gamma_m = \mu_m - \mu$, and

$$(\eta\gamma)_{ijkm} = (\mu_{ijkm} - \mu) - (\mu_{ijk} - \mu) - (\mu_m - \mu)$$

Equation (8.7) ignores the possibility of effects that involve the variables A and B. A more realistic model notes that subjects differ because they are at different levels of A, because they are at different levels of B, because they are in different AB combinations, and because even subjects within the same treatment classification differ due to individual differences. A mathematical form of the preceding verbal statement is

(8.8) $$\eta_{ijk} = \alpha_j + \beta_k + (\alpha\beta)_{jk} + \eta_{i/jk}$$

or

(8.8') $$(\mu_{ijk} - \mu) = (\mu_j - \mu) + (\mu_k - \mu) + (\mu_{jk} - \mu_j - \mu_k + \mu)$$
$$+ (\mu_{ijk} - \mu_{jk})$$

Equation (8.8') is an algebraic identity. The model can therefore be extended by appropriate substitution for η_{ijk} in Equation (8.7).

(8.9) $$Y_{ijkm} = \mu + \alpha_j + \beta_k + (\alpha\beta)_{jk} + \eta_{i/jk} + \gamma_m + (\eta\gamma)_{ijkm} + \epsilon_{ijkm}$$

Since subjects A and B all cross with C, it is reasonable to assume interaction effects involving C. Parallel to the analysis of subject effects, η_{ijk}, we might assume that the $S \times C$ interaction effect, $(\eta\gamma)_{ijkm}$, is contributed to by the joint effects of A and C; B and C; A, B, and C; and the pure, or residual, interaction of S and C, within a treatment classification. Accordingly, we have

(8.10) $$(\eta\gamma)_{ijkm} = (\alpha\gamma)_{jm} + (\beta\gamma)_{km} + (\alpha\beta\gamma)_{jkm} + (\eta\gamma)_{im/jk}$$

or

(8.10')

$$(\mu_{ijkm} - \mu_{ijk} - \mu_m + \mu) = (\mu_{jm} - \mu_j - \mu_m + \mu) + (\mu_{km} - \mu_k - \mu_m + \mu)$$
$$+ (\mu_{jkm} + \mu_j + \mu_k + \mu_m - \mu_{jk} - \mu_{jm} - \mu_{km} - \mu)$$
$$+ (\mu_{ijkm} - \mu_{ijk} - \mu_{jkm} + \mu_{jk})$$

Having accounted for all main and interaction effects that are suggested by the design, we may now state the final form of the model:

(8.11) $$Y_{ijkm} = \alpha_j + \beta_k + (\alpha\beta)_{jk} + \eta_{i/jk} + \gamma_m + (\alpha\gamma)_{jm} + (\beta\gamma)_{km}$$
$$+ (\alpha\beta\gamma)_{jkm} + (\eta\gamma)_{im/jk} + \epsilon_{ijkm}$$

It is assumed that A, B, and C are fixed effect variables; this implies

$$\sum_j \alpha_j = 0; \; \theta_A^2 = \frac{\sum_j \alpha_j^2}{a - 1}$$

$$\sum_k \beta_k = 0; \; \theta_B^2 = \frac{\sum_k \beta_k^2}{b - 1}$$

$$\sum_m \gamma_m = 0; \; \theta_C^2 = \frac{\sum_m \gamma_m^2}{c - 1}$$

$$\sum_j \sum_k (\alpha\beta)_{jk} = 0; \; \theta_{AB}^2 = \frac{\sum_j \sum_k (\alpha\beta)_{jk}^2}{(a - 1)(b - 1)}$$

$$\sum_j \sum_m (\alpha\gamma)_{jm} = 0; \; \theta_{AC}^2 = \frac{\sum_j \sum_m (\alpha\gamma)_{jm}^2}{(a - 1)(c - 1)}$$

TABLE 8-10
Analysis of variance for the mixed design, two between- and one within-subjects variables

SV	df	SS	EMS	F
Total	$abnc - 1$	$\sum_i^n \sum_j^a \sum_k^b \sum_m^c Y_{ijkm}^2 - C$		
Between S	$abn - 1$	$\dfrac{\sum_i^n \sum_j^a \sum_k^b \left(\sum_m^c Y_{ijkm}\right)}{c} - C$		
A	$a - 1$	$\dfrac{\sum_j^a \left(\sum_i^n \sum_k^b \sum_m^c Y_{ijkm}\right)^2}{nbc} - C$	$\sigma_e^2 + c\sigma_{S/AB}^2 + nbc\theta_A^2$	$\dfrac{MS_A}{MS_{S/AB}}$
B	$b - 1$	$\dfrac{\sum_k^b \left(\sum_i^n \sum_j^a \sum_m^c Y_{ijkm}\right)^2}{nac} - C$	$\sigma_e^2 + c\sigma_{S/AB}^2 + nac\theta_B^2$	$\dfrac{MS_B}{MS_{S/AB}}$
AB	$(a - 1)(b - 1)$	$\dfrac{\sum_j^a \sum_k^b \left(\sum_i^n \sum_m^c Y_{ijkm}\right)^2}{nc} - C - SS_A - SS_B$	$\sigma_e^2 + c\sigma_{S/AB}^2 + nc\theta_{AB}^2$	$\dfrac{MS_{AB}}{MS_{S/AB}}$
S/AB	$ab(n - 1)$	$SS_{B.S} - SS_A - SS_B - SS_{AB}$	$\sigma_e^2 + c\sigma_{S/AB}^2$	
Within S	$abn(c - 1)$	$SS_{tot} - SS_{B.S}$		
C	$(c - 1)$	$\dfrac{\sum_m^c \left(\sum_i^n \sum_j^a \sum_k^b Y_{ijkm}\right)^2}{nab} - C$	$\sigma_e^2 + \sigma_{SC/AB}^2 + nab\theta_C^2$	$\dfrac{MS_C}{MS_{SC/AB}}$

Source	df	SS	$E(MS)$	F
AC	$(a-1)(c-1)$	$\displaystyle\sum_j^a \sum_m^c \frac{\left(\sum_i^n \sum_k^b Y_{ijkm}\right)^2}{nb} - C - SS_A - SS_C$	$\sigma_e^2 + \sigma_{SC/AB}^2 + nb\bar\sigma_{AC}^2$	$\dfrac{MS_{AC}}{MS_{SC/AB}}$
BC	$(b-1)(c-1)$	$\displaystyle\sum_k^b \sum_m^c \frac{\left(\sum_i^n \sum_j^a Y_{ijkm}\right)^2}{na} - C - SS_B - SS_C$	$\sigma_e^2 + \sigma_{SC/AB}^2 + na\bar\sigma_{BC}^2$	$\dfrac{MS_{BC}}{MS_{SC/AB}}$
ABC	$(a-1)(b-1)(c-1)$	$\displaystyle\sum_j^a \sum_k^b \sum_m^c \frac{\left(\sum_i^n Y_{ijkm}\right)^2}{n} - C - SS_{AB} - SS_{AC} - SS_{BC}$ $- SS_A - SS_B - SS_C$	$\sigma_e^2 + \sigma_{SC/AB}^2 + n\theta_{ABC}^2$	$\dfrac{MS_{ABC}}{MS_{SC/AB}}$
SC/AB	$ab(n-1)(c-1)$	$SS_{W.S} - SS_C - SS_{AC} - SS_{BC} - SS_{ABC}$	$\sigma_e^2 + \sigma_{SC/AB}^2$	

$$\sum_k \sum_m (\beta\gamma)_{km} = 0; \; \theta^2_{BC} = \frac{\sum_k \sum_m (\beta\gamma)^2_{km}}{(b-1)(c-1)}$$

$$\sum_j \sum_k \sum_m (\alpha\beta\gamma)_{jkm} = 0; \; \theta^2_{ABC} = \frac{\sum_j \sum_k \sum_m (\alpha\beta\gamma)^2_{jkm}}{(a-1)(b-1)(c-1)}$$

The ϵ_{ijkm}, $\eta_{i/jk}$, and $(\eta\gamma)_{im/jk}$ effects are randomly sampled from infinite populations of such effects. The population distributions are normal with zero expected value and with variances σ^2_e, $\sigma^2_{S/AB}$, and $\sigma^2_{SC/AB}$, respectively.

The analysis of variance. The analysis of variance for the two between- and one within-subjects design is summarized in Table 8-10. The *SV* follow directly from Equation (8.12). The *df* are derived as in Section 8.2.2. The df_{tot}, as usual, are one less than the total number of scores, which is $abcn$ in the present case. This quantity is partitioned into two parts, the $df_{B.S}$, which is one less than the total number of subjects, and the $df_{W.S}$, which is the *df* for each subject $(c-1)$ pooled over the number of subjects. The *df* for all treatment main and interaction effects are identical to those presented for previous designs, and the *df* for the two nested effects can be readily obtained as residuals. Computational formulas for sums of squares all follow the precedents set in the preceding section and in preceding chapters. The results of applying the rules of thumb for generating *EMS* are similar to those achieved in Section 8.2; we again obtain two error terms, one for between-subjects effects and one for within-subjects effects.

A numerical example. An analysis of variance on the data of Table 8-11 will exemplify the computational process. We first compute

$$SS_{tot} = \sum_i^n \sum_j^a \sum_k^b \sum_m^c Y^2_{ijkm} - C$$

$$= (4)^2 + (8)^2 + \cdots + (6)^2 + (8)^2 - \frac{(169)^2}{24}$$

$$= 1,403.000 - 1,190.042$$

$$= 212.958$$

The total variability among subjects is

$$SS_{B.S} = \frac{\sum_i^n \sum_j^a \sum_k^b \left(\sum_m^c Y_{ijkm}\right)^2}{c} - C$$

$$= \frac{(22)^2 + (27)^2 + \cdots + (15)^2}{3} - \frac{(169)^2}{24}$$

$$= 3,721.000 - 1,190.042$$

$$= 50.291$$

This variability may be partitioned into several components:

TABLE 8-11

Data for a numerical example, two between- and one within-subjects design

			C_1	C_2	C_3	$\sum_m Y_{ijkm}$
A_1	B_1	S_{111}	4	8	10	22
		S_{211}	6	9	12	27
		$\sum_i Y_{i11m} = 10$		17	22	$\sum_i \sum_m Y_{i11m} = 49$
	B_2	S_{112}	3	7	11	21
		S_{212}	5	11	12	28
		$\sum_i Y_{i12m} = 8$		18	23	$\sum_i \sum_m Y_{i12m} = 49$
		$\sum_i \sum_k Y_{i1km} = 18$		35	45	$\sum_i \sum_k \sum_m Y_{i1km} = 98$
A_2	B_1	S_{121}	4	6	9	19
		S_{221}	5	8	8	21
		$\sum_i Y_{i21m} = 9$		14	17	$\sum_i \sum_m Y_{i21m} = 40$
	B_2	S_{122}	4	3	9	16
		S_{222}	1	6	8	15
		$\sum_i Y_{i22m} = 5$		9	17	$\sum_i \sum_m Y_{i22m} = 31$
		$\sum_i \sum_k Y_{i2km} = 14$		23	34	$\sum_i \sum_k \sum_m Y_{i2km} = 71$
		$\sum_i \sum_j \sum_k Y_{ijkm} = 32$		58	79	$\sum_i \sum_j \sum_k \sum_m Y_{ijkm} = 169$

Sub-totals for BC Cells

	C_1	C_2	C_3	$\sum_i \sum_j \sum_m Y_{ijkm}$
B_1	19	31	39	89
B_2	13	27	40	80
$\sum_i \sum_j \sum_k Y_{ijkm} = 32$		58	79	$\sum_i \sum_j \sum_k \sum_m Y_{ijkm} = 169$

$$SS_A = \frac{\sum\limits_{j}^{a} \left(\sum\limits_{i}^{n} \sum\limits_{k}^{b} \sum\limits_{m}^{c} Y_{ijkm} \right)^2}{nbc} - C$$

$$= \frac{(98)^2 + (71)^2}{12} - \frac{(169)^2}{24}$$

$$= 1,220.417 - 1,190.042$$

$$= 30.375$$

$$SS_B = \frac{\sum\limits_{k}^{b} \left(\sum\limits_{i}^{n} \sum\limits_{j}^{a} \sum\limits_{m}^{c} Y_{ijkm} \right)^2}{nac} - C$$

$$= \frac{(89)^2 + (80)^2}{12} - \frac{(169)^2}{24}$$

$$= 1,193.417 - 1,190.042$$

$$= 3.375$$

$$SS_{AB} = \frac{\sum\limits_{j}^{a} \sum\limits_{k}^{b} \left(\sum\limits_{i}^{n} \sum\limits_{m}^{c} Y_{ijkm} \right)^2}{nc} - C - SS_A - SS_B$$

$$= \frac{(49)^2 + (49)^2 + (40)^2 + (31)^2}{6} - \frac{(169)^2}{24} - SS_A - SS_B$$

$$= 1,227.167 - 1,190.042 - 30.375 - 3.375$$

$$= 3.375$$

$$SS_{S/AB} = SS_{B.S} - SS_A - SS_B - SS_{AB}$$
$$= 50.291 - 30.375 - 3.375 - 3.375$$
$$= 13.166$$

Note that the A, B, and AB terms may be swiftly computed by the single df approach first presented in Section 5.9. Thus,

$$SS_A = \frac{(98 - 71)^2}{24} \qquad SS_B = \frac{(89 - 80)^2}{24}$$

$$= 30.375 \qquad\qquad = 3.375$$

and

$$SS_{AB} = \frac{(49 - 49 - 40 + 31)^2}{24}$$

$$= 3.375$$

The within-subjects variability may be obtained as the difference between the total and the between-subjects variability:

$$SS_{W.S} = SS_{tot} - SS_{B.S}$$
$$= 212.958 - 50.291$$
$$= 162.667$$

This term is next partitioned into its components. We have

$$SS_C = \frac{\sum\limits_{m}^{c}\left(\sum\limits_{i}^{n}\sum\limits_{j}^{a}\sum\limits_{k}^{b} Y_{ijkm}\right)^2}{nab} - C$$

$$= \frac{(32)^2 + (58)^2 + (79)^2}{8} - \frac{(169)^2}{24}$$

$$= 1{,}328.625 - 1{,}190.042$$

$$= 138.583$$

$$SS_{AC} = \frac{\sum\limits_{j}^{a}\sum\limits_{m}^{c}\left(\sum\limits_{i}^{n}\sum\limits_{k}^{b} Y_{ijkm}\right)^2}{nb} - C - SS_A - SS_C$$

$$= \frac{(18)^2 + (35)^2 + \cdots + (34)^2}{4} - \frac{(169)^2}{24} - SS_A - SS_C$$

$$= 1{,}363.750 - 1{,}190.042 - 30.375 - 138.583$$

$$= 4.750$$

$$SS_{BC} = \frac{\sum\limits_{k}^{b}\sum\limits_{m}^{c}\left(\sum\limits_{i}^{n}\sum\limits_{j}^{a} Y_{ijkm}\right)^2}{na} - C - SS_B - SS_C$$

$$= \frac{(19)^2 + (31)^2 + \cdots + (40)^2}{4} - \frac{(169)^2}{24} - SS_B - SS_C$$

$$= 1{,}335.250 - 1{,}190.042 - 3.375 - 138.583$$

$$= 3.250$$

$$SS_{ABC} = \frac{\sum\limits_{j}^{a}\sum\limits_{k}^{b}\sum\limits_{m}^{c}\left(\sum\limits_{i}^{n} Y_{ijkm}\right)^2}{n} - C - SS_{AB} - SS_{AC} - SS_{BC} - SS_A$$
$$- SS_B - SS_C$$

$$= \frac{(10)^2 + (17)^2 + \cdots + (9)^2 + (17)^2}{2} - \frac{(169)^2}{24} - SS_A - SS_B$$
$$- SS_C - SS_{AB} - SS_{AC} - SS_{BC}$$

$$= 1{,}375.500 - 1{,}190.042 - 30.375 - 3.375 - 138.583 - 3.375$$
$$- 4.750 - 3.250$$

$$= 1.750$$

and

$$SS_{SC/AB} = SS_{\text{w.s}} - SS_C - SS_{AC} - SS_{BC} - SS_{ABC}$$
$$= 162.667 - 138.583 - 4.750 - 3.250 - 1.750$$
$$= 14.334$$

The final results of the analysis are summarized in Table 8-12. Clearly, only the A and C main effects are significant; the population mean for the

TABLE 8-12

Analysis of variance for the data of Table 8-11

SV	df	SS	MS	F
Total	23	212.958		
Between S	7	50.291		
A	1	30.375	30.375	9.227 *
B	1	3.375	3.375	1.025
AB	1	3.375	3.375	1.025
S/AB	4	13.166	3.292	
Within S	16	162.667		
C	2	138.583	69.292	38.667 *
AC	2	4.750	2.375	1.325
BC	2	3.250	1.625	.907
ABC	2	1.750	.875	.488
SC/AB	8	14.334	1.792	
				$*p<.01$

A_1 treatment is higher than that for the A_2 treatment, and the mean performance is also an increasing function of the level of C.

8.3.2 One between- and two within-subjects variables

This design is of interest because it requires consideration of a more complex analysis of within-subjects variability than any which have been previously discussed. The design is quite common; indeed, three and even four within-subjects variables are frequently manipulated. As an example of one experiment using this design, consider a study of paired-associate learning in which the subject must learn the 16 responses that are correct for the 16 stimuli presented to him. Trials to criterion (perhaps two errorless runs) is the dependent variable. The stimuli and responses are nonsense syllables. Half of the stimuli have high association values, and the other half have low association values; similarly, the responses are divided between high and low association syllables. Thus, four pairs are high-high (B_1C_1), four are low-high (B_2C_1), four are high-low (B_1C_2), and four are low-low (B_2C_2). Since each S must learn all 16 pairs, stimulus association value (B) and response association value (C) are both within-subjects variables.

Table 8-13 presents a data matrix for the class of designs under discussion. A random sample from a large population of subjects has been randomly distributed among the a levels of the between-subjects variable, A, with the restriction that there are exactly n subjects at each level. The within-subjects variables are B and C, and there are bc scores obtained from each subject. The order of presentation of the bc treatment combinations is randomized independently for each subject. The indices $i, j, k,$ and m are used in reference to the levels of subjects, A, B, and C, respectively.

TABLE 8-13
Data matrix for a mixed design, one between- and two within-subjects variables

	B_1				B_k				B_b		
	$C_1 \cdots$	C_m	$\cdots C_c$	$\cdots$	$C_1 \cdots$	C_m	$\cdots C_c$	$\cdots$	C_1	$C_m \cdots$	C_c
A_1											
S_{11}	Y_{1111}	Y_{111m}	Y_{111c}		Y_{11k1}	Y_{11km}	Y_{11kc}		Y_{11b1}	Y_{11bm}	Y_{11bc}
$\vdots$											
S_{i1}	Y_{i111}	Y_{i11m}	Y_{i11c}		Y_{i1k1}	Y_{i1km}	Y_{i1kc}		Y_{i1b1}	Y_{i1bm}	Y_{i1bc}
$\vdots$											
S_{n1}	Y_{n111}	Y_{n11m}	Y_{n11c}		Y_{n1k1}	Y_{n1km}	Y_{n1kc}		Y_{n1b1}	Y_{n1bm}	Y_{n1bc}
$\cdots$											
A_j											
$\vdots$ S_{ij} $\vdots$	Y_{ij11}	Y_{ij1m}	Y_{ij1c}		Y_{ijk1}	Y_{ijkm}	Y_{ijkc}		Y_{ijb1}	Y_{ijbm}	Y_{ijbc}
$\cdots$											
A_a											
$\vdots$ S_{ia} $\vdots$	Y_{ia11}	Y_{ia1m}	Y_{ia1c}		Y_{iak1}	Y_{iakm}	Y_{iakc}		Y_{iab1}	Y_{iabm}	Y_{iabc}

The model. As in preceding sections of this chapter, we use the developments of Chapter 7 as a point of departure. The design may be viewed as an $S \times B \times C$ design with *an* subjects. Then our first approximation to the final model is

$$Y_{ijkm} = \mu + \underset{\text{S effect}}{\eta_{ij}} + \underset{\text{B effect}}{\beta_k} + \underset{\text{C effect}}{\gamma_m} + \underset{\text{BC effect}}{(\beta\gamma)_{km}}$$

(8.12)

$$+ \underset{\text{SB effect}}{(\eta\beta)_{ijk}} + \underset{\text{SC effect}}{(\eta\gamma)_{ijm}} + \underset{\text{SBC effect}}{(\eta\beta\gamma)_{ijkm}} + \underset{\text{error}}{\epsilon_{ijkm}}$$

The effects that involve η are now partitioned as in the preceding sections. We have

(8.13)
$$\eta_{ij} = \alpha_j + \eta_{i/j}$$
$$(\eta\beta)_{ijk} = (\alpha\beta)_{jk} + (\eta\beta)_{ik/j}$$
$$(\eta\gamma)_{ijm} = (\alpha\gamma)_{jm} + (\eta\gamma)_{im/j}$$
$$(\eta\beta\gamma)_{ijkm} = (\alpha\beta\gamma)_{jkm} + (\eta\beta\gamma)_{ikm/j}$$

where

$$\alpha_j = \mu_j - \mu$$
$$\eta_{i/j} = \mu_{ij} - \mu_j$$
$$(\alpha\beta)_{jk} = \mu_{jk} - \mu_j - \mu_k + \mu$$
$$(\eta\beta)_{ik/j} = \mu_{ijk} - \mu_{ij} - \mu_{jk} + \mu_j$$
$$(\alpha\gamma)_{jm} = \mu_{jm} - \mu_j - \mu_m + \mu$$
$$(\eta\gamma)_{im/j} = \mu_{ijm} - \mu_{ij} - \mu_{jm} + \mu_j$$
$$(\alpha\beta\gamma)_{jkm} = \mu_{jkm} + \mu_j + \mu_k + \mu_m - \mu_{jk} - \mu_{jm} - \mu_{km} - \mu$$
$$(\eta\beta\gamma)_{ikm/j} = \mu_{ijkm} + \mu_{ij} + \mu_{jk} + \mu_{jm} - \mu_{ijk} - \mu_{ijm} - \mu_{jkm} - \mu_j$$

Referring back to Equation (8.13), we note that as in the past, the nested interaction effect is the pure, or residual, effect obtained by correcting the overall interaction effect for an interaction of between- and within-subjects variables. For example, the SBC/A effect, $(\eta\beta\gamma)_{ikm/j}$, is the difference between the SBC and the ABC effect.

Substituting from Equation (8.13) into Equation (8.12), we are able to present a statement of our model that provides for all those effects that might exist in the population.

(8.14)
$$Y_{ijkm} = \mu + \alpha_j + \eta_{i/j} + \beta_k + \gamma_m + (\beta\gamma)_{km} + (\alpha\beta)_{jk}$$
$$+ (\alpha\gamma)_{jm} + (\alpha\beta\gamma)_{jkm} + (\eta\beta)_{ik/j} + (\eta\gamma)_{im/j}$$
$$+ (\eta\beta\gamma)_{ikm/j} + \epsilon_{ijkm}$$

As usual, specific assumptions about the population parameters are required in order to derive *EMS* and in order that the ratios of mean squares that test the null hypotheses are distributed as *F*. It is assumed that the effects of the variables *A*, *B*, and *C* are fixed; the levels of these variables have been arbitrarily chosen. Consequently, the fixed effect population components (e.g., θ_A^2) are defined exactly as in Section 8.3.1, p. 191). It is assumed that subjects have been randomly sampled from a large population of subjects. Consequently, $\eta_{i/j}$, $(\eta\beta)_{ik/j}$, $(\eta\gamma)_{im/j}$, $(\eta\beta\gamma)_{ikm/j}$, as well as ϵ_{ijkm}, are assumed to be random samples from normally distributed populations with mean zero and variances $\sigma^2_{S/A}$, $\sigma^2_{SB/A}$, $\sigma^2_{SC/A}$, $\sigma^2_{SBC/A}$, and σ^2_e, respectively.

The analysis of variance. The *SV* of Table 8-14 parallel the terms in Equation (8.14), with the qualification that there is no separate error term corresponding to ϵ_{ijkm}. In the *df* column, only the nested subject × treatment interactions warrant comment. The previous section on the model provides the clue to these quantities. For example, it has been pointed out that the *SB/A* effect is the difference between the *SB* effect and the *AB* effect. It follows that $df_{SB/A} = df_{SB} - df_{AB}$, or

$$a(n-1)(b-1) = (an-1)(b-1) - (a-1)(b-1)$$

An alternative way of arriving at the above result is to view the nested interaction as a pool of *a SB* interactions, each computed at a different level of *A*. Then there are $(n-1)(b-1)$ *df* at each level of *A*, and the pooled result is $a(n-1)(b-1)$ *df*.

The *SS* calculations are also familiar, with the possible exception of the nested interaction terms. Either of the two approaches indicated for *df* can be used to calculate *SS*. For example, we could calculate an SS_{SB} as we would for a simple repeated measurements design and then subtract SS_{AB}, thereby obtaining $SS_{SB/A}$. As an alternative, the overall design could be treated as *a* two-factor repeated measurements designs. An *SB* interaction sum of squares could be computed for each of the *a* sets of data, and these would then be pooled. The author's preference for a computational formula is again based on the isomorphism of *df* and *SS*; this formula will ordinarily be the easiest to generate and the quickest to execute. For example, in the case of the *SB/A* term, we expand the *df*, obtaining

$$a(n-1)(b-1) = abn - an - ab + a$$

Remembering that there must be one squared term for each *df*, we have

$$\sum_j^a \sum_k^b \sum_i^n (\quad)^2 - \sum_j^a \sum_i^n (\quad)^2 - \sum_j^a \sum_k^b (\quad)^2 + \sum_j^a (\quad)^2$$

Indices not appearing outside the parentheses must appear within. Therefore, we obtain

$$\sum_j^a \sum_k^b \sum_i^n \left(\sum_m^c Y_{ijkm} \right)^2 - \sum_j^a \sum_i^n \left(\sum_k^b \sum_m^c Y_{ijkm} \right)^2 - \sum_j^a \sum_k^b \left(\sum_i^n \sum_m^c Y_{ijkm} \right)^2$$
$$+ \sum_j^a \left(\sum_i^n \sum_k^b \sum_m^c Y_{ijkm} \right)^2$$

Finally, we divide by the number of scores being summed prior to squaring, yielding

TABLE 8-14

Analysis of variance for the mixed design, one between- and two within-subjects variables

SV	df	SS	EMS	F
Total	$anbc - 1$	$\sum_i^n \sum_j^a \sum_k^b \sum_m^c Y_{ijkm}^2 - C$		
Between S	$an - 1$	$\dfrac{\sum_i^n \sum_j^a \left(\sum_k^b \sum_m^c Y_{ijkm} \right)^2}{bc} - C$		
A	$a - 1$	$\dfrac{\sum_j^a \left(\sum_i^n \sum_k^b \sum_m^c Y_{ijkm} \right)^2}{nbc} - C$	$\sigma_e^2 + bc\sigma_{S/A}^2 + nbc\theta_A^2$	$\dfrac{MS_A}{MS_{S/A}}$
S/A	$a(n - 1)$	$SS_{\text{B.S}} - SS_A$	$\sigma_e^2 + bc\sigma_{S/A}^2$	
Within S	$an(bc - 1)$	$SS_{\text{tot}} - SS_{\text{B.S}}$		
B	$b - 1$	$\dfrac{\sum_k^b \left(\sum_i^n \sum_j^a \sum_m^c Y_{ijkm} \right)^2}{nac} - C$	$\sigma_e^2 + c\sigma_{SB/A}^2 + nac\theta_B^2$	$\dfrac{MS_B}{MS_{SB/A}}$
AB	$(a - 1)(b - 1)$	$\dfrac{\sum_j^a \sum_k^b \left(\sum_i^n \sum_m^c Y_{ijkm} \right)^2}{nc} - C - SS_A - SS_B$	$\sigma_e^2 + c\sigma_{SB/A}^2 + nc\theta_{AB}^2$	$\dfrac{MS_{AB}}{MS_{SB/A}}$
SB/A	$a(n - 1)(b - 1)$	$\dfrac{\sum_i^n \sum_j^a \sum_k^b \left(\sum_m^c Y_{ijkm} \right)^2}{c} - \dfrac{\sum_i^n \sum_j^a \left(\sum_k^b \sum_m^c Y_{ijkm} \right)^2}{bc}$	$\sigma_e^2 + c\sigma_{SB/A}^2$	

Source	df	SS	E(MS)	F
C	$c-1$	$\dfrac{\sum_{j}^{a}\sum_{k}^{b}\left(\sum_{i}^{n}\sum_{m}^{c}Y_{ijkm}\right)^{2}}{nc}-\dfrac{\sum_{m}^{c}\left(\sum_{i}^{n}\sum_{j}^{a}\sum_{k}^{b}Y_{ijkm}\right)^{2}}{nab}+\dfrac{\sum_{j}^{a}\left(\sum_{i}^{n}\sum_{k}^{b}\sum_{m}^{c}Y_{ijkm}\right)^{2}}{nbc}-C$	$\sigma_e^2+b\sigma_{SC/A}^2+nab\theta_C^2$	$\dfrac{MS_C}{MS_{SC/A}}$
AC	$(a-1)(c-1)$	$\dfrac{\sum_{j}^{a}\sum_{m}^{c}\left(\sum_{i}^{n}\sum_{k}^{b}Y_{ijkm}\right)^{2}}{nb}-C-SS_A-SS_C$	$\sigma_e^2+b\sigma_{SC/A}^2+nb\theta_{AC}^2$	$\dfrac{MS_{AC}}{MS_{SC/A}}$
SC/A	$a(n-1)(c-1)$	$\dfrac{\sum_{i}^{n}\sum_{j}^{a}\sum_{m}^{c}\left(\sum_{k}^{b}Y_{ijkm}\right)^{2}}{b}-\dfrac{\sum_{j}^{a}\sum_{m}^{c}\left(\sum_{i}^{n}\sum_{k}^{b}Y_{ijkm}\right)^{2}}{nb}$	$\sigma_e^2+b\sigma_{SC/A}^2$	
BC	$(b-1)(c-1)$	$\dfrac{\sum_{k}^{b}\sum_{m}^{c}\left(\sum_{i}^{n}\sum_{j}^{a}Y_{ijkm}\right)^{2}}{na}-C-SS_B-SS_C$	$\sigma_e^2+\sigma_{SBC/A}^2+na\theta_{BC}^2$	$\dfrac{MS_{BC}}{MS_{SBC/A}}$
ABC	$(a-1)(b-1)(c-1)$	$\dfrac{\sum_{j}^{a}\sum_{k}^{b}\sum_{m}^{c}\left(\sum_{i}^{n}Y_{ijkm}\right)^{2}}{n}-C-SS_{AC}-SS_{BC}-SS_B-SS_{AB}-SS_A-SS_C$	$\sigma_e^2+\sigma_{SBC/A}^2+n\theta_{ABC}^2$	$\dfrac{MS_{ABC}}{MS_{SBC/A}}$
SBC/A	$a(n-1)(b-1)(c-1)$	$SS_{w.s}-SS_C-SS_{AC}-SS_{SC/A}-SS_B-SS_{AB}-SS_{SB/A}-SS_{BC}-SS_{ABC}$	$\sigma_e^2+\sigma_{SBC/A}^2$	

$$SS_{SB/A} = \frac{\sum_j^a \sum_k^b \sum_i^n \left(\sum_m^c Y_{ijkm} \right)^2}{c} - \frac{\sum_j^a \sum_i^n \left(\sum_k^b \sum_m^c Y_{ijkm} \right)^2}{bc}$$

$$- \frac{\sum_j^a \sum_k^b \left(\sum_i^n \sum_m^c Y_{ijkm} \right)^2}{nc} + \frac{\sum_j^a \left(\sum_i^n \sum_k^b \sum_m^c Y_{ijkm} \right)^2}{nbc}$$

Note that of the four terms comprising the computational formula for $SS_{SB/A}$, three have been previously calculated in the analysis of variance table. The quantity $\sum_i^n \sum_j^a (\sum_k^b \sum_m^c Y_{ijkm})^2/bc$ is computed in order to obtain $SS_{B.S}$; $\sum_j^a \sum_k^b (\sum_i^n \sum_m^c Y_{ijkm})^2/nc$ is computed as part of the calculations for SS_{AB}; and $\sum_j^a (\sum_i^n \sum_k^b \sum_m^c Y_{ijkm})^2/nbc$ is part of the calculation for SS_A. Thus, only one new term need be calculated in order to obtain the $SS_{SB/A}$.

The *EMS* follow from the rules of thumb presented earlier in this chapter. The reader would be well advised to check through each line to ensure that he understands the application of the rules. Once the *EMS* have been generated, the F tests present no problem. Each main or interaction effect is tested against the nested effect that follows most closely in the table.

A numerical example. Table 8-15 contains data for an illustrative analysis. In addition to the data, sub-totals are presented which will be of use during the analysis. We begin by computing the total sum of squares:

$$SS_{tot} = \sum_i \sum_j \sum_k \sum_m Y_{ijkm}^2 - C$$

$$= (3)^2 + (5)^2 + \cdots + (11)^2 - \frac{(412)^2}{48}$$

$$= 3{,}912.000 - 3{,}536.333$$

$$= 375.667$$

For the variability among subjects, we have

$$SS_{B.S} = \frac{\sum_i \sum_j \left(\sum_k \sum_m Y_{ijkm} \right)^2}{bc} - C$$

$$= \frac{(54)^2 + (56)^2 + \cdots + (80)^2 + (88)^2}{8} - \frac{(412)^2}{48}$$

$$= 3{,}647.000 - 3{,}536.333$$

$$= 110.667$$

This term has two components:

$$SS_A = \frac{\sum_j \left(\sum_i \sum_k \sum_m Y_{ijkm} \right)^2}{nbc} - C$$

$$= \frac{(110)^2 + (134)^2 + (168)^2}{16} - \frac{(412)^2}{48}$$

$$= 3{,}642.500 - 3{,}536.333$$

$$= 106.167$$

and

$$SS_{S/A} = SS_{\text{B.S}} - SS_A$$
$$= 110.667 - 106.167$$
$$= 4.500$$

We turn next to the within-subjects variability:

$$SS_{\text{W.S}} = SS_{\text{tot}} - SS_{\text{B.S}}$$
$$= 375.667 - 110.667$$
$$= 265.000$$

For the main effect of B, we can use the single df formula, thus saving some computational effort:

$$SS_B = \frac{(216 - 196)^2}{48}$$
$$= 8.333$$

For the AB interaction, we have

$$SS_{AB} = \frac{\sum_j \sum_k \left(\sum_i \sum_m Y_{ijkm} \right)^2}{nc} - C - SS_A - SS_B$$

$$= \frac{(44)^2 + (70)^2 + \cdots + (66)^2}{8} - \frac{(412)^2}{48} - 106.167 - 8.333$$

$$= 3,756.000 - 3,536.333 - 106.167 - 8.333$$

$$= 105.167$$

The error variability for the previous two terms is

$$SS_{SB/A} = \frac{\sum_i \sum_j \sum_k \left(\sum_m Y_{ijkm} \right)^2}{c} - \frac{\sum_i \sum_j \left(\sum_k \sum_m Y_{ijkm} \right)^2}{bc}$$

$$- \frac{\sum_j \sum_k \left(\sum_i \sum_m Y_{ijkm} \right)^2}{nc} + \frac{\sum_j \left(\sum_i \sum_k \sum_m Y_{ijkm} \right)^2}{nbc}$$

$$= \frac{(23)^2 + (31)^2 + \cdots + (52)^2 + (36)^2}{4} - 3,647.000$$

$$- 3,756.000 + 3,642.500$$

$$= 9.500$$

For the C main effect, we have

$$SS_C = \frac{\sum_m \left(\sum_i \sum_j \sum_k Y_{ijkm} \right)^2}{abn} - C$$

$$= \frac{(82)^2 + (90)^2 + (110)^2 + (130)^2}{12} - \frac{(412)^2}{48}$$

$$= 4,027.000 - 3,536.333$$

$$= 115.667$$

TABLE 8-15

Data and sub-totals for an analysis of variance, one between- and two within-subjects variables

		B_1					B_2					
		C_1	C_2	C_3	C_4	$\sum_m Y_{ij1m}$	C_1	C_2	C_3	C_4	$\sum_m Y_{ij2m}$	$\sum_k \sum_m Y_{ijkm}$
A_1	S_{11}	3	5	7	8	23	7	6	9	9	31	54
	S_{21}	2	5	6	8	21	8	5	10	12	35	56
		$\sum_i Y_{i11m} = 5$	10	13	16	$\sum_i \sum_m Y_{i11m} = 44$	$\sum_i Y_{i12m} = 15$	11	19	21	$\sum_i \sum_m Y_{i12m} = 66$	$\sum_i \sum_k \sum_m Y_{i1km} = 110$
A_2	S_{12}	8	9	9	11	37	6	7	7	9	29	66
	S_{22}	7	7	9	10	33	7	8	9	11	35	68
		$\sum_i Y_{i21m} = 15$	16	18	21	$\sum_i \sum_m Y_{i21m} = 70$	$\sum_i Y_{i22m} = 13$	15	16	20	$\sum_i \sum_m Y_{i22m} = 64$	$\sum_i \sum_k \sum_m Y_{i2km} = 134$
A_3	S_{13}	10	12	13	15	50	5	7	8	10	30	80
	S_{23}	11	11	14	16	52	8	8	9	11	36	88
		$\sum_i Y_{i31m} = 21$	23	27	31	$\sum_i \sum_m Y_{i31m} = 102$	$\sum_i Y_{i32m} = 13$	15	17	21	$\sum_i \sum_m Y_{i32m} = 66$	$\sum_i \sum_k \sum_m Y_{i3km} = 168$
		$\sum_i \sum_j Y_{ij1m} = 41$	49	58	68	$\sum_i \sum_j \sum_m Y_{ij1m} = 216$	$\sum_i \sum_j Y_{ij2m} = 41$	41	52	62	$\sum_i \sum_j \sum_m Y_{ij2m} = 196$	$\sum_i \sum_j \sum_k \sum_m Y_{ijkm} = 412$

Subjects $\times$ C Sub-totals $\left(\sum_k Y_{ijkm} \right)$

		C_1	C_2	C_3	C_4	$\sum_k \sum_m Y_{ijkm}$
A_1	S_{11}	10	11	16	17	54
	S_{21}	10	10	16	20	56
	$\sum_i \sum_k Y_{i1km} =$	20	21	32	37	$\sum_i \sum_k \sum_m Y_{i1km} = 110$
A_2	S_{12}	14	16	16	20	66
	S_{22}	14	15	18	21	68
	$\sum_i \sum_k Y_{i2km} =$	28	31	34	41	$\sum_i \sum_k \sum_m Y_{i2km} = 134$
A_3	S_{13}	15	19	21	25	80
	S_{23}	19	19	23	27	88
	$\sum_i \sum_k Y_{i3km} =$	34	38	44	52	$\sum_i \sum_k \sum_m Y_{i3km} = 168$
	$\sum_i \sum_j \sum_k Y_{ijkm} =$	82	90	110	130	$\sum_i \sum_j \sum_k \sum_m Y_{ijkm} = 412$

For the AC interaction, we have

$$SS_{AC} = \frac{\sum_j \sum_m \left(\sum_i \sum_k Y_{ijkm} \right)^2}{nb} - C - SS_A - SS_C$$

$$= \frac{(20)^2 + (21)^2 + \cdots + (44)^2 + (52)^2}{4} - \frac{(412)^2}{48} - 106.167 - 115.667$$

$$= 3{,}764.000 - 3{,}536.333 - 106.167 - 115.667$$

$$= 5.833$$

The error variability for the previous two terms is

$$SS_{SC/A} = \frac{\sum_i \sum_j \sum_m \left(\sum_k Y_{ijkm} \right)^2}{b} - \frac{\sum_i \sum_j \left(\sum_k \sum_m Y_{ijkm} \right)^2}{bc}$$

$$- \frac{\sum_j \sum_m \left(\sum_i \sum_k Y_{ijkm} \right)^2}{nb} + \frac{\sum_j \left(\sum_i \sum_k \sum_m Y_{ijkm} \right)^2}{nbc}$$

$$= \frac{(10)^2 + (11)^2 + \cdots + (23)^2 + (27)^2}{2} - 3{,}647.000$$

$$- 3{,}764.000 + 3{,}642.500$$

$$= 5.500$$

The BC interaction sum of squares is obtained by

$$SS_{BC} = \frac{\sum_k \sum_m \left(\sum_i \sum_j Y_{ijkm} \right)^2}{na} - C - SS_B - SS_C$$

$$= \frac{(41)^2 + (49)^2 + \cdots + (52)^2 + (62)^2}{6} - \frac{(412)^2}{48} - 8.333 - 115.667$$

$$= 3{,}663.667 - 3{,}536.333 - 8.333 - 115.667$$

$$= 3.333$$

We have next

$$SS_{ABC} = \frac{\sum_j \sum_k \sum_m \left(\sum_i Y_{ijkm} \right)^2}{n} - C - SS_A - SS_B - SS_C - SS_{AB}$$

$$- SS_{AC} - SS_{BC}$$

$$= \frac{(5)^2 + (10)^2 + \cdots + (17)^2 + (21)^2}{2} - C - SS_A - SS_B - SS_C$$

$$- SS_{AB} - SS_{AC} - SS_{BC}$$

$$= 3{,}889.000 - 3{,}536.333 - 106.167 - 8.333 - 115.667$$

$$- 105.167 - 5.833 - 3.333$$

$$= 8.167$$

The error variability for the two previous terms may be taken as a residual from the $SS_{\text{w.s}}$:

$$SS_{SBC/A} = SS_{w.s} - SS_B - SS_{AB} - SS_{SB/A} - SS_C - SS_{AC} - SS_{SC/A}$$
$$- SS_{BC} - SS_{ABC}$$

$$= 265.000 - 8.333 - 105.167 - 9.500 - 115.667 - 5.833$$
$$- 5.500 - 3.333 - 8.167$$

$$= 3.500$$

The final results of the analysis are summarized in Table 8-16.

TABLE 8-16

Analysis of variance for the data of Table 8-15

SV	df	SS	MS	F
Total	47	375.667		
Between S	5	110.667		
A	2	106.167	53.083	35.389 **
S/A	3	4.500	1.500	
Within S	42	265.000		
B	1	8.333	8.333	2.631
AB	2	105.167	52.583	16.603 *
SB/A	3	9.500	3.167	
C	3	115.667	38.556	63.103 **
AC	6	5.833	.972	1.591
SC/A	9	5.500	.611	
BC	3	3.333	1.111	2.856
ABC	6	8.167	1.361	3.499
SBC/A	9	3.500	.389	

$$* \ p < .025$$
$$** \ p < .01$$

8.4 CONCLUDING REMARKS

The mixed design is a compromise between the simplicity of the completely randomized design and the high relative efficiency of the simple repeated measurements design. In testing the null hypothesis that $\theta_A^2 = 0$ where A is a between-subjects variable, precision is usually low; this part of the design is essentially completely randomized. By introducing one or more within-subjects variables, fewer subjects are needed than would be required if all variables were between subjects, and a potentially precise test of the within-subjects effects is provided, since the error terms are not inflated by individual differences. But this saving of subjects and increase in precision costs something. As in the simpler repeated measurements designs of Chapter 7, the possibility of subject $\times$ treatment interactions are introduced, with the consequent possibilities of lowered efficiency (if the interaction with subjects is large) and heterogeneity of covariance. If the population covariances are not similar for all possible pairs of levels of within-subjects variables, only the F tests of within-subjects effects will be positively biased. For levels of the between-subjects variables, the expected covariances should all be zero if randomization has been properly carried out.

Tukey's single df test, described in Chapter 7, can be extended to test for nonadditivity in the mixed design. For example, in a one between- and one within-subjects design, a sum of squares for nonadditivity could be computed at each level of A. These a quantities could then be pooled, yielding a sum of squares for nonadditivity on a df which would be tested against the balance of the SB/A interaction. Transformations to additivity may also be sought following the guidelines of Chapter 7. If additivity is achieved, the nested interaction effects are dropped from the model and such terms as $\sigma^2_{SB/A}$ disappear from the EMS. The covariances will be homogeneous, and the tests of within-subjects effects will generally be efficient and unbiased.

In the absence of strong evidence to the contrary, most investigators assume that the nonadditive model presented in this chapter is appropriate. Therefore, it becomes important to be aware of the possibility of heterogeneity of covariance and the consequent positive bias of the tests of within-subjects effects. A conservative F test, parallel to that presented in Section 7.2.4, is available. Again, the numerator and denominator df are divided by the df for the within-subjects variable(s). For example, consider the one between- and two within-subjects design of the preceding section. For the conservative test of the null hypothesis that $\theta^2_B = 0$, F is evaluated as if the df were 1 and $a(n - 1)$ rather than $b - 1$ and $a(n - 1)(b - 1)$. The same df would be used to test C and BC effects. To test the null hypothesis that $\theta^2_{AB} = 0$ (A is a between-subjects variable and the interaction is a within-subjects term), we use $a - 1$ and $a(n - 1)$ rather than $(a - 1)(b - 1)$ and $a(n - 1)(b - 1)$. The same df are effective for the conservative tests of AC and ABC effects. For a more detailed discussion of the covariance problem and of nonadditivity in general, the reader is referred back to Chapter 7.

EXERCISES

8.1 There are n subjects in each of ab combinations of the variables A and B for a total of abn subjects. Each subject is tested under all combinations of C, D, and E. Give SV, df, EMS, and F ratios.

8.2 Carry out the appropriate analysis of variance on the data on page 211.

		B_1C_1	B_1C_2	B_1C_3	B_2C_1	B_2C_2	B_2C_3
	S_1	3	2	1	6	4	3
A_1	S_2	5	4	7	3	1	9
	S_3	8	6	8	5	7	2
	S_4	4	2	4	2	10	4
A_2	S_5	1	5	1	8	6	5
	S_6	6	3	7	9	6	3
	S_7	2	3	5	6	1	3
A_3	S_8	8	7	5	2	7	4
	S_9	1	4	4	8	3	8

8.3 We have *abc* combinations of the variables *A*, *B*, and *C*. Assuming that the levels of all three are randomly sampled, find the *EMS*. Are there any special problems which occur? How would the *EMS* and *F* tests be affected if it were known that $\sigma^2_{AB} = 0$?

HIERARCHICAL DESIGNS

9

9.1 INTRODUCTION

In Chapter 8 an examination was made of the models and analyses that are appropriate when subjects are nested within levels of the variable A and are crossed with the levels of a second variable, B. In this chapter the paradigm is extended to designs in-which there are several levels of nests. Thus, subjects may be nested within levels of a variable G, while the levels of G are in turn nested within the levels of A. Such designs are often labeled "hierarchical" in reference to the hierarchy of variables that is typical of them. The statistical models and computations are straightforward extensions of the developments of the preceding chapter.

Hierarchical designs have an important place in both psychological and educational research. To cite one example, consider a group dynamics experiment designed for the purpose of studying the effects of stress upon attitude change in the members of four-man conference teams. We might have several conference groups under a high stress and an equal number under a low stress condition; the resultant design might be characterized as *subjects within conference groups within levels of stress*. A similar example might be taken from educational psychology. Several first-grade classes are taught reading under one method while an equal number are taught under a second method; all students are tested at the end of the term. The design might be characterized as *subjects within classes within methods*. In both of our examples, it is reasonable to assume that the total variability among subjects has three potential sources: subjects' scores may differ because of

(a) Treatment effects. The variable A (e.g., stress, method) is a potential source.

(b) Group effects. Differences in the composition of groups (e.g., conference groups, school classes) may contribute to the variability in the data.

(c) Residual individual differences.   Even the scores of subjects within the same group may vary due to such factors as attitude or ability.

The primary new aspect of the hierarchical designs is the assumption that an individual's score is in part contributed to by the social group in which he participates.   To put it another way, whenever measures are obtained from individuals who in the course of experimental sessions interact with other individuals, variance due to the unique interrelationships within each group are to be considered in the statistical model.

Hierarchical designs do not necessarily involve social units, such as groups or school classes.   For example, we might have four difficult and four easy concept formation problems.   Since there are different problems at each difficulty level, problems are nested within levels of difficulty.   Before this chapter is concluded, an example of this type will be considered.   However, for the most part the chapter will be concerned with the more common *subjects-within-groups-within-treatments* design and several of its variants.

The importance of the material of Chapter 9 goes beyond the actual applications of the hierarchical designs.   The presentation of these designs and their analyses should further understanding of the establishment of structural models and the translation of models into analysis of variance tables.   Every design that the researcher may encounter cannot possibly be discussed.   However, the material of this chapter should help establish certain fundamental but widely applied principles of data analysis which were first introduced in Chapter 8.

9.2   GROUPS WITHIN TREATMENTS

9.2.1   The analysis of variance model

We begin by conceptualizing a treatment populations, differing systematically only with respect to the level of the treatment variable, A.   From each population, subjects are randomly selected in groups of size n; the sampling process ends when g groups of n subjects have been sampled from each population.   The resulting experimental layout is presented in Table 9-1.   The design involves a total of agn subjects with n subjects in each group, g groups at each level of A, and a levels of A.   The notational indices are

$$i = 1, 2, \cdots, n$$
$$j = 1, 2, \cdots, g$$
$$k = 1, 2, \cdots, a$$

Next, an equation is required to relate the representative score, Y_{ijk}, to the parameters of the population from which the sample is drawn.   We begin by ignoring the variable A; the design is viewed as a one-factor design, the "factor" being groups (G) with ag levels and n subjects at each level.   In accord with the one-factor model of Chapter 4, this view suggests

TABLE 9-1

Data matrix for the groups-within-treatments design

A_1			$\cdots$	A_k			$\cdots$	A_a		
G_{11}	$\cdots$	G_{g1}		G_{1k}	$\cdots$	G_{gk}		G_{1a}	G_{ja}	G_{ga}
Y_{111}		Y_{1g1}		Y_{11k}		Y_{1gk}		Y_{11a}	Y_{1ja}	Y_{1ga}
Y_{i11}		Y_{ig1}		Y_{i1k}		Y_{igk}		Y_{i1a}	Y_{ija}	Y_{iga}
Y_{n11}		Y_{ng1}		Y_{n1k}		Y_{ngk}		Y_{n1a}	Y_{nja}	Y_{nga}

TABLE 9-2

Analysis of variance for the groups-within-treatments design

SV	df	SS	EMS	F
Total	$agn - 1$	$\sum_i^n \sum_j^g \sum_k^a Y_{ijk}^2 - C$		
Between G	$ag - 1$	$\dfrac{\sum_j^g \sum_k^a \left(\sum_i^n Y_{ijk}\right)^2}{n} - C$		
A	$a - 1$	$\dfrac{\sum_k^a \left(\sum_j^g \sum_i^n Y_{ijk}\right)^2}{gn} - C$	$\sigma_e^2 + n\sigma_{G/A}^2 + ng\theta_A$	$\dfrac{MS_A}{MS_{G/A}}$
G/A	$a(g - 1)$	$SS_{B.G} - SS_A$	$\sigma_e^2 + n\sigma_{G/A}^2$	$\dfrac{MS_{G/A}}{MS_{S/G/A}}$
S/G/A	$ag(n - 1)$	$SS_{tot} - SS_{B.G}$	σ_e^2	

$$(9.1) \qquad\qquad Y_{ijk} = \mu + \gamma_{jk} + \epsilon_{ijk}$$

where $\gamma_{jk} = \mu_{jk} - \mu$, the overall effect of the jth group at the kth level of A, and $\epsilon_{ijk} = Y_{ijk} - \mu_{jk}$, the residual error component. Equation (9.1) disregards the possibility of an effect due to A_k. Presumably, group means differ not merely because the groups have different compositions, but also because some groups are at one level of A, others are at a different level. This line of reasoning suggests that part of the γ_{jk} effect is due to α_k, the effect due to the level of A in which the group exists. Accordingly, we subtract the contribution of α_k:

$$
\begin{aligned}
\gamma_{jk} - \alpha_k &= (\mu_{jk} - \mu) - (\mu_k - \mu) \\
&= \mu_{jk} - \mu_k \\
&= \gamma_{j/k}
\end{aligned}
$$

(9.2)

where $\gamma_{j/k}$ is the pure effect of the jkth group, uninflated by any contribution due to α_k. We may now substitute in Equation (9.1) for γ_{jk}, obtaining

$$(9.3) \qquad\qquad Y_{ijk} = \mu + \alpha_k + \gamma_{j/k} + \epsilon_{ijk}$$

Each score is contributed to by a treatment effect, a group effect, and a residual component reflecting error of measurement and individual differences.

A common error in the analysis of the group designs is the failure to consider group effects in the model. In this case, the analysis proceeds as if the design were a completely randomized one-factor design with gn subjects in each of a treatment groups. This failure to separate out the γ component from ϵ may result in an inflated F ratio, as will be shown in the next section.

To complete the presentation of the underlying theory, and in order to arrive at the *EMS*, the nature of the effects must be considered. It is assumed that the levels of A have been arbitrarily chosen by the experimenter, and consequently, that α_k is a fixed variable. Then, $\sum_k \alpha_k = 0$ and the variance component is defined as $\theta_A^2 = \sum_k^a \alpha_k^2/(a - 1)$. The group effect, $\gamma_{j/k}$, is viewed as a random variable, since the groups are clearly a random sample from the population of all possible groups of size n which could be composed. As usual, ϵ_{ijk} is also a random variable. The $\gamma_{j/k}$ and ϵ_{ijk} are assumed to be sampled from normally distributed populations with mean zero and variances $\sigma_{G/A}^2$ and σ_e^2, respectively.

9.2.2 The analysis of variance

Table 9-2 contains the *SV*, *df*, *SS*, *EMS*, and *F* for the *groups-within-treatments* design. One source exists for each term on the right-hand side of Equation (9.1). To facilitate the analysis, we have first divided our variability between two sources; ignoring the treatment variable, *A*, we have between-groups and within-groups variability. This breakdown corresponds to a model of the form of Equation (9.1). Subsequently, the between-groups source is further divided into the G/A and A components, as in the development of the model in Section 9.2.1.

The df are easily obtainable once we have noted the sources. For the nested term, G/A, we may make use of the fact that the between-groups term is a composite of the A and G/A terms. Therefore, $df_{\text{B.G}} - df_A = df_{G/A}$, or

$$(ag - 1) - (a - 1) = a(g - 1)$$

Alternatively, we note that G/A literally represents the summing, over all treatment levels, of the variability of group means about the mean of their treatment level. At each treatment level we have $g - 1$ df to represent the variability of g means about the treatment mean. Pooling over a levels, we again arrive at $a(g - 1)$ df.

The computational formulas in the SS column can be obtained from the df column. For example, the $ag - 1$ df for between groups requires ag squared quantities minus the correction term. Thus, we have

$$\sum_{j}^{g} \sum_{k}^{a} (\quad)^2 - C$$

Including the absent index, i, within the parentheses, we have

$$\sum_{j}^{g} \sum_{k}^{a} \left(\sum_{i}^{n} Y_{ijk} \right)^2 - C$$

Dividing by the number of scores within the parentheses, we have the final result,

$$SS_{\text{B.G}} = \frac{\sum_{j}^{g} \sum_{k}^{a} \left(\sum_{i}^{n} Y_{ijk} \right)^2}{n} - C$$

As a second example, expansion of $df_{G/A}$, yielding $ag - a$, leads to the result,

$$SS_{G/A} = \frac{\sum_{j}^{g} \sum_{k}^{a} \left(\sum_{i}^{n} Y_{ijk} \right)^2}{n} - \frac{\sum_{k}^{a} \left(\sum_{j}^{g} \sum_{i}^{n} Y_{ijk} \right)^2}{gn}$$

In this instance, it is simpler to note merely that the G/A term is the difference between the between-groups term and the A term. The result, presented in Table 9-2, is algebraically identical to that given above.

The EMS follow the rules of thumb developed in Chapter 8. Considering the A line first, we immediately set down σ_e^2 and the null hypothesis term, θ_A^2. Noting that the subscript G/A includes the letter A and that the essential letter, G, represents a random effects variable, we include $\sigma_{G/A}^2$ in the expectation. The remaining two lines should pose no problems.

On the basis of the EMS, it is clear that the treatment mean square should be tested against the mean square for groups within A. A little consideration of the error df will indicate that this F test may often be lacking in power. For example, suppose the experiment involves three four-man conference groups at each of three levels of A. The total of 36 subjects would generally be considered reasonable for a study involving three treatment levels, since 33 error df would be available if the design were a completely randomized one-factor design. However, the error df for the hierarchical design actually employed are only $3(3-1)$, or six. This number of error df is not likely to make the experimenter feel secure if he fails to reject the null hypothesis. One possible way out of the difficulty is to assume a different model; specifically, the experimenter might assume that the group structures do not contribute to error variability, and consequently, that the $\sigma_{G/A}^2$ component may be deleted wherever it appears in the *EMS* column of Table 9-2. In this case, both $MS_{G/A}$ and $MS_{S/G/A}$ are estimates of σ_e^2 and may therefore be combined to provide a new error term. The combining, or *pooling* as it is generally referred to, takes the form $(SS_{G/A} + SS_{S/G/A})/(df_{G/A} + df_{S/G/A})$, an error mean square distributed on 33 df. For reasons that will shortly be considered, pooling should not be carried out unless the data strongly indicate that $\sigma_{G/A}^2$ is a negligible quantity; appropriate criteria will be discussed in Section 11.2.2.

Since the decision on pooling must await the collection of data, in designing the experiment one must proceed on the assumption that $MS_{G/A}$ will be the error term. Consequently, the investigator planning an experiment which involves a group of subjects as a unit should carefully evaluate $df_{G/A}$, and if it is too small to provide an adequate test of treatment effects, modify his design accordingly.

What are the consequences if the G/A and $S/G/A$ terms are pooled when $\sigma_{G/A}^2$ contributes to the data variability? To answer this, we first derive the expectation of our new error term, which will be labeled $MS_{S/A}$. The expected sum of squares for G/A is

$$E(SS_{G/A}) = a(g-1)E(MS_{G/A})$$
$$= a(g-1)(\sigma_e^2 + n\sigma_{G/A}^2)$$

Similarly,

$$E(SS_{S/G/A}) = ag(n-1)\sigma_e^2$$

Then,

$$E(SS_{G/A} + SS_{S/G/A}) = a(gn-1)\sigma_e^2 + an(g-1)\sigma_{G/A}^2$$

The pooled df are

$$a(g-1) + ag(n-1) = a(gn-1)$$

The new error term is

$$MS_{S/A} = \frac{SS_{G/A} + SS_{S/G/A}}{a(gn-1)}$$

Its expectation is

$$E(MS_{S/A}) = \frac{a(gn-1)\sigma_e^2 + an(g-1)\sigma_{G/A}^2}{a(gn-1)}$$

$$= \sigma_e^2 + \frac{n(g-1)}{gn-1}\sigma_{G/A}^2$$

Now consider the test of the A main effect against the pooled error term, $MS_{S/A}$. If the null hypothesis is correct, $\theta_A^2 = 0$ and

$$E(F) = \frac{\sigma_e^2 + n\sigma_{G/A}^2}{\sigma_e^2 + \frac{n(g-1)}{gn-1}\sigma_{G/A}^2}$$

Since for any non-zero values of n and g, $n > n(g-1)/(gn-1)$, $E(F)$ must be greater than 1 if $\sigma_{G/A}^2$ is greater than zero, and the F test based on the pooled error term is positively biased; generally the obtained significance level will underestimate the true probability of a Type I error.

TABLE 9-3

Data for a groups-within-treatments design

| | A_1 | | | | A_2 | | |
	G_{11}	G_{21}	G_{31}		G_{12}	G_{22}	G_{32}
	5	7	16		24	9	17
	6	18	5		21	23	26
	18	4	9		12	28	24
	12	11	14		16	19	19
$\sum_i Y_{ij1} =$	41	40	44	$\sum_i Y_{ij2} =$	73	79	86

$$\sum_i \sum_j Y_{ij1} = 125 \qquad \sum_i \sum_j Y_{ij2} = 238$$

$$\sum_i \sum_j \sum_k Y_{ijk} = 363$$

9.2.3 A numerical example

Table 9-3 presents data for a groups-within-treatments design. We first obtain the total sum of squares:

$$SS_{tot} = \sum_{i=1}^{4} \sum_{j=1}^{3} \sum_{k=1}^{2} Y_{ijk}^2 - C$$

$$= 5^2 + 6^2 + \cdots + 24^2 + 19^2 - \frac{(363)^2}{24}$$

$$= 6,671.00 - 5,490.38$$

$$= 1,180.62$$

The measure of between-groups variability is

$$SS_{B.G} = \frac{\sum\limits_{j=1}^{3} \sum\limits_{k=1}^{2} \left(\sum\limits_{i=1}^{4} Y_{ijk} \right)^2}{4} - C$$

$$= \frac{(41)^2 + \cdots + (86)^2}{4} - \frac{(363)^2}{24}$$

$$= 6{,}045.75 - 5{,}490.38$$

$$= 555.37$$

Turning to the A source, we have

$$SS_A = \frac{\sum\limits_{k=1}^{2} \left(\sum\limits_{j=1}^{3} \sum\limits_{i=1}^{4} Y_{ijk} \right)^2}{12} - C$$

$$= \frac{(125)^2 + (238)^2}{12} - \frac{(363)^2}{24}$$

$$= 6{,}022.42 - 5{,}490.38$$

$$= 532.04$$

Subtracting SS_A from $SS_{B.G}$, we obtain the sum of squares for the nested group effect:

$$SS_{G/A} = SS_{B.G} - SS_A$$
$$= 555.37 - 532.04$$
$$= 23.33$$

The total variability may be partitioned into a between-groups and a within-groups component. Therefore,

$$SS_{S/G/A} = SS_{tot} - SS_{B.G}$$
$$= 1{,}180.62 - 555.37$$
$$= 625.25$$

The results of the analysis are summarized in Table 9-4. The difference

TABLE 9-4

Analysis of variance for the data of Table 9-3

SV	df	SS	MS	F
Total	23	1,180.62		
Between G	5	555.37		
A	1	532.04	532.04	92.98 *
G/A	4	23.33	5.83	
$S/G/A$	18	625.25	34.74	

$* \ p < .01$

in performance under treatments A_1 and A_2 is clearly significant. Since the ratio of G/A to $S/G/A$ mean squares is less than 1, these two sources might be pooled to provide a new error term to test the A effect; however, the F test of Table 9-4 is so clearly significant that this appears to be an unnecessary step.

9.3 A WITHIN-GROUPS VARIABLE

We next consider the situation where a variable is introduced within each group. There are again g groups at each of the a levels of the variable A. In addition, each group is divided into b levels of the variable B, with n subjects at each level. For example, there may be several conference groups working under a high stress condition and several others working under low stress. Within each conference group, half of the subjects may be high anxious (as measured by the Taylor Manifest Anxiety Scale), while the other half are low anxious. *Stress* is the A variable and *Anxiety* is the B variable.

This hierarchical design is represented in Table 9-5. The indices of notation are

$$i = 1, 2, \cdots, n$$
$$j = 1, 2, \cdots, g$$
$$k = 1, 2, \cdots, a$$
$$m = 1, 2, \cdots, b$$

The design involves bn subjects within each group, bgn subjects at each level of A, and $abgn$ subjects for the entire experiment.

9.3.1 The analysis of variance model

In developing an appropriate equation to describe the relationship between data and population parameters, it may help to first ignore the variable A. We then have a two-factor design; the factors are G and B. The discussion of two-factor designs in Chapter 5, particularly Equation (5.1), suggests

$$(9.4) \qquad Y_{ijkm} = \mu + \gamma_{jk} + \beta_m + (\gamma\beta)_{jkm} + \epsilon_{ijkm}$$

where $\gamma_{jk} = \mu_{jk} - \mu$; $\beta_m = \mu_m - \mu$; $(\gamma\beta)_{jkm} = \mu_{jkm} - \mu_{jk} - \mu_m + \mu$; and

$$\epsilon_{ijkm} = Y_{ijkm} - \mu_{jkm}$$

the residual error component. We next note that the mean for the jkth group may deviate from the grand mean, partly because the groups are different in their composition and partly because some groups are at one level of A while other groups are at a different level. In other words, the overall group effect, γ_{jk}, contains a "pure" group component and a treatment component. Accordingly, we may write

TABLE 9-5

Data matrix for a hierarchical design containing a within-groups variable

	A_1				A_k				A_a		
	G_{11} $\cdots$ G_{j1} $\cdots$ G_{g1}			$\cdots$	G_{1k} $\cdots$ G_{jk} $\cdots$ G_{gk}			$\cdots$	G_{1a} $\cdots$ G_{ja} $\cdots$ G_{ga}		
B_1	Y_{1111}	Y_{1j11}	Y_{1g11}		Y_{11k1}	Y_{1jk1}	Y_{1gk1}		Y_{11a1}	Y_{1ja1}	Y_{1ga1}
	Y_{i111}	Y_{ij11}	Y_{ig11}		Y_{i1k1}	Y_{ijk1}	Y_{igk1}		Y_{i1a1}	Y_{ija1}	Y_{iga1}
	Y_{n111}	Y_{nj11}	Y_{ng11}		Y_{n1k1}	Y_{njk1}	Y_{ngk1}		Y_{n1a1}	Y_{nja1}	Y_{nga1}
$\cdots$											
B_m	Y_{111m}	Y_{1j1m}	Y_{1g1m}		Y_{11km}	Y_{1jkm}	Y_{1gkm}		Y_{11am}	Y_{1jam}	Y_{1gam}
	Y_{i11m}	Y_{ij1m}	Y_{ig1m}		Y_{i1km}	Y_{ijkm}	Y_{igkm}		Y_{i1am}	Y_{ijam}	Y_{igam}
	Y_{n11m}	Y_{nj1m}	Y_{ng1m}		Y_{n1km}	Y_{njkm}	Y_{ngkm}		Y_{n1am}	Y_{njam}	Y_{ngam}
$\cdots$											
B_b	Y_{111b}	Y_{1j1b}	Y_{1g1b}		Y_{11kb}	Y_{1jkb}	Y_{1gkb}		Y_{11ab}	Y_{1jab}	Y_{1gab}
	Y_{i11b}	Y_{ij1b}	Y_{ig1b}		Y_{i1kb}	Y_{ijkb}	Y_{igkb}		Y_{i1ab}	Y_{ijab}	Y_{igab}
	Y_{n11b}	Y_{nj1b}	Y_{ng1b}		Y_{n1kb}	Y_{njkb}	Y_{ngkb}		Y_{n1ab}	Y_{njab}	Y_{ngab}

(9.5) $$(\mu_{jk} - \mu) = (\mu_{jk} - \mu_k) + (\mu_k - \mu)$$

or

(9.5′) $$\gamma_{jk} = \gamma_{j/k} + \alpha_k$$

Presumably, there is also an AB interaction, since all levels of A and B cross. Intuition and previous experience suggest that the effect is imbedded in the overall GB interaction. Accordingly, we subtract effects as follows:

(9.6) $$(\mu_{jkm} - \mu_{jk} - \mu_m + \mu) - (\mu_{km} - \mu_k - \mu_m + \mu)$$
$$= (\mu_{jkm} - \mu_{jk} - \mu_{km} + \mu_k)$$

or

(9.6′) $$(\gamma\beta)_{jkm} - (\alpha\beta)_{km} = (\gamma\beta)_{jm/k}$$

Substituting Equation (9.5′) and Equation (9.6′) into Equation (9.4), we have our final statement:

(9.7) $$Y_{ijkm} = \mu + \alpha_k + \gamma_{j/k} + \beta_m + (\alpha\beta)_{km} + (\gamma\beta)_{jm/k} + \epsilon_{ijkm}$$

Note that there are no interactions involving subjects, nor is there any AG or ABG effect. This is because subjects cross with none of the three other variables, and G does not cross with A. As a further help in establishing models for designs involving nesting, note that the interaction of a nested effect with another variable will also be nested. For example, the interaction of G/A with B is the nested interaction GB/A.

It is assumed that A and B are fixed effect variables, but that the groups are a random sample from a large population of such groups. Consequently,

$$\sum_k \alpha_k = \sum_m \beta_m = \sum_k \sum_m (\alpha\beta)_{km} = 0$$

The variance components for the fixed effects are

$$\theta_A^2 = \frac{\sum_k \alpha_k^2}{a - 1} \qquad \theta_B^2 = \frac{\sum_m \beta_m^2}{b - 1}$$

$$\theta_{AB}^2 = \frac{\sum_k \sum_m (\alpha\beta)_{km}^2}{(a - 1)(b - 1)}$$

$\gamma_{j/k}$, $(\gamma\beta)_{jm/k}$, and ϵ_{ijkm} are randomly sampled from normally distributed populations with mean zero and variances $\sigma_{G/A}^2$, $\sigma_{GB/A}^2$, and σ_e^2, respectively.

9.3.2 The analysis of variance

Table 9-6 presents the pertinent aspects of the analysis of variance. It is helpful to view the design first as a one-factor design with ag levels of the between-groups factor and bn subjects within each level. This gives us two overall sources, between groups and within groups. From Equation (9.5′) we know that the overall group source contains a nested group source and the A treatment source. The remaining parameters in Equation (9.7) must

TABLE 9-6

Analysis of variance for a hierarchical design containing a within-groups variable

SV	df	SS	EMS	F
Total	$abgn - 1$	$\displaystyle\sum_i^n\sum_j^g\sum_k^a\sum_m^b Y_{ijkm}^2 - C$		
Between G	$ag - 1$	$\displaystyle\frac{\sum_j^g\left(\sum_i^n\sum_k^a\sum_m^b Y_{ijkm}\right)^2}{nb} - C$		
A	$a - 1$	$\displaystyle\frac{\sum_k^a\left(\sum_i^n\sum_j^g\sum_m^b Y_{ijkm}\right)^2}{ngb} - C$	$\sigma_e^2 + nb\sigma_{G/A}^2 + nbg\theta_A^2$	$\dfrac{MS_A}{MS_{G/A}}$
G/A	$a(g - 1)$	$SS_{B.G} - SS_A$	$\sigma_e^2 + nb\sigma_{G/A}^2$	$\dfrac{MS_{G/A}}{MS_{S/GB/A}}$
Within G	$ag(bn - 1)$	$SS_{tot} - SS_{B.G}$		
B	$b - 1$	$\displaystyle\frac{\sum_m^b\left(\sum_i^n\sum_j^g\sum_k^a Y_{ijkm}\right)^2}{nga} - C$	$\sigma_e^2 + n\sigma_{GB/A}^2 + nga\theta_B^2$	$\dfrac{MS_B}{MS_{GB/A}}$
AB	$(a - 1)(b - 1)$	$\displaystyle\frac{\sum_k^a\sum_m^b\left(\sum_i^n\sum_j^g Y_{ijkm}\right)^2}{ng} - C - SS_A - SS_B$	$\sigma_e^2 + n\sigma_{GB/A}^2 + ng\theta_{AB}^2$	$\dfrac{MS_{AB}}{MS_{GB/A}}$
GB/A	$a(b - 1)(g - 1)$	$\displaystyle\frac{\sum_j^g\sum_k^a\sum_m^b\left(\sum_i^n Y_{ijkm}\right)^2}{n} - \frac{\sum_j^g\sum_k^a\left(\sum_i^n\sum_m^b Y_{ijkm}\right)^2}{nb} - \frac{\sum_k^a\sum_m^b\left(\sum_i^n\sum_j^g Y_{ijkm}\right)^2}{ng} + \frac{\sum_k^a\left(\sum_i^n\sum_j^g\sum_m^b Y_{ijkm}\right)^2}{ngb}$	$\sigma_e^2 + n\sigma_{GB/A}^2$	$\dfrac{MS_{GB/A}}{MS_{S/GB/A}}$
S/GB/A	$abg(n - 1)$	$SS_{W.G} - SS_B - SS_{AB} - SS_{GB/A}$	σ_e^2	

(Handwritten marginal notes: $a = 2$, $b = 3$, $g = 2$; checkmarks beside A, G/A, B, AB, GB/A, S/GB/A; and various numeric computations alongside the df and SS columns.*)*

therefore represent within-groups sources. The df column provides an excellent check on our breakdown of sources of variance. The initial division into between- and within-groups sources may be checked by noting that $df_{B.G}$ reflects the variability of ag means about the grand mean; therefore, $ag - 1$ is the required number. The $df_{W.G}$ reflects the variability of all bn scores within the group deviated about the group mean and then pooled over the ag groups; the result is $ag(bn - 1)$. Adding the two df quantities, we obtain $abgn - 1$, which is, of course, the correct total. The df for the A, B, and AB terms require no comment. The $df_{G/A}$ reflect the fact that g group means have been subtracted from the mean for the level of A in which the groups are nested (thus requiring $g - 1$ df), that this process has been repeated at all a levels of A, and that the squared deviations have then been pooled. Similarly, GB/A represents the interaction of groups and B for each level of A $[(g - 1)(b - 1)\ df]$ pooled over a levels of A. Finally, we note that there are $n - 1$ df for the variability of scores within each level of B within each group; pooling over b levels and ag groups gives the $df_{S/GB/A}$. Adding the various df together, we find that there are neither too few nor too many terms in the analysis; the individual terms sum to the appropriate total.

It may be helpful to note certain parallels between the developments here and in Chapter 8. The source of variance breakdown is very similar to that in Table 8-5, except that the nested subject effects of the preceding chapter are replaced by nested group effects and Table 9-6 contains one additional term, $S/GB/A$. As in the preceding chapter, any interaction involving a *within* variable is itself a *within* effect. Thus, AB was a within-subjects effect in Chapter 8; it is a within-groups effect in the present design.

The SS formulas should present no problems. As in the past, $SS_{GB/A}$ may be obtained by expanding the df,

$$a(g - 1)(b - 1) = abg - ab - ag + a$$

or by noting that the nested interaction is the difference between two interactions. The first approach is the basis for the formula in Table 9-6. The second approach, following Equation (9.6), yields an algebraically identical result:

$$SS_{GB/A} = SS_{GB} - SS_{AB}$$

$$= \left[\frac{\sum_{j}^{g} \sum_{k}^{a} \sum_{m}^{b} \left(\sum_{i}^{n} Y_{ijkm} \right)^2}{n} - C - SS_{B.G} - SS_B \right] - SS_{AB}$$

A third approach is available if we note that

$$SS_{GB/A} = SS_{GB/A_1} + \cdots + SS_{GB/A_a}$$

i.e., the nested interaction is actually the result of computing the GB variability at each level of A and then pooling over levels. While this last approach seems closest to the definition of GB/A, it is most laborious and least recommended.

Remembering that A and B are fixed effect variables and that groups are assumed to have random effects, we can readily verify that the entries in the EMS column follow the rules developed in Section 8.2.2. Once the EMS have been set down, appropriate F tests are immediately available.

9.3.3 A numerical example

Table 9-7 presents data and cell totals for a hierarchical design with one within-groups variable. The total variability is as usual

$$SS_{tot} = \sum_i^n \sum_j^g \sum_k^a \sum_m^b Y_{ijkm}^2 - C$$

$$= (4)^2 + (5)^2 + \cdots + (22)^2 - \frac{(328)^2}{24}$$

$$= 5{,}502.00 - 4{,}482.67$$

$$= 1{,}019.33$$

This quantity is then partitioned into between- and within-groups components:

$$SS_{B.G} = \frac{\sum_j^g \sum_k^a \left(\sum_i^n \sum_m^b Y_{ijkm} \right)^2}{nb} - C$$

$$= \frac{(32)^2 + \cdots + (81)^2}{4} - \frac{(328)^2}{24}$$

$$= 5{,}188.50 - 4{,}482.67$$

$$= 705.83$$

and

$$SS_{W.G} = SS_{tot} - SS_{B.G}$$
$$= 1{,}019.33 - 705.83$$
$$= 313.50$$

The A main effect contributes to the variability among groups. Therefore, we compute

$$SS_A = \frac{\sum_k^a \left(\sum_i^n \sum_j^g \sum_m^b Y_{ijkm} \right)^2}{ngb} - C$$

$$= \frac{(71)^2 + (88)^2 + (169)^2}{8} - \frac{(328)^2}{24}$$

$$= 5{,}168.92 - 4{,}482.67$$

$$= 686.25$$

The residual variability due to differences among groups is

TABLE 9-7

Data matrix for a hierarchical design including a within-groups variable

		A_1		A_2		A_3		
		G_{11}	G_{21}	G_{12}	G_{22}	G_{13}	G_{23}	
B_1		4	5	3	11	20	18	
		6	9	10	6	23	17	
		$\sum_i Y_{ij11} = 10$	14	$\sum_i Y_{ij21} = 13$	17	$\sum_i Y_{ij31} = 43$	35	
		$\sum_i \sum_j Y_{ij11} = 24$		$\sum_i \sum_j Y_{ij21} = 30$		$\sum_i \sum_j Y_{ij31} = 78$		$\sum_i \sum_j \sum_k Y_{ijk1} = 132$
B_2		8	10	12	14	19	24	
		14	15	15	17	26	22	
		$\sum_i Y_{ij12} = 22$	25	$\sum_i Y_{ij22} = 27$	31	$\sum_i Y_{ij32} = 45$	46	
		$\sum_i \sum_j Y_{ij12} = 47$		$\sum_i \sum_j Y_{ij22} = 58$		$\sum_i \sum_j Y_{ij32} = 91$		$\sum_i \sum_j \sum_k Y_{ijk2} = 196$
		$\sum_i \sum_j \sum_m Y_{ij1m} = 71$		$\sum_i \sum_j \sum_m Y_{ij2m} = 88$		$\sum_i \sum_j \sum_m Y_{ij3m} = 169$		$\sum_i \sum_j \sum_k \sum_m Y_{ijkm} = 328$

Group Totals

	A_1		A_2		A_3		
	G_{11}	G_{21}	G_{12}	G_{22}	G_{13}	G_{23}	
$\sum_m Y_{ijkm} = 32$	32	39	40	48	88	81	
$\sum_i \sum_j \sum_m Y_{ijkm} = 71$	71		88		169		
							$\sum_i \sum_j \sum_k \sum_m Y_{ijkm} = 328$

226

$$SS_{G/A} = SS_{B.G} - SS_A$$
$$= 705.83 - 686.25$$
$$= 19.53$$

We next analyze the within-groups variability. The effect of B may be swiftly computed by use of the single df formula:

$$SS_B = \frac{\left(\sum_i^n \sum_j^g \sum_k^b Y_{ijk1} - \sum_i^n \sum_j^g \sum_k^b Y_{ijk2} \right)^2}{24}$$

$$= \frac{(132 - 196)^2}{24}$$

$$= 170.67$$

The AB interaction is investigated next:

$$SS_{AB} = \frac{\sum_k^a \sum_m^b \left(\sum_i^n \sum_j^g Y_{ijkm} \right)^2}{ng} - C - SS_A - SS_B$$

$$= \frac{(24)^2 + \cdots + (91)^2}{4} - \frac{(328)^2}{24} - 686.25 - 170.67$$

$$= 5,353.50 - 4,482.67 - 686.25 - 170.67$$

$$= 13.91$$

Next, we have

$$SS_{GB/A} = \frac{\sum_j^g \sum_k^a \sum_m^b \left(\sum_i^n Y_{ijkm} \right)^2}{n} - \frac{\sum_k^a \sum_m^b \left(\sum_i^n \sum_j^g Y_{ijkm} \right)^2}{ng}$$
$$- \frac{\sum_j^g \sum_k^a \left(\sum_i^n \sum_m^b Y_{ijkm} \right)^2}{nb} + \frac{\sum_k^a \left(\sum_i^n \sum_j^g \sum_m^b Y_{ijkm} \right)^2}{ngb}$$

$$= \frac{(10)^2 + (14)^2 + \cdots + (46)^2}{2} - 5,188.50 - 5,353.50 + 5,168.92$$

$$= 10.92$$

Finally, we have the residual variability among subjects:

$$SS_{S/GB/A} = SS_{W.G} - SS_B - SS_{AB} - SS_{GB/A}$$
$$= 313.50 - 170.67 - 13.91 - 10.92$$
$$= 118.00$$

Table 9-8 summarizes the analysis. Even on the small number of df provided in the example, the A and B main effects are highly significant. No other sources are significant.

TABLE 9-8

Analysis of variance for the data of Table 9-7

SV	df	SS	MS	F
Total	23	1,019.33		
Between G	5	705.83		
A	2	686.25	343.13	52.71 **
G/A	3	19.53	6.51	
Within G	18	313.50		
B	1	170.67	170.67	46.89 *
AB	2	13.91	6.96	1.91
GB/A	3	10.92	3.64	.37
$S/GB/A$	12	118.00	9.83	

$**p < .005$
$*p < .01$

9.4   REPEATED MEASUREMENTS IN A HIERARCHICAL DESIGN

The design of Section 9.3 may be extended by requiring several measures from each subject. For example, we again have g groups under high stress (A_1) and g groups under low stress (A_2). Within each group there are n high anxious subjects (B_1) and n low anxious subjects (B_2). Each member of the group is required to solve each of four problems; *problems* is the within-subjects variable which we shall label C in this section. In general, we have g groups, sampled randomly from a large population of such groups, at each of a levels of the independent variable A. Within each group are b arbitrarily chosen levels of the independent variable B; there are n different subjects at each of these levels. Thus, we have bn subjects in each of ag groups for a total of $abgn$ subjects. A measure is obtained from each subject at each of c levels of the variable C. The design is represented in Table 9-9 at one level of A. The indices are

$$i = 1, 2, \cdots, n$$
$$j = 1, 2, \cdots, g$$
$$k = 1, 2, \cdots, a$$
$$m = 1, 2, \cdots, b$$
$$p = 1, 2, \cdots, c$$

9.4.1   The analysis of variance model

The simplest way to arrive at a statement of the equation which relates data and population parameters is to use Equation (9.7) as a starting point. All of the effects listed there should be present in the model under consideration. In addition, a within-subjects variable is added to the previous design. We

TABLE 9-9

Data matrix for a hierarchical design with repeated measurements

				C_1	C_2	$\cdots$	C_p	$\cdots$	C_c
			S_{1111}	Y_{11111}	Y_{11112}		Y_{1111p}		Y_{1111c}
			$\vdots$						
		B_1	S_{i111}	Y_{i1111}	Y_{i1112}		Y_{i111p}		Y_{i111c}
			$\vdots$						
			S_{n111}	Y_{n1111}	Y_{n1112}		Y_{n111p}		Y_{n111c}
		$\vdots$							
			S_{111m}	Y_{111m1}	Y_{111m2}		Y_{111mp}		Y_{111mc}
			$\vdots$						
	G_{11}	B_m	S_{i11m}	Y_{i11m1}	Y_{i11m2}		Y_{i11mp}		Y_{i11mc}
			$\vdots$						
			S_{n11m}	Y_{n11m1}	Y_{n11m2}		Y_{n11mp}		Y_{n11mc}
		$\vdots$							
			S_{111b}	Y_{111b1}	Y_{111b2}		Y_{111bp}		Y_{111bc}
			$\vdots$						
A_1	B_b		S_{i11b}	Y_{i11b1}	Y_{i11b2}		Y_{i11bp}		Y_{i11bc}
$\vdots$			$\vdots$						
			S_{n11b}	Y_{n11b1}	Y_{n11b2}		Y_{n11bp}		Y_{n11bc}
	$\vdots$								
			S_{1j1m}	Y_{1j1m1}	Y_{1j1m2}		Y_{1j1mp}		Y_{1j1mc}
			$\vdots$						
	G_{j1}	B_m	S_{ij1m}	Y_{ij1m1}	Y_{ij1m2}		Y_{ij1mp}		Y_{ij1mc}
			$\vdots$						
			S_{nj1m}	Y_{nj1m1}	Y_{nj1m2}		Y_{nj1mp}		Y_{nj1mc}
	$\vdots$								
			S_{1g1m}	Y_{1g1m1}	Y_{1g1m2}		Y_{1g1mp}		Y_{1g1mc}
			$\vdots$						
	$\bar{G}_{g1}$	B_m	S_{ig1m}	Y_{ig1m1}	Y_{ig1m2}		Y_{ig1mp}		Y_{ig1mc}
	$\vdots$								
			S_{ng1m}	Y_{ng1m1}	Y_{ng1m2}		Y_{ng1mp}		Y_{ng1mc}

may therefore now separate the error due to individual differences from the error of measurement. This results in the addition of $\eta_{i/jm/k}$ ($= \mu_{ijkm} - \mu_{jkm}$) to Equation (9.7). Furthermore, an overall within-subjects effect, $\mu_{ijkmp} - \mu_{ijkm}$, is added to the model. The result of these extensions of Equation (9.7) is

(9.8)
$$Y_{ijkmp} = \mu + \underset{\substack{A \\ \text{effect}}}{\alpha_k} + \underset{\substack{G/A \\ \text{effect}}}{\gamma_{j/k}} + \underset{\substack{B \\ \text{effect}}}{\beta_m} + \underset{\substack{AB \\ \text{effect}}}{(\alpha\beta)_{km}} + \underset{\substack{GB/A \\ \text{effect}}}{(\gamma\beta)_{jm/k}}$$

$$+ \underset{\substack{S/GB/A \\ \text{effect}}}{\eta_{i/jm/k}} + \underset{\substack{\text{within-subjects} \\ \text{effect}}}{(\mu_{ijkmp} - \mu_{ijkm})} + \underset{\substack{\text{error of} \\ \text{measurement}}}{\epsilon_{ijkmp}}$$

Presumably, the main and interaction effects involving C are imbedded within the overall within-subjects component. Since groups, subjects, A, and B all cross with C, we can readily generate the remaining terms of our model.

$$\delta_p = \mu_p - \mu \qquad [C \text{ effect}]$$
$$(\alpha\delta)_{kp} = \mu_{kp} - \mu_k - \mu_p + \mu \qquad [AC \text{ effect}]$$
$$(\gamma\delta)_{jp/k} = \mu_{jkp} - \mu_{jk} - \mu_{kp} + \mu_k \qquad [GC/A \text{ effect}]$$
$$(\beta\delta)_{mp} = \mu_{mp} - \mu_m - \mu_p + \mu \qquad [BC \text{ effect}]$$
$$(\alpha\beta\delta)_{kmp} = \mu_{kmp} + \mu_k + \mu_m + \mu_p - \mu_{km} - \mu_{kp} - \mu_{mp} - \mu \qquad [ABC \text{ effect}]$$
$$(\gamma\beta\delta)_{jmp/k} = \mu_{jkmp} + \mu_{jk} + \mu_{km} + \mu_{kp} - \mu_{jkm} - \mu_{ikp} - \mu_{kmp} - \mu_k$$
$$[GBC/A \text{ effect}]$$
$$(\eta\delta)_{ip/jm/k} = \mu_{ijkmp} - \mu_{ijkm} - \mu_{jkmp} + \mu_{jkm} \qquad [SC/GB/A \text{ effect}]$$

The sum of these seven effects is $\mu_{ijkmp} - \mu_{ijkm}$; thus, the within-subjects variability is accounted for. Our final equation is

(9.9)
$$Y_{ijkmp} = \mu + \underset{\substack{A \\ \text{effect}}}{\alpha_k} + \underset{\substack{G/A \\ \text{effect}}}{\gamma_{j/k}} + \underset{\substack{B \\ \text{effect}}}{\beta_m} + \underset{\substack{AB \\ \text{effect}}}{(\alpha\beta)_{km}} + \underset{\substack{GB/A \\ \text{effect}}}{(\gamma\beta)_{jm/k}}$$

$$+ \underset{\substack{S/GB/A \\ \text{effect}}}{\eta_{i/jm/k}} + \underset{\substack{C \\ \text{effect}}}{\delta_p} + \underset{\substack{AC \\ \text{effect}}}{(\alpha\delta)_{kp}} + \underset{\substack{GC/A \\ \text{effect}}}{(\gamma\delta)_{jp/k}} + \underset{\substack{BC \\ \text{effect}}}{(\beta\delta)_{mp}}$$

$$+ \underset{\substack{ABC \\ \text{effect}}}{(\alpha\beta\delta)_{kmp}} + \underset{\substack{GBC/A \\ \text{effect}}}{(\gamma\beta\delta)_{jmp/k}} + \underset{\substack{SC/GB/A \\ \text{effect}}}{(\eta\delta)_{ip/jm/k}} + \underset{\substack{\text{error of} \\ \text{measurement}}}{\epsilon_{ijkmp}}$$

9.4.2 The analysis of variance

The analysis of variance represented in Table 9-10 is less forbidding than it may appear. The key to the analysis lies in Equation (9.9), which dictates the sources of variance. The organization of these sources begins with the subject; in any design an effect must either be between subjects or within subjects. Since there are different subjects in each group, and consequently in each level of A, and also in each level of B, and since each subject is tested at all levels of C, the classification in the present design seems reasonable. The only question might be the status of interaction effects involving between- and within-subjects variables; in previous designs involving such interactions they were shown to be within-subjects effects. If any doubt exists in the present case, two checks are available. First, the effects that correspond to the between-subjects sources may be summed. The result after substitution of the population means is $\mu_{ijkm} - \mu$, which demonstrates that these effects totally account for the deviation of the subject's population mean from the grand mean, the between-subjects effect. Summing the remaining effects (excluding ϵ_{ijkmp}), we obtain $\mu_{ijkmp} - \mu_{ijkm}$, the deviation of the pth true score for a subject from the mean score for the subject, the within-subjects effect. The same type of check could be accomplished using df rather than the population effects. The sum of df for the sources classified as between subjects is $abgn - 1$, clearly the appropriate number for the total variability among subjects. Within subjects, we should have $c - 1$ df for each individual, multiplied by $abgn$ to reflect the pooling over subjects. This is the total obtained when the df for the within-subjects effects are added together. The reader should follow the two approaches just described to verify that the between- and within-groups classifications are also accurate.

It is extremely helpful to consider not only what the sources are, but also how they are to be organized. The appropriate classification of sources of variance, as, for example, into between- and within-groups categories, makes the table easier to digest and facilitates calculations of df and sums of squares. In addition, fewer mistakes in the selection of error terms will be made if the table is so laid out that each error term lies beneath the sources which it will be used to evaluate.

Once the SV have been determined and organized as in Table 9-10, df and SS columns are readily established. As always, the df are determined by a few simple principles, which we have used repeatedly:

(a) The df for an unnested main effect are one less than the number of levels of the variable involved. For example, the A source represents the variability of a means about the grand mean of the data matrix.

(b) The df for a nested main effect involve the computation of df for each level of nesting and then multiplication by the number of levels. For example, subjects are nested within groups $\times$ B combinations, which in turn are nested within levels of A. Thus, we have $n - 1$ df for each groups $\times$ B combination, multiplied by the number of such combinations, abg. The $df_{S/GB/A}$ are therefore equal to $abg(n - 1)$.

(c) The df for interaction effects are merely a product of the df for the effects involved. Thus $df_{SC/BG/A}$ equals $abg(n - 1) \times (c - 1)$.

The formulas for sum of squares computations in Table 9-10 are those which are considered most easily generated and executed. Alternatives exist,

TABLE 9-10
Analysis of variance for a hierarchical design with repeated measurements

SV	df	SS	EMS	F
Total	$abgnc - 1$	$\displaystyle\sum_i^n \sum_j^g \sum_k^a \sum_m^b \sum_p^c Y_{ijkmp}^2 - C$		
Between S	$abgn - 1$	$\dfrac{\displaystyle\sum_i^n \sum_j^g \sum_k^a \sum_m^b \left(\sum_p^c Y_{ijkmp}\right)^2}{c} - C$		
Between G	$ag - 1$	$\dfrac{\displaystyle\sum_j^g \sum_k^a \left(\sum_i^n \sum_m^b \sum_p^c Y_{ijkmp}\right)^2}{nbc} - C$		
A	$a - 1$	$\dfrac{\displaystyle\sum_k^a \left(\sum_i^n \sum_j^g \sum_m^b \sum_p^c Y_{ijkmp}\right)^2}{ngbc} - C$	$\sigma_e^2 + nbc\sigma_{G/A}^2 + c\sigma_{S/GB/A}^2 + nbgc\theta_A^2$	$\dfrac{MS_A}{MS_{G/A}}$
G/A	$a(g - 1)$	$SS_{\mathrm{B.G}} - SS_A$	$\sigma_e^2 + nbc\sigma_{G/A}^2 + c\sigma_{S/GB/A}^2$	
Within G	$ag(bn - 1)$	$SS_{\mathrm{B.S}} - SS_{\mathrm{B.G}}$		
B	$b - 1$	$\dfrac{\displaystyle\sum_m^b \left(\sum_i^n \sum_j^g \sum_k^a \sum_p^c Y_{ijkmp}\right)^2}{ngac} - C$	$\sigma_e^2 + c\sigma_{S/GB/A}^2 + nagc\theta_B^2$	$\dfrac{MS_B}{MS_{GB/A}}$
AB	$(a - 1)(b - 1)$	$\dfrac{\displaystyle\sum_k^a \sum_m^b \left(\sum_i^n \sum_j^g \sum_p^c Y_{ijkmp}\right)^2}{ngc} - C - SS_A - SS_B$	$\sigma_e^2 + c\sigma_{S/GB/A}^2 + ngc\theta_{AB}^2$	$\dfrac{MS_{AB}}{MS_{GB/A}}$

Source	df	SS	Expected mean square	F
GB/A	$a(g-1)(b-1)$	$\dfrac{\sum_j^g\sum_k^a\sum_m^b\left(\sum_i^n\sum_p^c Y_{ijkmp}\right)^2}{nc} - \dfrac{\sum_k^a\sum_m^b\left(\sum_i^n\sum_j^g\sum_p^c Y_{ijkmp}\right)^2}{nbc} - \dfrac{\sum_j^g\sum_k^a\left(\sum_i^n\sum_m^b\sum_p^c Y_{ijkmp}\right)^2}{ngc} + \dfrac{\sum_k^a\left(\sum_i^n\sum_j^g\sum_m^b\sum_p^c Y_{ijkmp}\right)^2}{ngbc}$	$\sigma_e^2 + c\sigma_{S/GB/A}^2 + nc\sigma_{GB/A}^2$	$\dfrac{MS_{GB/A}}{MS_{S/GB/A}}$
$S/GB/A$	$abg(n-1)$	$SS_{W.G} - SS_B - SS_{AB} - SS_{GB/A}$	$\sigma_e^2 + c\sigma_{S/GB/A}^2$	
Within S	$abgnc - 1$	$SS_{\text{tot}} - SS_{B.S}$		
C	$c-1$	$\dfrac{\sum_p^c\left(\sum_i^n\sum_j^g\sum_k^a\sum_m^b Y_{ijkmp}\right)^2}{ngab} - C$	$\sigma_e^2 + nb\sigma_{GC/A}^2 + \sigma_{SC/GB/A}^2 + ngba\theta_C^2$	$\dfrac{MS_C}{MS_{GC/A}}$
AC	$(a-1)(c-1)$	$\dfrac{\sum_k^a\sum_p^c\left(\sum_i^n\sum_j^g\sum_m^b Y_{ijkmp}\right)^2}{ngb} - C - SS_A - SS_C$	$\sigma_e^2 + nb\sigma_{GC/A}^2 + \sigma_{SC/GB/A}^2 + ngb\theta_{AC}^2$	$\dfrac{MS_{AC}}{MS_{GC/A}}$
GC/A	$a(g-1)(c-1)$	$\dfrac{\sum_j^g\sum_k^a\sum_p^c\left(\sum_i^n\sum_m^b Y_{ijkmp}\right)^2}{nb} - \dfrac{\sum_k^a\sum_p^c\left(\sum_i^n\sum_j^g\sum_m^b Y_{ijkmp}\right)^2}{nbg} - \dfrac{\sum_j^g\sum_k^a\left(\sum_i^n\sum_m^b\sum_p^c Y_{ijkmp}\right)^2}{nbc} + \dfrac{\sum_k^a\left(\sum_i^n\sum_j^g\sum_m^b\sum_p^c Y_{ijkmp}\right)^2}{ngbc}$	$\sigma_e^2 + nb\sigma_{GC/A}^2 + \sigma_{SC/GB/A}^2$	$\dfrac{MS_{GC/A}}{MS_{SC/GB/A}}$
BC	$(b-1)(c-1)$	$\dfrac{\sum_m^b\sum_p^c\left(\sum_i^n\sum_j^g\sum_k^a Y_{ijkmp}\right)^2}{nga} - C - SS_B - SS_C$	$\sigma_e^2 + nc\sigma_{GBC/A}^2 + \sigma_{SC/GB/A}^2 + nga\theta_{BC}^2$	$\dfrac{MS_{BC}}{MS_{GBC/A}}$

233

TABLE 9-10 (Continued)

SV	df	SS	EMS	F
ABC	$(a-1)(b-1)(c-1)$	$\dfrac{\sum\limits_k^a \sum\limits_m^b \sum\limits_p^c \left(\sum\limits_i^n \sum\limits_j^g Y_{ijkmp}\right)^2}{ng} - C - SS_{AB} - SS_{AC} - SS_{BC} - SS_A - SS_B - SS_C$	$\sigma_e^2 + n\sigma_{GBC/A}^2 + \sigma_{SC/GB/A}^2 + ng\theta_{ABC}^2$	$\dfrac{MS_{ABC}}{MS_{GBC/A}}$
GBC/A	$a(g-1)(b-1)(c-1)$	$\dfrac{\sum\limits_j^a \sum\limits_k^b \sum\limits_m^c \left(\sum\limits_i^n \sum\limits_p^g Y_{ijkmp}\right)^2}{n} + \dfrac{\sum\limits_k^a \sum\limits_m^b \sum\limits_p^c \left(\sum\limits_i^n \sum\limits_j^g Y_{ijkmp}\right)^2}{nbc}$ $+ \dfrac{\sum\limits_k^a \sum\limits_m^b \left(\sum\limits_i^n \sum\limits_j^g \sum\limits_p^c Y_{ijkmp}\right)^2}{ngc} + \dfrac{\sum\limits_j^a \sum\limits_k^c \left(\sum\limits_i^n \sum\limits_j^g \sum\limits_m^b Y_{ijkmp}\right)^2}{ngb}$ $- \dfrac{\sum\limits_k^a \sum\limits_m^b \left(\sum\limits_i^n \sum\limits_j^g \sum\limits_p^c Y_{ijkmp}\right)^2}{nb} - \dfrac{\sum\limits_j^a \sum\limits_k^c \left(\sum\limits_i^n \sum\limits_m^b Y_{ijkmp}\right)^2}{nc}$ $- \dfrac{\sum\limits_k^a \sum\limits_m^b \sum\limits_p^c \left(\sum\limits_i^n \sum\limits_j^g Y_{ijkmp}\right)^2}{ngbc} - \dfrac{\sum\limits_k^a \sum\limits_m^b \sum\limits_p^c \left(\sum\limits_i^n \sum\limits_j^g Y_{ijkmp}\right)^2}{ng}$	$\sigma_e^2 + n\sigma_{GBC/A}^2 + \sigma_{SC/GB/A}^2$	$\dfrac{MS_{GBC/A}}{MS_{SC/GB/A}}$
SC/GB/A	$abg(n-1)(c-1)$	$SS_{W.S} - SS_C - SS_{AC} - SS_{GC/A} - SS_{BC} - SS_{ABC} - SS_{GBC/A}$	$\sigma_e^2 + \sigma_{SC/GB/A}^2$	

particularly in the case of nested effects, which may be computed as a difference among interactions rather than by the expanded *df* approach.

The *EMS* are particularly important in the present design, since there are many sources and error terms. It is foolish to attempt to remember what is tested against what in this and similar designs. The best approach is to remember the rules of thumb of Chapter 8, which allow us to quickly generate *EMS* for any design; the *F* tests follow immediately. The reader should note that regardless of how many levels of nesting exist, the letters designating the source must be contained somewhere among the subscripts if a component is to be considered for inclusion in the *EMS*. However, only those subscripts to the left of the first slash are "essential." The component is included in the *EMS* only if after ignoring the letters which describe the source the essential subscripts all represent random effect variables. For example, in assessing the *EMS* for G/A, we consider (in addition to error variance and the null hypothesis term, $\sigma^2_{G/A}$)

$$\sigma^2_{GB/A}, \ \sigma^2_{S/GB/A}, \ \sigma^2_{GC/A}, \ \sigma^2_{GBC/A}, \ \sigma^2_{SC/GB/A}$$

Of these, only $\sigma^2_{S/GB/A}$ contains no fixed effect letter subscript in the "essential" position after ignoring G and A. As a second example, consider the BC source. We can consider

$$\theta^2_{ABC}, \ \sigma^2_{GBC/A}, \ \sigma^2_{SC/GB/A}$$

Ignoring B and C, we find that $\sigma^2_{GBC/A}$ and $\sigma^2_{SC/GB/A}$ enter into the *EMS*.

9.4.3 A numerical example

Table 9-11 presents data for a hierarchical design with repeated measurements. Squaring each score and summing, we obtain

$$SS_{tot} = \sum_{i}^{n} \sum_{j}^{g} \sum_{k}^{a} \sum_{m}^{b} \sum_{p}^{c} Y^2_{ijkmp} - C$$

$$= (4)^2 + (3)^2 + \cdots + (15)^2 - \frac{(4 + 3 + \cdots + 15)^2}{48}$$

$$= 3,515.00 - 2,806.02$$

$$= 708.98$$

We next obtain a measure of the overall variability among subjects:

$$SS_{B.S} = \frac{\sum_{i}^{n} \sum_{j}^{g} \sum_{k}^{a} \sum_{m}^{b} \left(\sum_{p}^{c} Y_{ijkmp} \right)^2}{c} - C$$

$$= \frac{(4 + 5 + 8)^2 + \cdots + (9 + 11 + 15)^2}{3} - \frac{(4 + 3 + \cdots + 15)^2}{48}$$

$$= 3,094.33 - 2,806.02$$

$$= 288.31$$

TABLE 9-11

Data for a hierarchical design with repeated measurements

| | | | B_1 | | | | B_2 | | |
			C_1	C_2	C_3		C_1	C_2	C_3
A_1	G_{11}	S_{1111}	4	5	8	S_{1112}	3	6	10
		S_{2111}	3	6	10	S_{2112}	4	5	9
	G_{21}	S_{1211}	4	7	8	S_{1212}	1	6	8
		S_{2211}	3	6	9	S_{2212}	4	2	12
A_2	G_{12}	S_{1121}	7	7	11	S_{1122}	9	8	16
		S_{2121}	4	8	14	S_{2122}	7	10	19
	G_{22}	S_{1221}	3	5	9	S_{1222}	10	12	13
		S_{2221}	2	7	8	S_{2222}	9	11	15

Part of the variability among subjects is due to the fact that some subjects are in one group, some are in a different group. To measure this variability among group means, we have

$$SS_{\text{B.G}} = \frac{\sum_{j}^{g} \sum_{k}^{a} \left(\sum_{i}^{n} \sum_{m}^{b} \sum_{p}^{c} Y_{ijkmp} \right)^2}{nbc} - C$$

$$= \frac{(4 + 5 + \cdots + 5 + 9)^2 + (4 + 7 + \cdots + 2 + 12)^2}{12} + \cdots$$

$$+ \frac{(3 + 5 + \cdots + 11 + 15)^2}{12} - \frac{(4 + 3 + \cdots + 15)^2}{48}$$

$$= 2{,}953.75 - 2{,}806.02$$

$$= 147.73$$

The overall variability among group means may be attributed to the effects of the treatment variable, A, and to a residual group variability. We have

$$SS_A = \frac{\sum_{k}^{a} \left(\sum_{i}^{n} \sum_{j}^{g} \sum_{m}^{b} \sum_{p}^{c} Y_{ijkmp} \right)^2}{ngbc} - C$$

$$= \frac{(4 + 5 + \cdots + 2 + 12)^2 + (7 + 7 + \cdots + 11 + 15)^2}{24}$$

$$- \frac{(4 + 3 + \cdots + 15)^2}{48}$$

$$= 2{,}942.71 - 2{,}806.02$$

$$= 136.69$$

and

$$SS_{G/A} = SS_{B.G} - SS_A$$
$$= 147.73 - 136.69$$
$$= 11.04$$

Part of the variability among subject means still remains to be accounted for. Since there are different subjects at each level of B, this treatment variable contributes to $SS_{B.S}$.   We have

$$SS_B = \frac{\sum\limits_{m}^{b}\left(\sum\limits_{i}^{n}\sum\limits_{j}^{g}\sum\limits_{k}^{a}\sum\limits_{p}^{c} Y_{ijkmp}\right)^2}{ngac} - C$$

$$= \frac{(4 + 5 + \cdots + 7 + 8)^2 + (3 + 6 + \cdots + 11 + 15)^2}{24}$$

$$- \frac{(4 + 3 + \cdots + 15)^2}{48}$$

$$= 2{,}860.21 - 2{,}806.02$$
$$= 54.19$$

The variable B crosses with A and groups.   We therefore compute

$$SS_{AB} = \frac{\sum\limits_{k}^{a}\sum\limits_{m}^{b}\left(\sum\limits_{i}^{n}\sum\limits_{j}^{g}\sum\limits_{p}^{c} Y_{ijkmp}\right)^2}{ngc} - C - SS_A - SS_B$$

$$= \frac{(4 + 5 + \cdots + 6 + 9)^2 + \cdots + (9 + 8 + \cdots + 11 + 15)^2}{12}$$

$$- C - SS_A - SS_B$$

$$= 3{,}064.58 - 2{,}806.02 - 136.69 - 54.19$$
$$= 67.68$$

and

$$SS_{GB/A} = \frac{\sum\limits_{j}^{g}\sum\limits_{k}^{a}\sum\limits_{m}^{b}\left(\sum\limits_{i}^{n}\sum\limits_{p}^{c} Y_{ijkmp}\right)^2}{nc} - \frac{\sum\limits_{j}^{g}\sum\limits_{k}^{a}\left(\sum\limits_{i}^{n}\sum\limits_{m}^{b}\sum\limits_{p}^{c} Y_{ijkmp}\right)^2}{nbc}$$

$$- \frac{\sum\limits_{k}^{a}\sum\limits_{m}^{b}\left(\sum\limits_{i}^{n}\sum\limits_{j}^{g}\sum\limits_{p}^{c} Y_{ijkmp}\right)^2}{ngc} + \frac{\sum\limits_{k}^{a}\left(\sum\limits_{i}^{n}\sum\limits_{j}^{g}\sum\limits_{m}^{b}\sum\limits_{p}^{c} Y_{ijkmp}\right)^2}{ngbc}$$

$$= \frac{(4 + 5 + \cdots + 6 + 10)^2}{6} + \cdots + \frac{(10 + 12 + \cdots + 11 + 15)^2}{6}$$

$$- 2{,}953.75 - 3{,}064.58 + 2{,}942.71$$

$$= 3{,}090.17 - 2{,}953.75 - 3{,}064.58 + 2{,}942.71$$
$$= 14.55$$

Note that only $\sum\limits_{j}^{g}\sum\limits_{k}^{a}\sum\limits_{m}^{b}(\sum\limits_{i}^{n}\sum\limits_{p}^{c} Y_{ijkmp})^2/nc$ is computed.   The remaining parts of $SS_{GB/A}$ have been calculated previously in order to obtain other sum of square terms. A check on the above calculation is provided by

$$SS_{GB/A} = \frac{\sum\limits_{j}^{g} \sum\limits_{k}^{a} \sum\limits_{m}^{b} \left(\sum\limits_{i}^{n} \sum\limits_{p}^{c} Y_{ijkmp} \right)^2}{nc} - C - SS_{B.G} - SS_B - SS_{AB}$$

$$= 3{,}090.17 - 2{,}806.02 - 147.73 - 54.19 - 67.68$$

$$= 14.55$$

The residual variability among subjects may now be computed:

$$SS_{S/GB/A} = SS_{B.S} - SS_{B.G} - SS_B - SS_{AB} - SS_{GB/A}$$

$$= 288.31 - 147.73 - 54.19 - 67.68 - 14.55$$

$$= 4.16$$

We now turn to the variability within subjects which is due to the presence of repeated measurements. We obtain the overall within-subjects term first:

$$SS_{W.S} = SS_{tot} - SS_{B.S}$$

$$= 708.98 - 288.31$$

$$= 420.67$$

The variability due to treatment C is

$$SS_C = \frac{\sum\limits_{p}^{c} \left(\sum\limits_{i}^{n} \sum\limits_{j}^{g} \sum\limits_{k}^{a} \sum\limits_{m}^{b} Y_{ijkmp} \right)^2}{ngab} - C$$

$$= \frac{(4 + 3 + \cdots + 10 + 9)^2 + (5 + 6 + \cdots + 12 + 11)^2 + (8 + 10 + \cdots + 13 + 15)^2}{16} - 2{,}806.02$$

$$= 3{,}143.19 - 2{,}806.02$$

$$= 337.17$$

For the AC interaction, we have

$$SS_{AC} = \frac{\sum\limits_{k}^{a} \sum\limits_{p}^{c} \left(\sum\limits_{i}^{n} \sum\limits_{j}^{g} \sum\limits_{m}^{b} Y_{ijkmp} \right)^2}{ngb} - C - SS_A - SS_C$$

$$= \frac{(4 + 3 + \cdots + 1 + 4)^2}{8} + \cdots + \frac{(11 + 14 + \cdots + 13 + 15)^2}{8} - 2{,}806.02 - 136.69 - 337.17$$

$$= 3{,}281.38 - 2{,}806.02 - 136.69 - 337.17$$

$$= 1.50$$

Both the C and AC terms are tested against GC/A; the sum of squares for this is

$$SS_{GC/A} = \frac{\sum\limits_{j}^{g}\sum\limits_{k}^{u}\sum\limits_{p}^{c}\left(\sum\limits_{i}^{n}\sum\limits_{m}^{b} Y_{ijkmp}\right)^{2}}{nb} - \frac{\sum\limits_{j}^{g}\sum\limits_{k}^{a}\left(\sum\limits_{i}^{n}\sum\limits_{m}^{b}\sum\limits_{p}^{c} Y_{ijkmp}\right)^{2}}{nbc}$$

$$- \frac{\sum\limits_{k}^{a}\sum\limits_{p}^{c}\left(\sum\limits_{i}^{n}\sum\limits_{m}^{b}\sum\limits_{j}^{g} Y_{ijkmp}\right)^{2}}{nbg} + \frac{\sum\limits_{k}^{a}\left(\sum\limits_{i}^{n}\sum\limits_{j}^{g}\sum\limits_{m}^{b}\sum\limits_{p}^{c} Y_{ijkmp}\right)^{2}}{ngbc}$$

$$= \frac{(4+3+3+4)^2 + \cdots + (9+8+13+15)^2}{4} - 2{,}953.75$$

$$- 3{,}281.38 + 2{,}942.71$$

$$= 3{,}311.75 - 2{,}953.75 - 3{,}281.38 + 2{,}942.71$$

$$= 19.33$$

For the BC interaction, we have

$$SS_{BC} = \frac{\sum\limits_{m}^{b}\sum\limits_{p}^{c}\left(\sum\limits_{i}^{n}\sum\limits_{j}^{g}\sum\limits_{k}^{a} Y_{ijkmp}\right)^{2}}{nga} - C - SS_B - SS_C$$

$$= \frac{(4+3+\cdots+3+2)^2}{8} + \cdots + \frac{(10+9+\cdots+13+15)^2}{8}$$

$$- 2{,}806.02 - 54.19 - 337.17$$

$$= 3{,}205.38 - 2{,}806.02 - 54.19 - 337.17$$

$$= 8.00$$

Next, we have

$$SS_{ABC} = \frac{\sum\limits_{k}^{a}\sum\limits_{m}^{b}\sum\limits_{p}^{c}\left(\sum\limits_{i}^{n}\sum\limits_{j}^{g} Y_{ijkmp}\right)^{2}}{ng} - C - SS_{AB} - SS_{AC} - SS_{BC} - SS_A$$

$$- SS_B - SS_C$$

$$= \frac{(4+3+4+3)^2 + \cdots + (16+19+13+15)^2}{4} - 2{,}806.02$$

$$- 67.68 - 1.50 - 8.00 - 136.69 - 54.19 - 337.17$$

$$= 3{,}411.75 - 2{,}806.02 - 67.68 - 1.50 - 8.00 - 136.69$$

$$- 54.19 - 337.17$$

$$= .50$$

The error variability for the two preceding terms is

$$SS_{GBC/A} = \frac{\sum\limits_{j}^{g}\sum\limits_{k}^{a}\sum\limits_{m}^{b}\sum\limits_{p}^{c}\left(\sum\limits_{i}^{n} Y_{ijkmp}\right)^2}{n} + \frac{\sum\limits_{j}^{g}\sum\limits_{k}^{a}\left(\sum\limits_{i}^{n}\sum\limits_{m}^{b}\sum\limits_{p}^{c} Y_{ijkmp}\right)^2}{nbc}$$

$$+ \frac{\sum\limits_{k}^{a}\sum\limits_{m}^{b}\left(\sum\limits_{i}^{n}\sum\limits_{j}^{g}\sum\limits_{p}^{c} Y_{ijkmp}\right)^2}{ngc} + \frac{\sum\limits_{k}^{a}\sum\limits_{p}^{c}\left(\sum\limits_{i}^{n}\sum\limits_{j}^{g}\sum\limits_{m}^{b} Y_{ijkmp}\right)^2}{ngb}$$

$$- \frac{\sum\limits_{j}^{g}\sum\limits_{k}^{a}\sum\limits_{m}^{b}\left(\sum\limits_{i}^{n}\sum\limits_{p}^{c} Y_{ijkmp}\right)^2}{nc} - \frac{\sum\limits_{j}^{g}\sum\limits_{k}^{a}\sum\limits_{p}^{c}\left(\sum\limits_{i}^{n}\sum\limits_{m}^{b} Y_{ijkmp}\right)^2}{nb}$$

$$- \frac{\sum\limits_{k}^{a}\sum\limits_{m}^{b}\sum\limits_{p}^{c}\left(\sum\limits_{i}^{n}\sum\limits_{j}^{g} Y_{ijkmp}\right)^2}{ng} - \frac{\sum\limits_{k}^{a}\left(\sum\limits_{i}^{n}\sum\limits_{j}^{g}\sum\limits_{m}^{b}\sum\limits_{p}^{c} Y_{ijkmp}\right)^2}{ngbc}$$

$$= \frac{(4+3)^2 + \cdots + (13+15)^2}{2} + 2{,}953.75 + 3{,}064.58$$

$$+ 3{,}281.38 - 3{,}090.17 - 3{,}311.75 - 3{,}411.75 - 2{,}942.71$$

$$= 3{,}464.50 + 2{,}953.75 + 3{,}064.58 + 3{,}281.38 - 3{,}090.17$$
$$- 3{,}311.75 - 3{,}411.75 - 2{,}942.71$$

$$= 7.83$$

An alternative formula, which provides a partial check on $SS_{GBC/A}$, is

$$SS_{GBC/A} = \frac{\sum\limits_{j}^{g}\sum\limits_{k}^{a}\sum\limits_{m}^{b}\sum\limits_{p}^{c}\left(\sum\limits_{i}^{n} Y_{ijkmp}\right)^2}{n} - C - SS_A - SS_{G/A} - SS_B - SS_C$$

$$- SS_{GB/A} - SS_{GC/A} - SS_{BC} - SS_{AB} - SS_{AC} - SS_{ABC}$$

$$= 3{,}464.50 - 2{,}806.02 - 136.69 - 11.04 - 54.19 - 337.17$$
$$- 14.55 - 19.33 - 8.00 - 67.68 - 1.50 - .50$$

$$= 7.83$$

The $SS_{SC/GB/A}$ is the residual within-subjects variability. Therefore,

$$SS_{SC/GB/A} = SS_{\text{w.s}} - SS_C - SS_{AC} - SS_{GC/A} - SS_{BC} - SS_{ABC} - SS_{GBC/A}$$

$$= 420.67 - 337.17 - 1.50 - 19.33 - 8.00 - .50 - 7.83$$

$$= 46.34$$

Table 9-12 presents the completed analysis.

9.5 CONCLUDING REMARKS

Our presentation has been limited to designs in which subjects are nested within levels of some variable, G, which is in turn nested within levels of some variable, A. There are numerous variations on the designs that have been considered. There could be several between-groups variables, several

TABLE 9-12

Analysis of variance for the data of Table 9-11

SV	df	SS	MS	F
Total	47	708.98	15.08	
Between S	15	288.31	19.22	
Between G	3	147.73	49.24	
A	1	136.69	136.69	24.76 *
G/A	2	11.04	5.52	
Within G	12	140.58	11.72	
B	1	54.19	54.19	7.44
AB	1	67.68	67.68	9.30
GB/A	2	14.55	7.28	14.00
$S/GB/A$	8	4.16	.52	
Within S	32	420.67	13.15	
C	2	337.17	168.59	34.90 **
AC	2	1.50	.75	.16
GC/A	4	19.33	4.83	2.46
BC	2	8.00	4.00	2.04
ABC	2	.50	.25	.13
GBC/A	4	7.83	1.96	.68
$SC/GB/A$	16	46.34	2.90	

$*p < .05$
$**p < .01$

between-subjects-within-groups variables, and several within-subjects variables. Less frequently, within-subjects variables may be nested within each other. An example was given in Section 9.1; problems were nested within levels of difficulty. In the general case, there might be an subjects, randomized among the a levels of the treatment variable A. We obtain bc measures from each subject. However, the b levels of B at C_1 are not the same as the b levels at C_2, and so on; B is nested within levels of C. In terms of our previous example, B is problems and C is difficulty level. Noting that there are S/A, A, B/C, C, and the possible interactions AC, SB/AC, SC/A, and AB/C, we arrive at the structural equation

$$Y_{ijkm} = \underset{\substack{A \\ \text{effect}}}{\alpha_j} + \underset{\substack{S/A \\ \text{effect}}}{\eta_{i/j}} + \underset{\substack{C \\ \text{effect}}}{\gamma_m} + \underset{\substack{B/C \\ \text{effect}}}{\beta_{k/m}} + \underset{\substack{AC \\ \text{effect}}}{(\alpha\gamma)_{jm}}$$

(9.13)

$$+ \underset{\substack{AB/C \\ \text{effect}}}{(\alpha\beta)_{jk/m}} + \underset{\substack{SC/A \\ \text{effect}}}{(\eta\gamma)_{im/j}} + \underset{\substack{SB/AC \\ \text{effect}}}{(\eta\beta)_{ik/jm}} + \epsilon_{ijkm}$$

which is sufficient to generate the sources of Table 9-13. The EMS are based on the assumption that A, B, and C are all fixed variables.

TABLE 9-13
Analysis of variance for a design with nesting within subjects

SV	df	SS	EMS	F
Total	$abcn - 1$	$\displaystyle\sum_i^n \sum_j^a \sum_k^b \sum_m^c Y_{ijkm}^2 - C$		
Between S	$an - 1$	$\dfrac{\displaystyle\sum_i^n \sum_j^a \left(\sum_k^b \sum_m^c Y_{ijkm} \right)^2}{bc} - C$		
A	$a - 1$	$\dfrac{\displaystyle\sum_j^a \left(\sum_i^n \sum_k^b \sum_m^c Y_{ijkm} \right)^2}{nbc} - C$	$\sigma_e^2 + bc\sigma_{S/A}^2 + nbc\theta_A^2$	$\dfrac{MS_A}{MS_{S/A}}$
S/A	$a(n - 1)$	$SS_{\text{B.S}} - SS_A$	$\sigma_e^2 + bc\sigma_{S/A}^2$	
Within S	$an(bc - 1)$	$SS_{\text{tot}} - SS_{\text{B.S}}$		
C	$c - 1$	$\dfrac{\displaystyle\sum_m^c \left(\sum_i^n \sum_j^a \sum_k^b Y_{ijkm} \right)^2}{nab} - C$	$\sigma_e^2 + b\sigma_{SC/A}^2 + nab\theta_C^2$	$\dfrac{MS_C}{MS_{SC/A}}$
AC	$(a - 1)(c - 1)$	$\dfrac{\displaystyle\sum_j^a \sum_m^c \left(\sum_i^n \sum_k^b Y_{ijkm} \right)^2}{nb} - C - SS_A - SS_C$	$\sigma_e^2 + b\sigma_{SC/A}^2 + nb\theta_{AC}^2$	$\dfrac{MS_{AC}}{MS_{SC/A}}$
SC/A	$a(n - 1)(c - 1)$	$\dfrac{\displaystyle\sum_i^n \sum_j^a \sum_m^c \left(\sum_k^b Y_{ijkm} \right)^2}{b} - \dfrac{\displaystyle\sum_i^n \sum_j^a \sum_m^c \left(\sum_k^b \sum_m^c Y_{ijkm} \right)^2}{bc}$	$\sigma_e^2 + b\sigma_{SC/A}^2$	

Source	df	SS	E(MS)	F
B/C	$c(b-1)$	$-\dfrac{\sum_j^a \sum_m^c \left(\sum_i^n \sum_k^b Y_{ijkm}\right)^2}{nb} + \dfrac{\sum_j^a \left(\sum_i^n \sum_k^b \sum_m^c Y_{ijkm}\right)^2}{nbc}$	$\sigma_e^2 + \sigma_{SB/AC}^2 + na\theta_{B/C}^2$	$\dfrac{MS_{B/C}}{MS_{SB/AC}}$
AB/C	$c(a-1)(b-1)$	$-\dfrac{\sum_k^b \sum_m^c \left(\sum_i^n \sum_j^a Y_{ijkm}\right)^2}{na} - \dfrac{\sum_m^c \left(\sum_i^n \sum_j^a \sum_k^b Y_{ijkm}\right)^2}{nab} + \dfrac{\sum_j^a \sum_k^b \sum_m^c \left(\sum_i^n Y_{ijkm}\right)^2}{n} + \dfrac{\sum_j^a \sum_k^b \left(\sum_i^n \sum_m^c Y_{ijkm}\right)^2}{nc} - \dfrac{\sum_j^a \sum_m^c \left(\sum_i^n \sum_k^b Y_{ijkm}\right)^2}{nab}$	$\sigma_e^2 + \sigma_{SB/AC}^2 + n\theta_{AB/C}^2$	$\dfrac{MS_{AB/C}}{MS_{SB/AC}}$
SB/AC	$ac(n-1)(b-1)$	$SS_{W.S} - SS_C - SS_{AC} - SS_{SC/A} - SS_{B/C} - SS_{AB/C}$	$\sigma_e^2 + \sigma_{SB/AC}^2$	

In closing, we note two pitfalls of the designs considered in this chapter. As pointed out earlier, there is the danger that certain F tests will lack power due to too few error df. This will most often occur when some nested group effect is the error term. Unless there are grounds for pooling to obtain an error term on more df, there is little the experimenter can do after the data are collected. This being the case, it is important to work out the actual analysis of sources and df prior to the collection of data and to modify the design in whatever ways seem necessary to obtain powerful tests of effects of interest. The second pitfall is the occasional failure to replicate groups within levels of A, essentially confounding groups and levels of A. If one class is taught by one method and another by a second, is a difference in class means due to the different methods or to differences in the personal interactions within the two classes? We need some measure of variability among classes taught by the same method in order to determine the effect of the treatment. Experimenters often do not realize that the failure to repli-cate groups within levels is not particularly different from running one sub-ject at each level of A in a simple completely randomized one-factor design.

EXERCISES

9.1 Analyze the following data set.

A_1		A_2		A_3	
G_{11}	G_{21}	G_{12}	G_{22}	G_{13}	G_{23}
5	8	11	32	12	18
21	23	15	18	22	31
14	10	16	26	36	38
12	17	23	25	18	37
8	15	27	26	34	28
16	20	31	17	41	32

9.2 There are three measures on each subject in the groups nested within levels of A. Analyze the data.

			B_1	B_2	B_3				B_1	B_2	B_3
		S_{111}	5	8	12			S_{112}	18	21	28
	G_{11}	S_{211}	7	8	14		G_{12}	S_{212}	17	19	23
		S_{311}	8	10	17			S_{312}	14	18	24
		S_{411}	7	11	16			S_{412}	16	21	27
A_1						A_2					
		S_{121}	10	12	19			S_{122}	15	21	32
	G_{21}	S_{221}	8	10	20		G_{22}	S_{222}	14	18	29
		S_{321}	7	11	17			S_{322}	15	23	28
		S_{421}	8	12	18			S_{422}	17	22	31

9.3 Six high schools are chosen at random for an experiment on teaching machines, which are introduced into three of the schools and not into the other three. Two introductory French classes are randomly selected from each school. There are ten students in each class, each of whom is given a mid-term and final examination. These constitute the measures. Give the *SV*, *df*, *EMS* and error terms.

9.4 Thirty-two subjects are randomly assigned to eight 4-man groups, four of which are task-oriented and four of which are ego-oriented. Each group is required to solve three problems under stress and three other problems under no stress. The score for each group is number of trials it takes the group to solve the problems. Give the *SV*, *df*, *EMS*, and error terms.

9.5 An experiment was performed on the effects of socioeconomic status and intelligence upon self-evaluation. Three school districts, each of a different social stratum, were chosen for participation in the experiment. Ten schools were selected at random from among the elementary schools in each district (i.e., a total of 30 schools). Ten high and ten low I.Q. subjects were selected from each school. Each subject was given a self-evaluation scale, the dependent variable. The experimenter performed the following analysis.

SV	*df*
District (*D*)	2
Intelligence level (*I*)	1
D × *I*	2
Within error	594
Total	599

Can you suggest an alternative analysis (include error terms)? What inference might be added? Changed? Why?

LATIN SQUARE DESIGNS

10

10.1 INTRODUCTION

The repeated measurements design of Chapter 7 permits the removal of variance due to individual differences, thus increasing the precision of the F test of the treatments effect. Much of the remaining error variance is attributable to the fact that scores have been obtained at different points in time within each sequence of treatment administrations. Careful randomization of the order of presentation minimizes bias in the F test due to these temporal effects, but their presence contributes to the imprecision of the design. The Latin square design permits the systematic removal of main effects due to the sequence in which treatments are presented and due to the ordinal position within the sequence (i.e., the point in the sequence at which treatment A_j is administered). This design shares the advantages of the repeated measurements design in requiring fewer subjects than the completely randomized design and in removing between-subjects variability. In addition, variability due to temporal effects is also removed from the error term and may be independently evaluated. Of course, the pitfalls of nonadditivity and heterogeneity of covariance are present in the Latin square design, as in any repeated measurements design. In particular, nonadditivity may create more serious difficulties than those considered in Chapter 7.

10.2 THE LATIN SQUARE

Consider the following arrangement of treatments:

$$\begin{bmatrix} A_1 & A_2 & A_3 \\ A_2 & A_3 & A_1 \\ A_3 & A_1 & A_2 \end{bmatrix}$$

The characteristic that defines this arrangement as a Latin square is the occurrence of each treatment exactly once in each row and in each column. The above square is only one of several possible. It is generally referred to as a *standard square*, since the first row and first column are in standard order (i.e., A_1, A_2, A_3). Interchanging rows and also columns, we might obtain

$$\begin{bmatrix} A_1 & A_3 & A_2 \\ A_3 & A_2 & A_1 \\ A_2 & A_1 & A_3 \end{bmatrix}$$

This is one of $3!2! - 1$ nonstandard squares obtainable from the standard square previously exhibited. If there are four treatment levels, there are four possible standard squares. Since each of these can, by permutation of rows and columns, give rise to $4!3! - 1$ nonstandard squares, the total number of 4×4 Latin squares is $4(4!3! - 1) + 4$, or 576. As we add levels of A, even more marked increases occur in the possible number of squares.

Sets of standard squares are available in several sources. A very extensive presentation is the set of tables in Fisher and Yates.* A standard square should be chosen at random from the complete set. Then randomly permute all the rows, all the columns, and finally the letters. For example, suppose we choose at random the following 6×6 standard square

$$\begin{bmatrix} A_1 & A_2 & A_3 & A_4 & A_5 & A_6 \\ A_2 & A_4 & A_5 & A_3 & A_6 & A_1 \\ A_3 & A_6 & A_1 & A_5 & A_4 & A_2 \\ A_4 & A_1 & A_2 & A_6 & A_3 & A_5 \\ A_5 & A_3 & A_6 & A_1 & A_2 & A_4 \\ A_6 & A_5 & A_4 & A_2 & A_1 & A_3 \end{bmatrix}$$

We note the order of appearance of the numbers 1 through 6 in a table of random numbers; we might obtain $\langle 1, 3, 2, 4, 6, 5 \rangle$. Then the rows are permuted so that the first row is still first, the third row is now second, the second row is now third, and so on. The result of the permutation of rows is

$$\begin{bmatrix} A_1 & A_2 & A_3 & A_4 & A_5 & A_6 \\ A_3 & A_6 & A_1 & A_5 & A_4 & A_2 \\ A_2 & A_4 & A_5 & A_3 & A_6 & A_1 \\ A_4 & A_1 & A_2 & A_6 & A_3 & A_5 \\ A_6 & A_5 & A_4 & A_2 & A_1 & A_3 \\ A_5 & A_3 & A_6 & A_1 & A_2 & A_4 \end{bmatrix}$$

We next permute all columns; we might have the random sequence $\langle 4, 1, 6, 2, 5, 3 \rangle$. Then the square becomes

* R. A. Fisher and F. Yates, *Statistical Tables for Biological, Agricultural and Medical Research* (Edinburgh: Oliver & Boyd, 1955), pp. 80–82.

$$\begin{bmatrix} A_4 & A_1 & A_6 & A_2 & A_5 & A_3 \\ A_5 & A_3 & A_2 & A_6 & A_4 & A_1 \\ A_3 & A_2 & A_1 & A_4 & A_6 & A_5 \\ A_6 & A_4 & A_5 & A_1 & A_3 & A_2 \\ A_2 & A_6 & A_3 & A_5 & A_1 & A_4 \\ A_1 & A_5 & A_4 & A_3 & A_2 & A_6 \end{bmatrix}$$

The random sequence dictating the permuting of letters might be $\langle 2, 4, 5, 1, 6, 3 \rangle$. The A_1's in the above square are replaced by A_2's, the A_2's by A_4's, the A_3's by A_5's, and so on. Then we have

$$\begin{bmatrix} A_1 & A_2 & A_3 & A_4 & A_6 & A_5 \\ A_6 & A_5 & A_4 & A_3 & A_1 & A_2 \\ A_5 & A_4 & A_2 & A_1 & A_3 & A_6 \\ A_3 & A_1 & A_6 & A_2 & A_5 & A_4 \\ A_4 & A_3 & A_5 & A_6 & A_2 & A_1 \\ A_2 & A_6 & A_1 & A_5 & A_4 & A_3 \end{bmatrix}$$

This square may be viewed as a random selection from the population of 6×6 squares.

10.3 A SIMPLE LATIN SQUARE DESIGN

10.3.1 Confounding in Latin square designs

The Latin square design provides no way of separating out certain variability contributions due to main effects from the contributions due to interaction. As a result, the ratio of mean squares designed to test the null hypothesis may not be distributed as F. Before further consideration of the consequences, the problem will be illustrated in more detail.

First, consider a 2×2 Latin square. Assume that each row represents a single subject; then S_1 receives A_1 first and A_2 second, while S_2 experiences the treatments in the reverse order; for example, we might have

$$\begin{array}{cc} & \begin{array}{cc} C_1 & C_2 \end{array} \\ \begin{array}{c} S_1 \\ \\ S_2 \end{array} & \begin{bmatrix} (A_1) & (A_2) \\ 5 & 8 \\ (A_2) & (A_1) \\ 6 & 9 \end{bmatrix} \end{array}$$

Using the single *df* approach of Section 5.9, $SS_S = (5 + 8 - 6 - 9)^2/4 = 1$. Now consider the interaction sum of squares for columns $\times$ treatments. Reorganizing the data matrix, we have

$$\begin{array}{cc} & \begin{array}{cc} C_1 & C_2 \end{array} \\ \begin{array}{c} A_1 \\ \\ A_2 \end{array} & \begin{bmatrix} (S_1) & (S_2) \\ 5 & 9 \\ (S_2) & (S_1) \\ 6 & 8 \end{bmatrix} \end{array}$$

and the sum of squares is $SS_{AC} = (5 + 8 - 9 - 6)^2/4 = 1$. The finding that the SS_S is equal to the SS_{AC} is typical of the 2×2 Latin square. In fact, it can be shown that the sum of squares for the main effect of any one variable will always be equal to the sum of squares for the interaction effect of the other two variables. Thus, the treatment main effect is confounded with the subject $\times$ column interaction ($SS_A = SS_{SC}$) and the column effect cannot be distinguished from the subject $\times$ treatment interaction ($SS_C = SS_{SA}$). As a consequence of this confounding of main and interaction effects in the 2×2 design, the F test of a main effect can be interpreted only if it is assumed that the population variance due to the interaction of the other two variables is zero. For example, the SS_A can be interpreted to reflect variability due to differences in the effects of A_1 and A_2 only if we assume that σ_{SC}^2 is negligible.

Confounding exists in larger squares, but it is not complete. To illustrate the nature of the confounding, we will compare the relation of main and interaction effects in a 3^3 factorial design with those in a 3×3 Latin square. We first consider the factorial arrangement, noting the example presented in Table 10-1. If $2/9$ is added to every score at C_2 and subtracted from every

TABLE 10-1

Data and sub-totals from a 3^3 factorial design

	C_1			C_2			C_3			
	A_1	A_2	A_3	A_1	A_2	A_3	A_1	A_2	A_3	
B_1	4	1	6	2	4	1	1	4	2	
B_2	5	2	3	1	7	5	3	8	6	
B_3	6	1	4	3	3	4	1	5	4	
	15	4	13	6	14	10	5	17	12	Grand
	C_1 Total = 32			C_2 Total = 30			C_3 Total = 34			Total = 96

Sub-totals for AB Cells

	A_1	A_2	A_3	B Totals
B_1	7	9	9	25
B_2	9	17	14	40
B_3	10	9	12	31
A Totals	26	35	35	96

score at C_3, the C main effect has been removed (i.e., SS_C is now zero), as may be seen in Table 10-2. However, note that the AB interaction effects are clearly unchanged. This is because C and AB effects are independent quantities in the complete factorial design.

We next turn to the Latin square approach. Table 10-3 presents a Latin

TABLE 10-2

Data of Table 10-1 after adjustment for C effects

	C_1			C_2			C_3			
	A_1	A_2	A_3	A_1	A_2	A_3	A_1	A_2	A_3	
B_1	4	1	6	$2\frac{2}{9}$	$4\frac{2}{9}$	$1\frac{2}{9}$	$\frac{7}{9}$	$3\frac{7}{9}$	$1\frac{7}{9}$	
B_2	5	2	3	$1\frac{2}{9}$	$7\frac{2}{9}$	$5\frac{2}{9}$	$2\frac{7}{9}$	$7\frac{7}{9}$	$5\frac{7}{9}$	
B_3	6	1	4	$3\frac{2}{9}$	$3\frac{2}{9}$	$4\frac{2}{9}$	$\frac{7}{9}$	$4\frac{7}{9}$	$3\frac{7}{9}$	
	15	4	13	$6\frac{2}{9}$	$14\frac{2}{9}$	$10\frac{2}{9}$	$4\frac{1}{3}$	$16\frac{1}{3}$	$11\frac{1}{3}$	Grand
	C_1 Total $= 32$			C_2 Total $= 32$			C_3 Total $= 32$			Total $= 96$

Sub-totals for AB Cells

	A_1	A_2	A_3	B Totals
B_1	7	9	9	25
B_2	9	17	14	40
B_3	10	9	12	31
A Totals	26	35	35	96

square that involves three levels of each of three variables. If 4/9 is added to all the C_1 scores, 1/9 is added to all the C_2 scores, and 5/9 is subtracted from all the C_3 scores, the C main effects are removed from the data matrix. The BC interaction effects have not been changed; the distance between any two rows in any column is exactly what it was before the adjustment. This

TABLE 10-3

Data from a Latin square design

	C_1	C_2	C_3	B Totals
B_1	(A_1) 4	(A_2) 4	(A_3) 2	10
B_2	(A_3) 3	(A_1) 1	(A_2) 8	12
B_3	(A_2) 1	(A_3) 4	(A_1) 1	6
A Totals	8	9	11	28

is apparent in Table 10-4. The reader should verify that the adjustment has also not affected the variability due to the AC interaction effects. However, the AB interaction variability is changed. Retabling the data, prior to the adjustment for C effects we had

TABLE 10-4

Data of Table 10-3 after adjustment for C effects

	C_1	C_2	C_3	B Totals
B_1	$4\frac{4}{9}$	$4\frac{1}{9}$	$1\frac{4}{9}$	10
B_2	$3\frac{4}{9}$	$1\frac{1}{9}$	$7\frac{4}{9}$	12
B_3	$1\frac{4}{9}$	$4\frac{1}{9}$	$\frac{4}{9}$	6
A Totals	$9\frac{1}{3}$	$9\frac{1}{3}$	$9\frac{1}{3}$	28

$$
\begin{array}{c}
\quad\quad B_1 \quad\quad B_2 \quad\quad B_3 \\
A_1 \begin{bmatrix} (C_1) & (C_2) & (C_3) \\ 4 & 1 & 1 \\ (C_2) & (C_3) & (C_1) \\ 4 & 8 & 1 \\ (C_3) & (C_1) & (C_2) \\ 2 & 3 & 4 \end{bmatrix} \\
A_2 \\
A_3
\end{array}
$$

We now have

$$
\begin{array}{c}
\quad\quad B_1 \quad\quad B_2 \quad\quad B_3 \\
A_1 \begin{bmatrix} (C_1) & (C_2) & (C_3) \\ 4\frac{4}{9} & 1\frac{1}{9} & \frac{4}{9} \\ (C_2) & (C_3) & (C_1) \\ 4\frac{1}{9} & 7\frac{4}{9} & 1\frac{4}{9} \\ (C_3) & (C_1) & (C_2) \\ 1\frac{4}{9} & 3\frac{4}{9} & 4\frac{1}{9} \end{bmatrix} \\
A_2 \\
A_3
\end{array}
$$

The sums of squares for the AB interaction are not the same for the two data sets. The situation is not quite the same as in the 2×2 Latin square. In that case, the SS_{AB} would be reduced to zero if variability due to C were removed from the matrix. In the larger squares, confounding is not complete. However, neither are main and interaction effects completely independent as in the factorial design considered earlier. In the factorial example, removal of variability due to C left the variability due to the AB interaction completely unaffected.

The confounding of main and interaction effects is a potential source of trouble in the use of Latin square designs. However, the existence of this problem does not preclude the use of the design. Transformations may be found which eliminate interaction effects, permitting a clear interpretation of tests of main effects. Even in the presence of interaction effects, reasonable interpretations of the F ratio will often be available.

10.3.2   A general nonadditive model for the Latin square

Consider an $a \times a$ Latin square, selected at random from the population of squares in the manner described in Section 10.2. Each row represents a subject who undergoes that particular sequence of treatments, and each column represents an ordinal position within the sequence. To best understand the analysis of variance for this design, and in particular the implications of the confounding discussed in the preceding section, we begin our development with an extremely general model, suggested by Wilk and Kempthorne.* They assume that all possible interactions among rows, columns, and treatments may exist in the population and therefore may contribute to the variability in the data matrix. The specific structural equation is

$$(10.1) \quad Y_{ijk} = \mu + \eta_i + \alpha_j + \gamma_k + (\eta\alpha)_{ij} + (\eta\gamma)_{ik} + (\alpha\gamma)_{jk} + (\eta\alpha\gamma)_{ijk} + \epsilon_{ijk}$$

where

$\eta_i = \mu_i - \mu$, the effect of the ith subject

$\alpha_j = \mu_j - \mu$, the effect of the jth level of the treatment variable, A

$\gamma_k = \mu_k - \mu$, the effect of the kth ordinal position

$(\eta\alpha)_{ij} = \mu_{ij} - \mu_i - \mu_j + \mu$, the interaction effect of the ith subject and the jth level of A

$(\eta\gamma)_{ik} = \mu_{ik} - \mu_i - \mu_k + \mu$, the interaction effect of the ith subject and the kth ordinal position

$(\alpha\gamma)_{jk} = \mu_{jk} - \mu_j - \mu_k + \mu$, the interaction effect of the jth level of A and the kth ordinal position

$(\eta\alpha\gamma)_{ijk} = \mu_{ijk} + \mu_i + \mu_j + \mu_k - \mu_{ij} - \mu_{ik} - \mu_{jk} - \mu$, the second-order interaction effect of the ith subject, jth level of A, and the kth ordinal position

$\epsilon_{ijk} =$ the residual error component associated with a score obtained from the ith subject under treatment A_j in the kth position in time.

It is assumed that the effects of treatments and columns are fixed; thus

$$\sum_k \alpha_j = \sum_j \gamma_k = \sum_j \sum_k (\alpha\gamma)_{jk} = 0$$

Row (subject) effects are assumed to be random. Consequently, η_i and all interaction effects involving η_i, as well as ϵ_{ijk}, are assumed to be randomly and independently sampled from normal distributions with zero means. The population variances are

Effect	Variance
η_i	σ_S^2
$(\eta\alpha)_{ij}$	σ_{SA}^2
$(\eta\gamma)_{ik}$	σ_{SC}^2
$(\eta\alpha\gamma)_{ijk}$	σ_{SCA}^2
ϵ_{ijk}	σ_e^2

* M. B. Wilk and O. Kempthorne. "Nonadditivities in a Latin Square," *Journal of the American Statistical Association*, 52:218–236 (1957).

We use θ_A^2, θ_C^2, and θ_{AC}^2 to represent the variances of the fixed effects, α_j, γ_k, and $(\alpha\gamma)_{jk}$.

10.3.3 The analysis of variance

Table 10-5 presents the *SV*, *df*, *SS*, *EMS* and *F* ratios for an $a \times a$ Latin square assuming the Wilk-Kempthorne model presented above. The first thing to note is that only four sources of variance can be distinguished, despite the abundance of terms in Equation 10-1. This follows from our earlier numerical demonstration that the main and interaction effects are not completely independent. Another way of justifying this breakdown is to turn to the *df* column. The total *df* are $a^2 - 1$. Subtracting the *df* for the three main effects, we have

$$df_{\text{res}} = (a^2 - 1) - 3(a - 1)$$
$$= a^2 - 3a + 2$$
$$= (a - 1)(a - 2)$$

What happens if we assume an interaction (int) source of variance independent of the main effects? The SS_{int} and df_{int} must come from the residual sum of squares and *df*. The *df* for any first-order interaction will be $(a - 1)(a - 1)$, a quantity which is larger than the df_{res}. Therefore, an interaction sum of squares cannot be extracted from the residual sum of squares.

Turning to the *EMS*, it is clear that they are not completely described by the rules of thumb presented in Chapter 8. However, some rules can be laid down. As usual, σ_e^2 and the null hypothesis components contribute to all terms. Next, note that our previous rules of thumb, while inadequate to completely specify the *EMS*, do enable us to provide some of the components. For example, σ_{SA}^2 does contribute to the *A* source and σ_{SC}^2 does contribute to the *C* source. The remaining components in each of the first three lines are accounted for by the confounding that we previously illustrated. Since *S* is partially confounded with *CA*, θ_{AC}^2 contributes to the *S* line. For the same reason, σ_{SA}^2 contributes to the *C* line, σ_{SC}^2 contributes to the *A* line, and σ_{SCA}^2 contributes to each of the first three lines. The residual includes all possible interaction components.

Under the general model assumed in the preceding section, the *F* tests are negatively biased; there will be too few rejections of the null hypothesis. If σ_S^2 equals zero,

$$E(F) = \frac{\sigma_e^2 + (1 - 1/a)\sigma_{SCA}^2 + \theta_{AC}^2}{\sigma_e^2 + (1 - 2/a)\sigma_{SCA}^2 + \sigma_{SC}^2 + \sigma_{SA}^2 + \theta_{AC}^2}$$

which is clearly less than one. The same is true of the test of the *A* main effect; under the null hypothesis ($H_0\colon \theta_A^2 = 0$),

$$E(F) = \frac{\sigma_e^2 + (1 - 2/a)\sigma_{SCA}^2 + \sigma_{SC}^2 + \sigma_{SA}^2}{\sigma_e^2 + (1 - 2/a)\sigma_{SCA}^2 + \sigma_{SC}^2 + \sigma_{SA}^2 + \theta_{AC}^2}$$

TABLE 10-5
Analysis of variance for a single Latin square

SV	df	SS	EMS	F
Total	$a^2 - 1$	$\sum_i \sum_j \sum_k Y_{ijk}^2 - C$		
S	$a - 1$	$\dfrac{\sum_i \left(\sum_j \sum_k Y_{ijk}\right)^2}{a} - C$	$\sigma_e^2 + \left(1 - \dfrac{1}{a}\right)\sigma_{SCA}^2 + \theta_{AC}^2 + n\sigma_S^2$	$\dfrac{MS_S}{MS_{\text{res}}}$
Columns	$a - 1$	$\dfrac{\sum_k \left(\sum_i \sum_j Y_{ijk}\right)^2}{a} - C$	$\sigma_e^2 + \left(1 - \dfrac{2}{a}\right)\sigma_{SCA}^2 + \sigma_{SC}^2 + \sigma_{SA}^2 + n\theta_C^2$	$\dfrac{MS_C}{MS_{\text{res}}}$
A	$a - 1$	$\dfrac{\sum_j \left(\sum_i \sum_k Y_{ijk}\right)^2}{a} - C$	$\sigma_e^2 + \left(1 - \dfrac{2}{a}\right)\sigma_{SCA}^2 + \sigma_{SA}^2 + \sigma_{SC}^2 + n\theta_A^2$	$\dfrac{MS_A}{MS_{\text{res}}}$
Residual	$(a - 1)(a - 2)$	$SS_{\text{tot}} - SS_S - SS_C - SS_A$	$\sigma_e^2 + \left(1 - \dfrac{2}{a}\right)\sigma_{SCA}^2 + \sigma_{SC}^2 + \sigma_{SA}^2 + \theta_{AC}^2$	

A similar expression holds for $E(F)$ when the C main effect is tested. As a general rule, we may conclude that when there are grounds for suspecting that θ^2_{AC} is greater than zero, nonsignificant F ratios for C and A effects must be regarded with extreme caution. In testing S, the magnitude of σ^2_{SA} and σ^2_{SC} are relevant to our inference; however, the F test of S will rarely be of interest.

Tukey* has suggested a test for nonadditivity in the Latin square which is similar in rationale and computations to that presented in Chapter 7 for the repeated measurements design. We will omit the procedure, but we note that if the result of the test is significant, a transformation may be sought to reduce nonadditivity. Wilk and Kempthorne† suggest an alternative approach: that transformation yielding the largest F ratio for the A effect should be chosen. Since (a) the F ratio for treatments will increase as interaction variability decreases, (b) this F ratio is our primary interest, and (c) the F for treatments is easier to compute than Tukey's single df test, this would seem to be a sensible criterion for selecting a transformation.

One final comment about the model is in order. If an additive model is valid (i.e., if population interaction effects are all zero), then the EMS are simply

S	$\sigma^2_e + a\sigma^2_S$
C	$\sigma^2_e + a\theta^2_C$
A	$\sigma^2_e + a\theta^2_A$
res	σ^2_e

and the residual is clearly an unbiased error term.

10.3.4 A numerical example

Table 10-6 presents the design, data, and sub-totals for an experiment using a single 4×4 Latin square. Each subject is tested at all four levels of A in the order indicated. We first calculate

$$C = \frac{(172)^2}{16}$$

$$= 1{,}849$$

The SS_{tot} are obtained in the usual way:

$$SS_{\text{tot}} = 4^2 + 8^2 + \cdots + 9^2 + 15^2 - C$$

$$= 2{,}350 - 1{,}849$$

$$= 501$$

* J. W. Tukey, "Test for Nonadditivity in the Latin Square," *Biometrics*, 11:111–113 (1955).

† Wilk and Kempthorne, *op. cit.*

TABLE 10-6

Data for a single Latin square design

	C_1	C_2	C_3	C_4	$\sum_j \sum_k Y_{ijk}$
S_1	(A_3) 4	(A_1) 8	(A_2) 3	(A_4) 16	31
S_2	(A_1) 12	(A_3) 6	(A_4) 19	(A_2) 7	44
S_3	(A_2) 9	(A_4) 23	(A_1) 11	(A_3) 5	48
S_4	(A_4) 17	(A_2) 8	(A_3) 9	(A_1) 15	49
$\sum_i \sum_j Y_{ijk} = 42$		45	42	43	$\sum_i \sum_j \sum_k Y_{ijk} = 172$

A Sub-totals

A_1	A_2	A_3	A_4
46	27	24	75

Next, we calculate a measure of the variability among subjects:

$$SS_S = \frac{(31)^2 + \cdots + (49)^2}{4} - C$$

$$= 1{,}900.5 - 1{,}849.0$$

$$= 51.5$$

A measure of variability due to temporal effects is given by

$$SS_C = \frac{(42)^2 + \cdots + (43)^2}{4} - C$$

$$= 1{,}850.5 - 1{,}849.0$$

$$= 1.5$$

The effect of the treatment variable is given by

$$SS_A = \frac{(46)^2 + \cdots + (75)^2}{4} - C$$

$$= 2{,}261.5 - 1{,}849.0$$

$$= 412.5$$

Subtracting the variability due to rows, columns, and treatments from the total, we obtain

$$SS_{\text{res}} = 501.0 - 51.5 - 1.5 - 412.5$$

$$= 35.5$$

The results of the analysis are summarized in Table 10-7.

TABLE 10-7

Analysis of variance for the data of Table 10-6

SV	df	SS	MS	F
Total	15	501.0	33.400	
S	3	51.5	17.167	2.9013
Columns	3	1.5	.500	.085
A	3	412.5	127.500	21.548 *
Residual	6	35.5	5.917	

$*p < .005$

10.3.5 A modification of the simple Latin square

Suppose that subjects will be required to learn four lists of nonsense syllables, differing with respect to stimulus similarity (high, A_1; low, A_2) and response similarity (high, B_1; low, B_2). We might use this design:

$$
\begin{array}{c c c c c}
 & C_1 & C_2 & C_3 & C_4 \\
S_1 & A_1B_2 & A_1B_1 & A_2B_1 & A_2B_2 \\
S_2 & A_1B_1 & A_1B_2 & A_2B_2 & A_2B_1 \\
S_3 & A_2B_2 & A_2B_1 & A_1B_2 & A_1B_1 \\
S_4 & A_2B_1 & A_2B_2 & A_1B_1 & A_1B_2
\end{array}
$$

Thus, S_1 is first tested under the high stimulus similarity, low response similarity (A_1B_2) condition, next under the high stimulus similarity, high response similarity (A_1B_1) condition, and so on. Each subject is tested under *all combinations of two treatment variables;* in the Latin square as previously discussed, each subject was tested under *all levels of a single variable.* The analysis presented in Table 10-8 is a slight modification of that presented in Table 10-5. The key point is that the df and SS for treatment combinations (analogous to df_A and SS_A in Table 10-5) can be partitioned into several components of interest.

The use of this design permits us to study the main and interaction effects of two treatment variables. In fact, the design could be extended to more variables. For example, there might be two levels of each of three treatment variables; then each of eight subjects is tested eight times, each measurement coming from a different ABD combination. The seven df for treatment combinations can be partitioned into seven quantities, representing three main effects, three first-order interactions, and one second-order interaction. The reader should also realize that this approach is not limited to two levels of the treatment variables. We could have 12 measurements from four levels of A and three levels of B; the 11 df yield an A effect on three df, a B effect on two df, and an AB effect on six df.

To illustrate the calculations, we will consider the data of Table 10-9. Each of four subjects has gone through a different sequence of four combina-

TABLE 10-8

Analysis of variance for a modified Latin square design

SV	df	SS *	F
Total	$a^2b^2 - 1$	$\sum_i \sum_j \sum_k \sum_m Y_{ijkm}^2 - C$	
S	$ab - 1$	$\dfrac{\sum_i \left(\sum_j \sum_k \sum_m Y_{ijkm} \right)^2}{ab} - C$	$\dfrac{MS_S}{MS_{\text{res}}}$
Columns	$ab - 1$	$\dfrac{\sum_m \left(\sum_i \sum_j \sum_k Y_{ijkm} \right)^2}{ab} - C$	$\dfrac{MS_C}{MS_{\text{res}}}$
Treatment combinations	$ab - 1$	$\dfrac{\sum_j \sum_k \left(\sum_i \sum_m Y_{ijkm} \right)^2}{ab} - C$	
A	$a - 1$	$\dfrac{\sum_j \left(\sum_i \sum_k \sum_m Y_{ijkm} \right)^2}{ab^2} - C$	$\dfrac{MS_A}{MS_{\text{res}}}$
B	$b - 1$	$\dfrac{\sum_k \left(\sum_i \sum_j \sum_m Y_{ijkm} \right)^2}{a^2b} - C$	$\dfrac{MS_B}{MS_{\text{res}}}$
AB	$(a - 1)(b - 1)$	$SS_{\text{T.C}} - SS_A - SS_B$	$\dfrac{MS_{AB}}{MS_{\text{res}}}$
Residual	$(ab - 1)(ab - 2)$	$SS_{\text{tot}} - SS_S - SS_C - SS_{\text{T.C}}$	

* i indexes the subject
j indexes the level of A
k indexes the level of B
m indexes the level of C

tions of levels of two independent variables; we are particularly interested in assessing the main and interaction effects of these two variables. Calculating the correction term in the usual way, we have

$$C = \frac{(175)^2}{16}$$

$$= 1{,}914.063$$

Then the total variability is

$$SS_{\text{tot}} = (5)^2 + (17)^2 + \cdots + (15)^2 + (7)^2 - C$$

$$= 2{,}391.000 - 1{,}914.063$$

$$= 476.937$$

Turning next to the variability among subjects (rows),

TABLE 10-9

Data for a modified Latin square design

	C_1	C_2	C_3	C_4	$\sum_j \sum_k \sum_m Y_{ijkm}$
S_1	(A_1B_1) 5	(A_2B_1) 17	(A_2B_2) 14	(A_1B_2) 8	44
S_2	(A_2B_1) 16	(A_1B_2) 4	(A_1B_1) 6	(A_2B_2) 20	46
S_3	(A_2B_2) 14	(A_1B_1) 8	(A_1B_2) 3	(A_2B_1) 19	44
S_4	(A_1B_2) 6	(A_2B_2) 13	(A_2B_1) 15	(A_1B_1) 7	41
$\sum_i \sum_j \sum_k Y_{ijkm} = 41$		42	38	54	$\sum_i \sum_j \sum_k \sum_m Y_{ijkm} = 175$

AB Sub-totals

A_1B_1	A_2B_1	A_2B_2	A_1B_2
26	67	61	21

$$SS_S = \frac{(44)^2 + \cdots + (41)^2}{4} - C$$

$$= 1,917.250 - 1,914.063$$

$$= 3.187$$

For C we have

$$SS_C = \frac{(41)^2 + \cdots + (54)^2}{4} - C$$

$$= 1,951.250 - 1,914.063$$

$$= 37.187$$

Next, we consider the treatment combinations:

$$SS_{T.C} = \frac{(26)^2 + \cdots + (21)^2}{4} - C$$

$$= 2,331.750 - 1,914.063$$

$$= 417.687$$

Part of the treatment variability is due to A, part to B, and the remainder to their interaction. Taking advantage of the fact that these terms are all distributed on 1 *df*, we may use the shortcut formula of Section 5.9:

$$SS_A = \frac{(67 + 61 - 26 - 21)^2}{16}$$

$$= 410.063$$

$$SS_B = \frac{(26 + 67 - 61 - 21)^2}{16}$$

$$= 7.563$$

and

$$SS_{AB} = \frac{(26 + 61 - 67 - 21)^2}{16}$$

$$= .063$$

Since $SS_A + SS_B + SS_{AB} = SS_{\text{T.C}}$ within a rounding error, our calculations check out. We now compute the residual:

$$SS_{\text{res}} = SS_{\text{tot}} - SS_S - SS_C - SS_{\text{T.C}}$$

$$= 476.937 - 3.187 - 37.187 - 417.687$$

$$= 18.876$$

The results of the analysis are summarized in Table 10-10.

TABLE 10-10

Analysis of variance for the data of Table 10-9

SV	df	SS	MS	F
Total	15	476.937	31.796	
S	3	3.187	1.062	.338
Columns	3	37.187	12.396	3.940
Treatment combinations	3	417.687		
A	1	410.063	410.063	130.344 *
B	1	7.563	7.563	2.404
AB	1	.063	.063	.02
Residual	6	18.876	3.146	
				*$p < .001$

10.4 THE GRECO-LATIN SQUARE

10.4.1 The design and its analysis

Consider the following two 4×4 Latin squares:

$$\begin{bmatrix} A_3 & A_1 & A_2 & A_4 \\ A_4 & A_2 & A_1 & A_3 \\ A_1 & A_3 & A_4 & A_2 \\ A_2 & A_4 & A_3 & A_1 \end{bmatrix} \quad \begin{bmatrix} B_1 & B_4 & B_2 & B_3 \\ B_4 & B_1 & B_3 & B_2 \\ B_2 & B_3 & B_1 & B_4 \\ B_3 & B_2 & B_4 & B_1 \end{bmatrix}$$

These squares are said to be *orthogonal*, since if superimposed, each combination of A and B treatment levels appears exactly once in the resultant square. Superimposing the above two squares, we obtain

$$\begin{bmatrix} A_3B_1 & A_1B_4 & A_2B_2 & A_4B_3 \\ A_4B_4 & A_2B_1 & A_1B_3 & A_3B_2 \\ A_1B_2 & A_3B_3 & A_4B_1 & A_2B_4 \\ A_2B_3 & A_4B_2 & A_3B_4 & A_1B_1 \end{bmatrix}$$

The above square is called a Greco-Latin square, since it is common practice to label the A_j by Latin letters and the B_k by Greek letters. For example, the designations A, B, C, and D might be used in place of A_1, A_2, A_3, and A_4, and the designations of the levels of B could be replaced by α, β, γ, and δ. Sets of orthogonal squares may be obtained in the previously cited book of tables edited by Fisher and Yates. However, it should be noted that tables for some orthogonal pairs are not readily available, for example, those for six or ten treatment levels.

In using the Greco-Latin design, each subject would go through each combination of A and B levels in the order designated for his particular row. Thus, employing the design presented above, S_1 would first be tested under the A_3B_1 treatment combination, next under the A_1B_4 combination, and so on. Each subject is exposed to only some of the combinations (in contrast to the design of Section 10.3.5), and each combination appears exactly once in the design.

The appropriate additive model is

(10.2) $$Y_{ijkm} = \mu + \eta_i + \alpha_j + \beta_k + \gamma_m + \epsilon_{ijkm}$$

where

$\eta_i = \mu_i - \mu$, the effect of the ith subject

$\alpha_j = \mu_j - \mu$, the effect of the jth level of A

$\beta_k = \mu_k - \mu$, the effect of the kth level of B

$\gamma_m = \mu_m - \mu$, the effect of the mth column of the square (position in time)

$\epsilon_{ijkm} = Y_{ijkm} - \mu_{ijkm}$, the residual error component

Only η_i and ϵ_{ijkm} are assumed to be randomly sampled. If interactions exist, the effects are confounded with the main effects of the two treatment variables, A and B, and with C (column) effects. Equation (10.2) would have to be appropriately revised, and the consequence of this nonadditivity will again be negatively biased F tests of main effects. More important in deciding whether to employ the Greco-Latin design is the possibility that the AB interaction, if it exists, will be of interest. If this is the case, the experimenter should avoid the Greco-Latin design, since it does not permit an independent evaluation of interaction effects. A better approach might be the Latin square design of Section 10.3.5. The Greco-Latin design involves fewer measurements for each subject, but the Latin square permits the evaluation of the AB interaction. Still other ways to deal with two treatments in a Latin square design will be considered in Section 10.6.

Table 10-11 presents the SV, df, SS, EMS, and F ratios; the EMS are based on the model of Equation (10.2). Note that the 3×3 design should not be used, since if $a = 3$, the error df are zero.

10.4.2 A numerical example

Table 10-12 presents a Greco-Latin design, illustrative data, and sub-totals to expedite computations of sums of squares. The correction term is

TABLE 10-12

Data and sub-totals for a Greco-Latin design

	C_1	C_2	C_3	C_4	$\sum_j \sum_k \sum_m Y_{ijkm}$
S_1	(A_3B_1) 5	(A_4B_3) 14	(A_1B_4) 16	(A_2B_2) 10	45
S_2	(A_4B_4) 20	(A_3B_2) 17	(A_2B_1) 4	(A_1B_3) 18	59
S_3	(A_1B_2) 11	(A_2B_4) 16	(A_3B_3) 16	(A_4B_1) 6	49
S_4	(A_2B_3) 15	(A_1B_1) 5	(A_4B_2) 14	(A_3B_4) 18	52
$\sum_i \sum_j \sum_k Y_{ijkm} =$	51	52	50	52	$\sum_i \sum_j \sum_k \sum_m Y_{ijkm} = 205$

Treatment Sub-totals

A_1	A_2	A_3	A_4	B_1	B_2	B_3	B_4
50	45	56	54	20	52	63	70

$$C = \frac{(205)^2}{16}$$
$$= 2{,}626.563$$

The total variability is
$$SS_{tot} = (5)^2 + (14)^2 + \cdots + (14)^2 + (18)^2 - C$$
$$= 418.437$$

The row and column variabilities are computed as
$$SS_S = \frac{(45)^2 + \cdots + (52)^2}{4} - C$$
$$= 2{,}652.750 - 2{,}626.563$$
$$= 26.187$$

TABLE 10-11

Analysis of variance for a Greco-Latin design

SV	df	SS	EMS	F
Total	$a^2 - 1$	$\displaystyle\sum_i \sum_j \sum_k \sum_m Y_{ijkm}^2 - C$		
S	$a - 1$	$\dfrac{\displaystyle\sum_i \left(\sum_j \sum_k \sum_m Y_{ijkm}\right)^2}{a} - C$	$\sigma_e^2 + a\sigma_S^2$	$\dfrac{MS_S}{MS_{\text{res}}}$
Columns	$a - 1$	$\dfrac{\displaystyle\sum_m \left(\sum_i \sum_j \sum_k Y_{ijkm}\right)^2}{a} - C$	$\sigma_e^2 + a\theta_C^2$	$\dfrac{MS_C}{MS_{\text{res}}}$
A	$a - 1$	$\dfrac{\displaystyle\sum_j \left(\sum_i \sum_k \sum_m Y_{ijkm}\right)^2}{a} - C$	$\sigma_e^2 + a\theta_A^2$	$\dfrac{MS_A}{MS_{\text{res}}}$
B	$a - 1$	$\dfrac{\displaystyle\sum_k \left(\sum_i \sum_j \sum_m Y_{ijkm}\right)^2}{a} - C$	$\sigma_e^2 + a\theta_B^2$	$\dfrac{MS_B}{MS_{\text{res}}}$
Residual	$(a - 1)(a - 3)$	$SS_{\text{tot}} - SS_S - SS_C - SS_A - SS_B$	σ_e^2	

and

$$SS_C = \frac{(51)^2 + \cdots + (52)^2}{4} - C$$

$$= 2{,}627.250 - 2{,}626.563$$

$$= .687$$

Variability due to the A treatment is computed as

$$SS_A = \frac{(50)^2 + \cdots + (54)^2}{4} - C$$

$$= 2{,}644.250 - 2{,}626.563$$

$$= 17.687$$

Variability due to B is computed as

$$SS_B = \frac{(20)^2 + \cdots + (70)^2}{4} - C$$

$$= 2{,}993.250 - 2{,}626.563$$

$$= 366.687$$

The residual variability is

$$SS_{res} = SS_{tot} - SS_S - SS_C - SS_A - SS_B$$

$$= 418.437 - 26.187 - .687 - 17.687 - 366.687$$

$$= 7.189$$

Table 10-13 summarizes the results of the analysis.

TABLE 10-13

Analysis of variance for the data of Table 10-12

SV	df	SS	MS	F
Total	15	418.437		
S	3	26.187	8.729	3.643
Columns	3	.687	.229	.096
A	3	17.687	5.896	2.461
B	3	366.687	122.229	51.013 *
Residual	3	7.189	2.396	

$*p < .005$

10.5 REPLICATING A LATIN SQUARE

Even when the additive model is appropriate for the simple Latin square design, the gain in efficiency (relative to other designs) may be offset by lower power.   This is because psychologists do not generally use more than five treatment levels (if that many), and the error *df* are $(a - 1)(a - 2)$.   One way of increasing the error *df*, and consequently the precision of the design, is to run *an* subjects, *n* through each sequence of a single square.   In this section, the model and analysis for this approach will be discussed.   In Section 10.6, further extensions of this design will be considered.

10.5.1   The analysis of variance model

It is assumed that a single $a \times a$ Latin square has been randomly sampled from the population of squares.   A total of *an* subjects are randomly distributed among the *a* rows (sequences) of the square, with *n* subjects in each row; there are *a* scores for each subject.   A representative score would be Y_{ijkm}, where

    i indexes the subject within the row $(i = 1, 2, \cdots, n)$,
    j indexes the level of the treatment variable, A $(j = 1, 2, \cdots, a)$,
    k indexes the column in the square $(k = 1, 2, \cdots, a)$,
    m indexes the row within the square $(m = 1, 2, \cdots, a)$.

As an example of the design, *a* might equal 4 and *n* might equal 2.   Then, we might represent the design by

$$
\begin{array}{cccc}
C_1 & C_2 & C_3 & C_4
\end{array}
$$

$$
\begin{array}{c}
S_{11},\ S_{21} \\
S_{12},\ S_{22} \\
S_{13},\ S_{23} \\
S_{14},\ S_{24}
\end{array}
\begin{bmatrix}
A_2 & A_4 & A_3 & A_1 \\
A_1 & A_3 & A_2 & A_4 \\
A_4 & A_2 & A_1 & A_3 \\
A_3 & A_1 & A_4 & A_2
\end{bmatrix}
$$

There are many models which might relate Y_{ijkm} and the population parameters.   One frequent assumption is that population variance due to sequence and sequence–interaction effects is negligible.   This assumption is reasonable if the treatment presentations have been sufficiently spaced or if the independent and dependent variables are of such a nature that *carry-over effects* are negligible, i.e., the presentation of one treatment does not influence the subsequent response to a second treatment.   The appropriate model is then

(10.3) $\qquad Y_{ijkm} = \mu + \eta_{i/m} + \alpha_j + \gamma_k + (\alpha\gamma)_{jk} + \epsilon_{ijkm}$

where

$\qquad \eta_{i/m} = \mu_{i..m} - \mu_{...m}$, the effect of the *i*th subject in the *m*th row
$\qquad \alpha_j = \mu_{.j..} - \mu$, the effect of the *j*th level of A
$\qquad \gamma_k = \mu_{..k.} - \mu$, the effect of the *k*th level of C
$\qquad (\alpha\gamma)_{jk} = \mu_{.jk.} - \mu_{.j..} - \mu_{..k.} + \mu$, the $A \times C$ interaction effect
$\qquad \epsilon_{ijkm} = $ the residual error component

We assume that $\eta_{i/m}$ and ϵ_{ijkm} are both independent, normally distributed variables with expected values of zero and variances $\sigma_{S/R}^2$ and σ_e^2, respectively.

Further, it is assumed that each population of effects is very large. All other effects are assumed to be fixed.

10.5.2 The analysis of variance

Table 10-14 presents the sources of variance, *df*, sums of squares formulas, and *EMS* for the replicated square design, assuming the model of Section 10.5.1. The total variability is analyzed in a manner similar to that of Chapters 8 and 9. Since there are *a* scores for each of *an* subjects, there are a total of $a^2n - 1$ *df*. Part of this variability is due to variability among subjects; this accounts for $an - 1$ *df*. The remaining $an(a - 1)$ *df* represent the within-subjects variability. Subjects may differ because they are in different rows in the square. In addition, there will be variability among subjects within rows due to individual differences. Thus the between-subjects variability is partitioned into two components: R and S/R. The interpretation of the test of R against S/R will be considered shortly when we deal with *EMS*.

The partitioning of the within-subjects variability follows that of the single Latin square of Section 10.3, except that because of the replication within rows, there is an additional source, the (within-cells) *residual*, $a(n - 1)(a - 1)$ *df*. The *square uniqueness* term is equivalent to the residual term in the analysis of Section 10.3 (they are both on $(a - 1)(a - 2)$ *df* and represent residual variability *among* cells); the label was suggested by Grant* and indicates that this source may contain patterns of interaction unique to the particular square selected.

The *EMS* follow directly from Equation (10.3), which implies an absence of effects due to the sequence of presentations and its interactions. In this case, the source labeled R may be viewed as the *between-subjects component of the AC interaction* since the test of R against S/R implies

$$E(F) = \frac{\sigma_e^2 + a\sigma_{S/R}^2 + n\theta_{AC}^2}{\sigma_e^2 + a\sigma_{S/R}^2}$$

and tests

$$H_0: \theta_{AC}^2 = 0$$

Still assuming the validity of Equation (10.3), and therefore the *EMS* of Table 10-14, we also have unbiased (and quite precise) tests of A, C, and square uniqueness. The last is interpreted as a test of the *within-subjects component of AC* since

$$E(F) = \frac{\sigma_e^2 + n\theta_{AC}^2}{\sigma_e^2}$$

It is reasonable to consider the implications of an alternative model, analogous to the Wilk-Kempthorne model of Section 10.3.2 [Equation (10.1)].

---

* D. A. Grant, "The Latin Square Principle in the Design and Analysis of Psychological Experiments," *Psychological Bulletin*, 45:427–443 (1948).

TABLE 10-14

Analysis of variance for the replicated square design

SV	df	SS	EMS	F
Total	$a^2 n - 1$	$\sum_i \sum_j \sum_k \sum_m Y_{ijkm}^2 - C$		
Between S	$an - 1$			
R	$a - 1$	$\dfrac{\sum_i \sum_j \left(\sum_k \sum_m Y_{ijkm} \right)^2}{a} - C$	$\sigma_e^2 + a\sigma_{S/R}^2 + n\theta_{AC}^2$	$\dfrac{MS_R}{MS_{S/R}}$
S/R	$a(n-1)$	$SS_{\text{B.S}} - SS_R$	$\sigma_e^2 + a\sigma_{S/R}^2$	
Within S	$an(a - 1)$	$SS_{\text{tot}} - SS_{\text{B.S}}$		
C	$a - 1$	$\dfrac{\sum_k \left(\sum_i \sum_j \sum_m Y_{ijkm} \right)^2}{an} - C$	$\sigma_e^2 + na\theta_C^2$	$\dfrac{MS_C}{MS_{\text{res}}}$
A	$a - 1$	$\dfrac{\sum_j \left(\sum_i \sum_k \sum_m Y_{ijkm} \right)^2}{an} - C$	$\sigma_e^2 + na\theta_A^2$	$\dfrac{MS_A}{MS_{\text{res}}}$
S.U AC	$(a - 1)(a - 2)$	$\dfrac{\sum_i \sum_j \sum_k \left(\sum_m Y_{ijkm} \right)^2}{n} - C - SS_A - SS_C$	$\sigma_e^2 + n\theta_{AC}^2$	$\dfrac{MS_{\text{S.U}}}{MS_{\text{res}}}$
Residual	$a(n - 1)(a - 1)$	$SS_{\text{w.s}} - SS_C - SS_A - SS_{\text{S.U}}$	σ_e^2	

Handwritten annotations:

- *(df column)* Between S: $rn - 1$; R: $r - 1$; S/R: $r(n-1)$; Within S: $rn(a-1)$; C: $(c-1)$
- *S.U AC — "corrected for R.":* $(a-1)(c-1) - (r-1)$; $(c-1)-(a-1)-(c-1)-(r-1)$
- *Residual:* $r(n-1)(c-1)$
- *(left margin)* $a = c = 1$
- *(bottom) (perhaps of ... uniqueness) pooling ... can we df*

267

Specifically, we are interested in the consequences when there is some likelihood that the sequence of presentations of treatments, and its interactions, contribute to the variability in the population. The appropriate model might be

$$(10.3') \quad Y_{ijkm} = \mu + \eta_{i/m} + \alpha_j + \gamma_k + \rho_m + (\alpha\gamma)_{jk} + (\alpha\rho)_{jm}$$
$$+ (\gamma\rho)_{km} + (\alpha\gamma\rho)_{jkm} + \epsilon_{ijkm}$$

where

$\rho_m = \mu_{...m} - \mu$, the effect of the mth sequence

$(\alpha\rho)_{jm} = \mu_{.j.m} - \mu_{.j..} - \mu_{...m} + \mu$, the $A \times$ sequence interaction effect

$(\gamma\rho)_{km} = \mu_{..km} - \mu_{..k.} - \mu_{...m} + \mu$, the sequence $\times C$ interaction effect

$(\alpha\gamma\rho)_{jkm} = \mu_{.jkm} + \mu_{.j..} + \mu_{..k.} + \mu_{...m} - \mu_{.jk.} - \mu_{.j.m} - \mu_{..km} - \mu$, the $A \times C \times$ sequence interaction effect

and all other terms have been previously defined.

We assume that $\eta_{i/m}$, ρ_m, $(\alpha\rho)_{jm}$, $(\gamma\rho)_{km}$, $(\alpha\gamma\rho)_{jkm}$ and ϵ_{ijkm} are all independent, normally distributed variables with expected values of zero and variances (respectively) $\sigma^2_{S/\text{Seq}}$, σ^2_{Seq}, $\sigma^2_{A \times \text{Seq}}$, $\sigma^2_{C \times \text{Seq}}$, $\sigma^2_{AC \times \text{Seq}}$, and σ^2_e. Further, it is assumed that each population of effects is very large. All other effects are assumed to be fixed.

The appropriate *EMS* for the general model now under consideration have not been derived. However, the *EMS* for the simple Latin square design (Table 10-5) suggest some inferences. Square uniqueness, which is computationally (and in *df*) equivalent to the residual of Table 10-5, will include the variances of interaction effects. Thus, like the residual of Table 10-5, it can result in negatively biased *F* tests if used as an error term for *C* and *A* effects. On the other hand, the residual of Table 10-14 is a within-subjects residual and should not be affected by interactions among *R*, *C*, and *A*. Since it is assumed that such interactions contribute to the *EMS* for main effects, the residual can result in positive bias if used as an error term.*

If the experimenter is not certain that sequence effects are negligible, a reasonable test procedure would be to compute $MS_{\text{s.u}}/MS_{\text{res}}$ and $MS_R/MS_{S/R}$. If these ratios are not significant (a criterion for significance is discussed in Chapter 11), the assumption of additivity is tenable; *all* interaction variance components are assumed to be zero; and S.U and the residual have a common expectation and should therefore be pooled to provide a more powerful and precise *F* test than that yielded by either term alone. If either the preliminary *F* test of S.U against the residual or of *R* against S/R is significant, then some, if not all, interaction effects are non-zero. In this case, S.U should be used as the error term for *C* and *A*; since the bias is negative, a significant result would be a valid ground for rejecting the null hypothesis. A nonsignificant result, using S.U as an error term, still poses

---

* Employing a model which differs slightly from that of Equation (10.3′), Gourlay arrives at essentially the conclusions just stated. The reference is N. Gourlay, "*F* Test Bias for Experimental Designs of the Latin Square Type," *Psychometrika*, 20:237–287 (1955).

an inferential problem: is the null hypothesis true (i.e., does θ_A^2 equal zero) or are the treatment effects non-zero but small relative to the AC effects? To resolve this dilemma, it is suggested that a transformation to an additive scale be sought. The success of the transformation will be indicated if the preliminary F ratios are small. The pooled error term may then be used to test treatment and column effects. The procedure just described does not provide information about AC effects independent of other interaction effects. If such information is important to the investigator, he should not use the Latin square design unless he is certain that interaction effects involving sequences of presentations can be ruled out.

10.5.3 A numerical example

Table 10-15 presents an illustration of the replicated square design. The analysis of variance follows that for the simple Latin square design with only a few exceptions. We calculate

$$C = \frac{(373)^2}{18}$$

$$= 7,729.389$$

and

$$SS_{\text{tot}} = (9)^2 + (12)^2 + \cdots + (33)^2 + (26)^2 - C$$

$$= 887.611$$

The variability between subjects is given by

$$SS_{\text{B.S}} = \frac{(59)^2 + \cdots + (76)^2 + (59)^2}{3} - C$$

$$= 82.944$$

This is partitioned into

$$SS_R = \frac{(118)^2 + (120)^2 + (135)^2}{6} - C$$

$$= 28.778$$

and

$$SS_{S/R} = SS_{\text{B.S}} - SS_R$$

$$= 54.166$$

We next obtain a measure of the within-subjects variability:

$$SS_{\text{W.S}} = SS_{\text{tot}} - SS_{\text{B.S}}$$

$$= 804.667$$

This can be further partitioned into several components:

$$SS_A = \frac{(120)^2 + (126)^2 + (127)^2}{6} - C$$

$$= 4.778$$

TABLE 10-15

Data for a replicated square design

		A_2	A_3	A_1	$\sum_j \sum_k Y_{ijkm}$
	S_{11}	9	23	27	59
R_1					
	S_{21}	12	25	22	59
	$\sum_i Y_{ijk1} = 21$		48	49	$\sum_i \sum_j \sum_k Y_{ijk1} = 118$
		A_1	A_2	A_3	
	S_{12}	15	20	22	57
R_2					
	S_{22}	8	26	29	63
	$\sum_i Y_{ijk2} = 23$		46	51	$\sum_i \sum_j \sum_k Y_{ijk2} = 120$
		A_3	A_1	A_2	
	S_{13}	16	27	33	76
R_3					
	S_{23}	12	21	26	59
	$\sum_i Y_{ijk3} = 28$		48	59	$\sum_i \sum_j \sum_k Y_{ijk3} = 135$
	$\sum_i \sum_m Y_{ijkm} = 72$		142	159	$\sum_i \sum_j \sum_k \sum_m Y_{ijkm} = 373$

A Sub-totals

A_1	A_2	A_3
120	126	127

$$SS_C = \frac{(72)^2 + (142)^2 + (159)^2}{6} - C$$
$$= 708.778$$

$$SS_{\text{s.u}} = \frac{(21)^2 + (48)^2 + \cdots + (48)^2 + (59)^2}{2} - C - SS_R - SS_A - SS_C$$
$$= 8.777$$

and

$$SS_{\text{res}} = SS_{\text{w.s}} - SS_A - SS_C - SS_{\text{s.u}}$$
$$= 82.335$$

The df for S.U are $(a - 1)(a - 2)$, or 2, and those for the residual are $a(a - 1)(n - 1)$, or 6. Therefore,

$$\frac{MS_{\text{s.u}}}{MS_{\text{res}}} = \frac{4.389}{13.723}$$

Since the F is clearly not significant, it seems reasonable to pool the S.U and residual terms to obtain increased power. The result is

$$MS_{\text{error}} = \frac{82.335 + 8.777}{6 + 2}$$

$$= 11.389$$

The analysis is summarized in Table 10-16.

TABLE 10-16

Analysis of variance for the data of Table 10-15

SV	df	SS	MS	F
Total	17	887.611		
Between S	5	82.944		
R	2	28.778	14.389	.797
S/R	3	54.166	18.055	
Within S	12	804.667		
A	2	4.778	2.389	.210
C	2	708.778	354.389	31.117 *
Error	8	91.112	11.389	
				*$p < .001$

10.6 BETWEEN-SQUARES TREATMENT VARIABLES

The replicated square design, described in Section 10.5, can be extended to permit the investigation of additional treatment variables. As before, there could be exactly a sequences. However, n of the subjects in a particular sequence would be at B_1, n more at B_2, and so on, giving a total of abn subjects, bn in each of a sequences. As an example of the application of this design, consider the measurement of reaction time under each of four levels of stress (A). Three experimental groups of two subjects each are tested under all stress levels; the groups differ with respect to level of anxiety (B). In this case, $a = 4$, $b = 3$, and $n = 2$. In general,

i indexes the subjects within a row at a level of B,
j indexes the level of A,
k indexes the level of B,
m indexes the level of C (position in time),
p indexes the row in a level of B.

TABLE 10-17
Analysis of variance for the replicated square design with a between-squares factor

SV	df	SS	EMS	F
Total	$a^2bn - 1$	$\sum_i \sum_j \sum_k \sum_m \sum_p Y^2_{ijkmp} - C$		
Between S	$abn - 1$	$\dfrac{\sum_i \left(\sum_m \sum_p \left(\sum_j \sum_k Y_{ijkmp} \right) \right)^2}{a} - C$		
R	$a - 1$	$\dfrac{\sum_p \left(\sum_i \sum_j \sum_k \sum_m Y_{ijkmp} \right)^2}{abn} - C$	$\sigma_e^2 + a\sigma^2_{S/RB} + abn\theta^2_{AC}$	$\dfrac{MS_R}{MS_{S/RB}}$
B	$b - 1$	$\dfrac{\sum_m \left(\sum_i \sum_j \sum_k \sum_p Y_{ijkmp} \right)^2}{a^2n} - C$	$\sigma_e^2 + a\sigma^2_{S/RB} + a^2n\theta^2_B$	$\dfrac{MS_B}{MS_{S/RB}}$
RB	$(a-1)(b-1)$	$\dfrac{\sum_m \sum_p \left(\sum_i \sum_j \sum_k Y_{ijkmp} \right)^2}{an} - C - SS_R - SS_B$	$\sigma_e^2 + a\sigma^2_{S/RB} + an\theta^2_{ABC}$	$\dfrac{MS_{RB}}{MS_{S/RB}}$
S/RB	$ab(n-1)$	$SS_{B.S} - SS_R - SS_B - SS_{RB}$	$\sigma_e^2 + a\sigma^2_{S/RB}$	
Within S	$abn(a-1)$	$SS_{tot} - SS_{B.S}$		
A	$a - 1$	$\dfrac{\sum_j \left(\sum_i \sum_k \sum_m \sum_p Y_{ijkmp} \right)^2}{abn} - C$	$\sigma_e^2 + abn\theta^2_A$	$\dfrac{MS_A}{MS_{res}}$
C	$a - 1$	$\dfrac{\sum_k \left(\sum_i \sum_j \sum_m \sum_p Y_{ijkmp} \right)^2}{abn} - C$	$\sigma_e^2 + abn\theta^2_C$	$\dfrac{MS_C}{MS_{res}}$

Source	df	SS	E(MS)	F
AB	$(a-1)(b-1)$	$\dfrac{\sum_j \sum_m \left(\sum_i \sum_k \sum_p Y_{ijkmp}\right)^2}{an} - C - SS_A - SS_B$	$\sigma_e^2 + an\theta_{AB}^2$	$\dfrac{MS_{AB}}{MS_{\text{res}}}$
BC	$(b-1)(a-1)$	$\dfrac{\sum_k \sum_m \left(\sum_i \sum_j \sum_p Y_{ijkmp}\right)^2}{an} - C - SS_B - SS_C$	$\sigma_e^2 + an\theta_{BC}^2$	$\dfrac{MS_{BC}}{MS_{\text{res}}}$
$S.U$	$(a-1)(a-2)$	$\dfrac{\sum_j \sum_k \sum_p \left(\sum_i \sum_m Y_{ijkmp}\right)^2}{bn} - C - SS_R - SS_C - SS_A$	$\sigma_e^2 + bn\theta_{AC}^2$	$\dfrac{MS_{S.U}}{MS_{\text{res}}}$
$S.U \times B$	$(a-1)(a-2)(b-1)$	$\dfrac{\sum_j \sum_k \sum_m \sum_p \left(\sum_i Y_{ijkmp}\right)^2}{n} - C - SS_B - SS_R$ $- SS_{RB} - SS_A - SS_C - SS_{AB} - SS_{BC} - SS_{S.U}$	$\sigma_e^2 + n\theta_{ABC}^2$	$\dfrac{MS_{S.U \times B}}{MS_{\text{res}}}$
Residual	$ab(a-1)(n-1)$	$SS_{W.S} - SS_A - SS_C - SS_{AB} - SS_{BC} - SS_{S.U}$ $- S.U \times B$	σ_e^2	

The layout of the design in our example might be

$$
\begin{array}{c}

\end{array}
\begin{array}{cccc}
C_1 & C_2 & C_3 & C_4
\end{array}
$$

$$
B_1
\begin{array}{c}
S_{111}, S_{211} \\
S_{112}, S_{212} \\
S_{113}, S_{213} \\
S_{114}, S_{214}
\end{array}
\begin{bmatrix}
A_4 & A_2 & A_1 & A_3 \\
A_2 & A_3 & A_4 & A_1 \\
A_1 & A_4 & A_3 & A_2 \\
A_3 & A_1 & A_2 & A_4
\end{bmatrix}
$$

$$
B_2
\begin{array}{c}
S_{121}, S_{221} \\
S_{122}, S_{222} \\
S_{123}, S_{223} \\
S_{124}, S_{224}
\end{array}
\begin{bmatrix}
A_4 & A_2 & A_1 & A_3 \\
A_2 & A_3 & A_4 & A_1 \\
A_1 & A_4 & A_3 & A_2 \\
A_3 & A_1 & A_2 & A_4
\end{bmatrix}
$$

$$
B_3
\begin{array}{c}
S_{131}, S_{231} \\
S_{132}, S_{232} \\
S_{133}, S_{233} \\
S_{134}, S_{234}
\end{array}
\begin{bmatrix}
A_4 & A_2 & A_1 & A_3 \\
A_2 & A_3 & A_4 & A_1 \\
A_1 & A_4 & A_3 & A_2 \\
A_3 & A_1 & A_2 & A_4
\end{bmatrix}
$$

The design under discussion permits the evaluation of main effects and interactions of A and B using fewer subjects than a completely randomized design, fewer measurements per subject than a simple repeated measurements design, and a potentially more efficient test of A and AB than the mixed design of Chapter 8.

10.6.1 The analysis of variance

Table 10-17 presents the *SV, df, SS, EMS* and *F* ratios. The between-subjects variability is partitioned in the same way as in Section 8.3, in which we dealt with two between-subjects variables. In the present case, R and B are the two between-subjects variables. The within-subjects effects are generated if one remembers that there is confounding between any main effect associated with the square (i.e., R, C, A) and the interaction of the other two variables. However, note that B can interact with each of the main effects associated with the square and with square uniqueness as well.

The model that has been chosen is a simple extension of Equation (10.3). Carry-over effects are assumed to be negligible; therefore, we have the equation:

$$(10.4) \quad Y_{ijkmp} = \mu + \eta_{i/kp} + \alpha_j + \beta_k + \gamma_m + (\alpha\beta)_{jk} + (\alpha\gamma)_{jm}$$
$$+ (\beta\gamma)_{km} + (\alpha\beta\gamma)_{jkm} + \epsilon_{ijkmp}$$

This equation generates the *EMS* for Table 10-17, which in turn indicate the appropriate error terms. Furthermore, it should be apparent that if Equation (10.4) is valid, R may be interpreted as a between-subjects measure of AC, RB as a between-subjects measure of ABC, S.U as a within-subjects measure of AC, and S.U $\times$ B as a within-subjects measure of ABC. As in Section 10.5, the F tests of A and C effects against the residual will be positively biased if the sequence of treatment presentations interacts with A or C. If there is reason to suspect such carry-over effects, the following preliminary tests may be carried out:

$$F = \frac{MS_R}{MS_{S/RB}} \qquad F = \frac{MS_{S.U}}{MS_{res}}$$

$$F = \frac{MS_{RB}}{MS_{S/RB}} \qquad F = \frac{MS_{S.U \times B}}{MS_{res}}$$

If any of these are significant, a transformation to additivity should be sought.

Note that if sequence interactions are suspect, our recommended procedure provides no way of testing for AC or ABC effects. There is no test that permits determination of which interaction component is present when, for example, S.U is significant. Such a result only reveals that *some* interaction component is present. A significant S.U can only be interpreted as AC (or S.U $\times B$ as ABC) if there is a strong a priori reason for assuming Equation (10.4) to be valid. Such an assumption might be founded on previous experimentation and on knowledge of the independent and dependent variables, i.e., knowledge of the experimental situation.

10.6.2 A numerical example

Table 10-18 presents data from a 3×3 Latin square replicated four times, twice at each of two levels of B. Sub-totals that are required in the calculation of sums of squares have also been computed. The correction term is

$$C = \frac{(416)^2}{36}$$

$$= 4,807.111$$

The total variability is

$$SS_{tot} = (12)^2 + (4)^2 + \cdots + (18)^2 + (16)^2 - C$$
$$= 5,814.000 - 4,807.111$$
$$= 1,006.889$$

We next obtain the between-subjects variability:

$$SS_{B.S} = \frac{(26)^2 + (28)^2 + \cdots + (37)^2 + (43)^2}{3} - C$$

$$= 5,218.000 - 4,807.111$$

$$= 410.889$$

This is now further partitioned:

$$SS_R = \frac{(54 + 102)^2 + (51 + 71)^2 + (58 + 80)^2}{12} - C$$

$$= 4,855.333 - 4,807.111$$

$$= 48.222$$

TABLE 10-18
Data for a replicated Latin square design with a between-squares factor

B_1

	A_1	A_3	A_2	$\sum_j Y_{ijlmp}$
S_{111}	12	4	10	26
S_{211}	14	6	8	28
$\sum_i Y_{ijlm1} = 26$		10	18	$\sum_j\sum_i Y_{ijlm1} = 54$

	A_2	A_1	A_3	
S_{112}	6	9	3	18
S_{212}	11	17	5	33
$\sum_i Y_{ijlm2} = 17$		26	8	$\sum_j\sum_i Y_{ijlm2} = 51$

	A_3	A_2	A_1	
S_{113}	5	12	18	35
S_{213}	7	6	10	23
$\sum_i Y_{ijlm3} = 12$		18	28	$\sum_j\sum_i Y_{ijlm3} = 58$

$\sum_i Y_{ijlmp} = 55$	54	54		$\sum_i\sum_m Y_{ijlmp} = 163$

B_2

	A_1	A_3	A_2	$\sum_j Y_{ij2mp}$
S_{121}	19	11	20	50
S_{221}	21	11	20	52
$\sum_i Y_{ij2m1} = 40$		22	40	$\sum_j\sum_i Y_{ij2m1} = 102$

	A_2	A_1	A_3	
S_{122}	16	18	8	42
S_{222}	14	12	3	29
$\sum_i Y_{ij2m2} = 30$		30	11	$\sum_j\sum_i Y_{ij2m2} = 71$

	A_3	A_2	A_1	
S_{123}	6	17	14	37
S_{223}	9	18	16	43
$\sum_i Y_{ij2m3} = 15$		35	30	$\sum_j\sum_i Y_{ij2m3} = 80$

$\sum_i Y_{ij2mp} = 85$	87	81		$\sum_i\sum_m Y_{ij2mp} = 253$

A Sub-totals

	A_1	A_2	A_3	
B_1	80	53	30	208
B_2	100	105	48	208
	180	158	78	416

C Sub-totals

	C_1	C_2	C_3	
B_1	55	54	54	163
B_2	85	87	81	253
	140	141	135	416

$$SS_B = \frac{(163 - 253)^2}{36}$$

$$= 225.000$$

$$SS_{RB} = \frac{(54)^2 + \cdots + (80)^2}{6} - C - SS_R - SS_B$$

$$= 5,121.000 - 4,807.111 - 48.222 - 225.000$$

$$= 40.667$$

and

$$SS_{S/RB} = SS_{B.S} - SS_R - SS_B - SS_{RB}$$
$$= 370.222$$

The within-subjects variability is computed next:

$$SS_{W.S} = SS_{tot} - SS_{B.S}$$
$$= 596.000$$

Partitioning this, we obtain

$$SS_C = \frac{(140)^2 + (141)^2 + (135)^2}{12} - C$$

$$= 4,808.833 - 4,807.111$$

$$= 1.722$$

$$SS_A = \frac{(180)^2 + (158)^2 + (78)^2}{12} - C$$

$$= 5,287.333 - 4,807.111$$

$$= 480.222$$

$$SS_{BC} = \frac{(55)^2 + (54)^2 + \cdots + (81)^2}{6} - C - SS_B - SS_C$$

$$= 5,035.333 - 4,807.111 - 225.000 - 1.722$$

$$= 2.500$$

$$SS_{AB} = \frac{(80)^2 + (53)^2 + \cdots + (48)^2}{6} - C - SS_A - SS_B$$

$$= 5,573.000 - 4,807.111 - 480.222 - 225.000$$

$$= 60.667$$

$$SS_{S.U} = \frac{(26 + 40)^2 + (10 + 22)^2 + \cdots + (28 + 30)^2}{4}$$
$$- C - SS_R - SS_C - SS_A$$

$$= 5,338.000 - 4,807.111 - 48.222 - 1.722 - 480.222$$

$$= .723$$

$$SS_{8.U\times B} = \frac{(26)^2 + (10)^2 + \cdots + (35)^2 + (30)^2}{2} - C - SS_B - SS_{8.U}$$

$$- SS_{RB} - SS_R - SS_{BC} - SS_C - SS_{AB} - SS_A$$

$$= 5{,}668.000 - 4{,}807.111 - 225.000 - .723 - 40.667$$

$$- 48.222 - 2.500 - 1.722 - 60.667 - 480.222$$

$$= 1.166$$

and

$$SS_{res} = SS_{W.8} - SS_C - SS_A - SS_{BC} - SS_{AB} - SS_{8.U} - SS_{8.U\times B}$$

$$= 48.000$$

Table 10-19 summarizes the results of the analysis.

TABLE 10-19

Analysis of variance for the data of Table 10-18

SV	df	SS	MS	F
Total	35	1,006.889		
Between S	11	410.889		
R	2	48.222	24.111	.391
B	1	225.000	225.000	3.646
RB	2	40.667	20.334	.330
S/RB	6	370.222	61.704	
Within S	24	596.000		
C	2	1.722	.861	.215
A	2	480.222	240.111	60.028 **
BC	2	2.500	1.250	.313
AB	2	60.667	30.334	7.584 *
S.U	2	.723	.362	.091
S.U $\times B$	2	1.166	.583	.146
Residual	12	48.000	4.000	

$$**p < .001$$
$$*p < .01$$

10.7 CONCLUDING REMARKS

The assets of the Latin square designs are clear—the need for fewer subjects, the reduction of systematic treatment biases through counter-balancing, the reduction of error variance through the removal of variability due to individual differences and temporal effects. The dangers are less immediately obvious, but it is hoped that the development in this chapter has made it clear that problems do exist. Heterogeneity of covariance, always a possibility in repeated measurement designs (see Section 7.2.4 for a discussion of the consequences and of possible approaches to the problem), may inflate the probability of Type I errors. Furthermore, carry-over effects may be present; i.e., the effect of a treatment may depend upon which of several treatments preceded it, and these effects may further be a function of the particular levels of A and C in question. Such effects can result in negative bias in the F tests for the single Latin square design. In the replicated square design, the residual error term will yield unbiased F tests if *random* interaction effects are negligible; otherwise there will be positive bias. Square uniqueness might be employed as an error term for testing treatment effects; however, if there are column $\times$ treatment interaction effects, this test will be negatively biased.

In view of the problem of bias just discussed, it is recommended that the experimenter consider the relative merits of other designs when planning his investigation. However, situations will exist for which the potential advantages of the Latin square will outweigh its disadvantages. This will particularly be the case when carry-over effects are expected to be minimal or when the experimenter has reason to believe that his particular measures are amenable to a transformation to additivity. Carry-over effects would be expected to be minimal in experiments in which sensory or physiological processes, or simple motor responses, are measured. For example, in his previously cited article, Grant refers to a study of pursuit movement (Corrigan and Brogden*) using the replicated square design. The results of the nonadditivity tests (R against S/R, S.U against residual) were not significant. In investigations of this type, the Latin square provides an efficient way of attaining clear-cut inferences about the behavior in question.

EXERCISES

10.1 Analyze the data from the following Greco-Latin design:

(A_3B_1)	(A_4B_3)	(A_1B_4)	(A_2B_2)
5	14	7	6
(A_4B_4)	(A_3B_2)	(A_2B_1)	(A_1B_3)
7	4	9	18
(A_1B_2)	(A_2B_4)	(A_3B_3)	(A_4B_1)
19	10	8	12
(A_2B_3)	(A_1B_1)	(A_4B_2)	(A_3B_4)
5	13	16	12

10.2 Each of 36 subjects was tested on four signal detection problems, which varied with respect to the location of the target. Subjects differed with respect to the sequence of presentations of the problems (four sequences were used) and with respect to the instructions read to them (three sets of instructions). Present the appropriate analysis of variance table.

* R. E. Corrigan and W. J. Brogden, "The Trigonometric Relationship of Precision and Angle of Linear Pursuit-Movements," *American Journal of Psychology*, 62:90–98 (1949).

10.3 Suppose location and brightness of target were both varied in Exercise 10.2; each subject sees four of 16 possible combinations of location and brightness within a Greco-Latin design. Again, there are 36 subjects, and *instructions* is a between-subjects variable. Give the *SV* and *df*. Suggest some alternative variations of the Latin square design for investigating these variables. Assess the relative merits of the various designs.

10.4 In an experiment on gambling behavior, 48 subjects are run through each of the following four treatment combinations:

A_1 = High gain—High loss A_3 = Low gain—High loss
A_2 = High gain—Low loss A_4 = Low gain—Low loss

Four sequences are established, yielding one 4×4 Latin square replicated 12 times. One-third of the subjects are run under high odds, one-third under 50-50 odds, one-third under low odds. Present the *SV*, *df*, error terms.

10.5 An investigator uses a single Latin square to compare six treatment levels. He obtains five measures under each condition, or 30 measures per subject. This results in a 6×6 Latin square with five measures in each cell. Present a model for the design; then give the appropriate *SV*, *df*, and error term(s).

10.6 108 subjects are randomly distributed among nine combinations of the variables *A*, *B*, and *C*. The design is

$$
\begin{array}{c} \\ A_1 \\ A_2 \\ A_3 \end{array}
\begin{array}{ccc} B_1 & B_2 & B_3 \\ \left[\begin{array}{ccc} C_1 & C_2 & C_3 \\ C_2 & C_3 & C_1 \\ C_3 & C_1 & C_2 \end{array}\right] \end{array}
$$

There are exactly 12 subjects in each of the nine cells, with one measurement per subject. State an appropriate model; give the *SV*, *df*, error term(s). What problems might this design pose? What might its advantages be over a complete factorial design?

SUPPLEMENTARY READING

There are countless possible variations of the Latin square design and of other designs involving the confounding of effects. These designs can be very efficient; they can also present the types of inferential problems discussed in this chapter. The reader who is interested in pursuing the topic further will find many designs and analyses in

COCHRAN, W. G. and G. M. COX, *Experimental Designs*, 2d ed. New York: Wiley, 1957.

Much of the relevant theory is presented in

KEMPTHORNE, O., *The Design and Analysis of Experiments*. New York: Wiley, 1952.

EXPECTED MEAN SQUARES

11

11.1 INTRODUCTION

Throughout this text, the *expected mean square* (*EMS*) has been a key concept. The *EMS* has been used to tackle such problems as the choice of error terms, the relative efficiency of designs, and the direction and extent of bias in *F* tests. These applications of the concept of the *EMS* are far from exhaustive; the purpose of this chapter is to extend the reader's knowledge of the uses of the *EMS*. We begin by examining certain problems in null hypothesis testing which have thus far not been considered. Subsequently point and interval estimation of the components that comprise our expectations will be discussed. Finally, it will be noted how the *EMS* provides information about the reliability of measurement.

11.2 SIGNIFICANCE TESTS

11.2.1 Quasi-*F* ratios

Consider an experiment in which n subjects (S) are required to detect the presence of each of t targets (T) under each of w levels of white noise (W). The levels of noise are arbitrarily selected. The locations of the targets are randomly selected from a continuum of locations available in a 4-ft. square field. The appropriate *SV*, *df*, and *EMS* are presented in Table 11-1. One important implication of the *EMS* column is that there is no appropriate error term for the *W* source of variance. By an appropriate error term, we again mean that the expectation contains all the components of the numerator *EMS* except the null hypothesis component.

The error term (for *W*) problem could be approached by assuming that σ^2_{WS} or σ^2_{WT} is zero, but unless this is truly so the *F* tests will be biased. It is

TABLE 11-1

Analysis of variance for one fixed and two random effect variables

SV	df	EMS
W	$w - 1$	$\sigma_e^2 + n\sigma_{WT}^2 + t\sigma_{WS}^2 + \sigma_{WTS}^2 + tn\theta_W^2$
T	$t - 1$	$\sigma_e^2 + w\sigma_{TS}^2 + nw\sigma_T^2$
S	$n - 1$	$\sigma_e^2 + w\sigma_{TS}^2 + wt\sigma_S^2$
WT	$(w - 1)(t - 1)$	$\sigma_e^2 + \sigma_{WTS}^2 + n\sigma_{WT}^2$
WS	$(w - 1)(n - 1)$	$\sigma_e^2 + \sigma_{WTS}^2 + t\sigma_{WS}^2$
TS	$(t - 1)(n - 1)$	$\sigma_e^2 + w\sigma_{TS}^2$
WTS	$(w - 1)(t - 1)(n - 1)$	$\sigma_e^2 + \sigma_{WTS}^2$

also possible that after some trial and error, a transformation might be found which would make the assumption true, but this is not certain. We require additional ammunition for our attack on the W effect (which, incidentally, is likely to be the effect of most interest to the experimenter). A careful examination of the EMS suggests the appropriate method. We note that

$$E(MS_{WT}) + E(MS_{WS}) - E(MS_{WTS}) = (\sigma_e^2 + \sigma_{WTS}^2 + n\sigma_{WT}^2)$$
$$+ (\sigma_e^2 + \sigma_{WTS}^2 + t\sigma_{WS}^2)$$
$$(11.1) \qquad\qquad\qquad - (\sigma_e^2 + \sigma_{WTS}^2)$$
$$= \sigma_e^2 + t\sigma_{WS}^2 + n\sigma_{WT}^2 + \sigma_{WTS}^2$$

and

$$(11.2) \quad \frac{E(MS_W)}{E(MS_{WT}) + E(MS_{WS}) - E(MS_{WTS})}$$
$$= \frac{\sigma_e^2 + t\sigma_{WS}^2 + n\sigma_{WT}^2 + \sigma_{WTS}^2 + tn\theta_W^2}{\sigma_e^2 + t\sigma_{WS}^2 + n\sigma_{WT}^2 + \sigma_{WTS}^2}$$

which has the virtue of equaling 1 if the null hypothesis ($\theta_W^2 = 0$) is true. Thus,

$$\frac{MS_W}{MS_{WT} + MS_{WS} - MS_{WTS}}$$

has the look of an F ratio. Is it an F ratio? Satterthwaite* has shown that the linear combination of mean squares is distributed approximately as a χ^2 divided by its df, and since it can be shown that MS_W also has the χ^2 distribution and that numerator and denominator are independent, we have a statistic which is approximately distributed as F. The only remaining question is,

---

* F. E. Satterthwaite, "An Approximate Distribution of Estimates of Variance Components," *Biometrics Bulletin*, 2:110–114 (1946).

What are the appropriate *df*? To answer, we define the *combination of mean squares*, $CMS = MS_A \pm MS_B \pm MS_C \pm \cdots$. Then,

(11.3)
$$df_{CMS} = \frac{(CMS)^2}{\dfrac{(MS_A)^2}{df_A} + \dfrac{(MS_B)^2}{df_B} + \dfrac{(MS_C)^2}{df_C} + \cdots}$$

rounded to the nearest integer.

In our target detection example, the *CMS* for testing the effects of W is $MS_{WT} + MS_{WS} - MS_{WTS}$. According to Equation (11.3), this quantity is distributed on

$$\frac{(MS_{WT} + MS_{WS} - MS_{WTS})^2}{\dfrac{(MS_{WT})^2}{(w-1)(t-1)} + \dfrac{(MS_{WS})^2}{(w-1)(n-1)} + \dfrac{(MS_{WTS})^2}{(w-1)(t-1)(n-1)}}$$

df.

What is the basis for the *CMS* selected to test the W effects? Simply enough, we require an *EMS* which contains σ_{WS}^2 and one which contains σ_{WT}^2; furthermore, we attempt to avoid expectations which introduce components not in the numerator expectations. Finally, we subtract whichever expectation is needed to adjust the coefficients of our components. Since we have $2\sigma_e^2$ after adding the WS and WT terms, we must remove a σ_e^2; similarly, a σ_{WTS}^2 must be removed. The same approach can be applied to a variety of designs.

11.2.2 Pooling in the analysis of variance

In Chapter 9 it was noted that the appropriate error term in the hierarchical designs is often distributed on a rather small number of *df*; consequently, the F test lacked power. The problem is not restricted to any one set of designs, and it seems reasonable to consider a possible remedy. As an example, we will use the design of Section 9.3.

There are g groups at each of a levels of A. Each group consists of bn subjects randomly assigned to the b levels of the variable B. Turning back to Table 9-6, we note that A is tested against G/A, and B and AB are tested against the GB/A term. There is a conspicuous waste here; the $MS_{S/GB/A}$, which is distributed on more *df* than either of our appropriate error terms, serves only to test the relatively uninteresting group effects. However, suppose that group effects were negligible. Specifically, we assume

(11.4)
$$Y_{ijkm} = \mu + \alpha_k + \beta_m + (\alpha\beta)_{km} + \epsilon_{ijkm}$$

which substitutes for Equation (9.7). Note that no effects involving groups are assumed to contribute to the subject's score. As a result, we have the new set of *EMS* of Table 11-2. Table 11-2 suggests that G/A, GB/A, and $S/GB/A$ might be combined in some way, since all three are estimates of the same population variance, σ_e^2. We pool these terms as follows:

$$MS_{S/AB} = \frac{SS_{G/A} + SS_{GB/A} + SS_{S/GB/A}}{a(g-1) + a(g-1)(b-1) + abg(n-1)}$$

(11.5)

$$= \frac{SS_{G/A} + SS_{GB/A} + SS_{S/GB/A}}{ab(ng-1)}$$

TABLE 11-2

EMS for a hierarchical design assuming no group effects

SV	EMS
A	$\sigma_e^2 + ngb\theta_A^2$
G/A	σ_e^2
B	$\sigma_e^2 + nga\theta_B^2$
AB	$\sigma_e^2 + ng\theta_{AB}^2$
GB/A	σ_e^2
S/GB/A	σ_e^2

Note that pooling is defined as adding sums of squares and dividing by the sums of *df* for the terms involved. The resulting analysis is presented in Table 11-3. Assuming that Equation (11.4) correctly describes the effects contributing to the data, we now have considerably more power in our *F* tests.

Pooling might be done on any set of terms which are assumed to represent the same population variances. As a second example, in a completely randomized three-factor design the θ_{AC}^2 and θ_{BC}^2 might be assumed to be negli-

TABLE 11-3

Analysis of variance after pooling of sources in Table 11-2

SV	df	EMS
A	$a - 1$	$\sigma_e^2 + ngb\theta_A^2$
B	$b - 1$	$\sigma_e^2 + nga\theta_B^2$
AB	$(a-1)(b-1)$	$\sigma_e^2 + ng\theta_{AB}^2$
S/AB	$ab(gn-1)$	σ_e^2

gible. The *AC* and *BC* sources might therefore be pooled with *S/ABC*, yielding the analysis of variance of Table 11-4.

The advantage that potentially accrues from pooling is immediately evident. In both of our examples, after pooling we have had considerably more error *df* than prior to pooling, and consequently the power of the *F* test has been increased, *if assumptions that we have made are correct*. In addition to increased power, there is also increased simplicity. The analysis of vari-

TABLE 11-4

Analysis of variance of a three-factor design after pooling of AC, BC, and S/ABC sources

SV	df	EMS
A	$a - 1$	$\sigma_e^2 + nbc\theta_A^2$
B	$b - 1$	$\sigma_e^2 + nac\theta_B^2$
C	$c - 1$	$\sigma_e^2 + nab\theta_C^2$
AB	$(a - 1)(b - 1)$	$\sigma_e^2 + nc\theta_{AB}^2$
ABC	$(a - 1)(b - 1)(c - 1)$	$\sigma_e^2 + n\theta_{ABC}^2$
Pooled residual	$[(a - 1) + (b - 1)](c - 1) + abc(n - 1)$	σ_e^2

ance table is less cluttered and therefore easier to interpret and to discuss in a report of the experiment. The pertinent sources of variance, those that make a major contribution to the data matrix, are the only ones that appear in the table.

What if the assumptions upon which the pooling is based are incorrect? Suppose that in the immediately preceding example the assumption that θ_{BC}^2 equals zero is incorrect. Then the residual term of Table 11-4 estimates

$$\frac{[(a - 1)(c - 1) + abc(n - 1)]\sigma_e^2 + (b - 1)(c - 1)(\sigma_e^2 + na\theta_{BC}^2)}{(a - 1)(c - 1) + abc(n - 1) + (b - 1)(c - 1)}$$

$$= \sigma_e^2 + \frac{(b - 1)(c - 1)na\theta_{BC}^2}{(c - 1)(a + b - 2) + abc(n - 1)}$$

Since the above quantity is clearly greater than σ_e^2, the use of the residual error term could result in negatively biased F tests; $E(F) < 1$, and therefore the increase in df could be more than offset by the increase in the error mean square. As a consequence, power can conceivably be lost, rather than gained, by pooling. Furthermore, it is also possible that the probability of a Type I error may be raised above the nominal α level.

To summarize, if certain variance components can reasonably be assumed to be zero, several mean squares share a common expectation and may all appear to be the appropriate error term for one or more of the other effects in the analysis. In this case, the terms having the common expectation should be pooled, providing an error term on more df than previously, and consequently a more powerful F test. In addition, the presentation of the analysis of variance is considerably simplified. On the other hand, if certain variance components are incorrectly assumed to be zero and pooling is carried out, two or more terms that estimate different population variances will have been combined. If this pooled term is now used as an error term for other lines in the analysis of variance table, the probabilities of Type I and Type II errors may be affected.

At this point, the obvious question is, When can we reasonably assume, for the purpose of pooling, that a variance component is zero? While several answers have been proposed to this question, the most extensive investigations have been carried out by Bozivich and her colleagues.* In the re-remainder of this section, we will consider their recommendations about pooling.

The simplest type of situation in which pooling is in question is represented in Table 11-5. The effects do not have to be hierarchical; however,

TABLE 11-5

Analysis of variance where pooling of two terms is possible

SV	df	MS	EMS
A	$n_3 = a - 1$	V_3	$\sigma_e^2 + n\sigma_{G/A}^2 + ng\theta_A^2 = \sigma_3^2$
G/A	$n_2 = a(g - 1)$	V_2	$\sigma_e^2 + n\sigma_{G/A}^2 = \sigma_2^2$
$S/G/A$	$n_1 = ag(n - 1)$	V_1	$\sigma_e^2 = \sigma_1^2$

it is assumed that

(a) all components are random except the treatment component (θ_A^2), which may be either random or fixed,

(b) $\sigma_3^2 \geq \sigma_2^2 \geq \sigma_1^2$.

Two testing procedures are relevant in this situation:

(a) *sometimes pool:* V_2 is tested against V_1 to determine whether $\sigma_2^2 = \sigma_1^2$. If the result of this test is not significant, then the two lines are pooled, yielding the error term V_{12}, against which V_3 is tested. If V_2/V_1 is significant, V_2 is used as the error term;

(b) *never pool:* V_2 is used as the error term without preliminary testing against V_1.

We require a basis for choosing between the two procedures, and if we decide on the sometimes pool procedure, we will require a criterion of significance for the preliminary F test. Reasonable criteria are the actual probability of a Type I error as well as the power of the F test of the treatment line (V_3), when the sometimes pool procedure is used. With regard to Type I errors, Bozivich *et al.* find that when a significant level of .25 is employed in the preliminary test and a level of .05 in the test of treatment effects, the true probability of a Type I error will generally not exceed .10. The exceptions occur if $n_3 \geq n_2$ (which would rarely occur) or if $n_1 \geq 5n_2$. In these latter instances, the α for the preliminary test should be .50.

* Helen Bozivich, T. A. Bancroft, and H. O. Hartley, "Power of Analysis of Variance Test Procedures for Certain Incompletely Specified Models," *Annals of Mathematical Statistics*, 27:1017–1043 (1956).

With regard to the question of power, it may actually be less for the sometimes pool procedure than for the never pool procedure. This again depends upon the *df* and the α levels chosen for the preliminary test and for the test of treatments. Assuming that α for the test of V_2 against V_1 is .25 and that α for the test of treatment effects is .05, the sometimes pool procedure will generally result in a more powerful test of treatments than will V_2 alone when σ_2^2/σ_1^2 is less than 1.5; when this ratio is greater than 2.0, the never pool procedure will generally result in a more powerful test. We never know the actual value of σ_2^2/σ_1^2; we can merely estimate on the basis of the preliminary F ratio from the present and previous studies.

To summarize, if the experimenter can assume that σ_2^2/σ_1^2 is small, then a preliminary test should be carried out at $\alpha = .25$ or $\alpha = .50$, depending upon the *df*. If this test is not significant, a pooled error term should be used for the subsequent test of the A main effect. Under this recommendation, the actual significance level should not be unreasonably inflated, and there is reasonable likelihood of an increase in power over the never pool procedure. The assumption regarding σ_2^2/σ_1^2 might be based on knowledge of the experimental situation (e.g., in a social experiment, it may be unlikely that groups really do contribute to the variability in the data beyond the contribution due to individual differences) or upon an analysis of the results of preliminary tests in several previous related experiments. If there is reason to doubt that σ_2^2/σ_1^2 is small, then the preliminary test should be omitted and V_2 should be the error term for V_1.

Recently, the investigation of pooling has been extended to situations involving the possible pooling of three lines. For example, consider Table 11-6, in which V_3 is the appropriate error term for V_4. Assuming $\sigma_3^2 \geq \sigma_2^2 \geq \sigma_1^2$, the possibility exists of pooling the V_3 and V_2 lines or the V_3, V_2 and

TABLE 11-6

Analysis of variance where pooling of three terms is possible

SV	df	MS	EMS
A	n_4	V_4	σ_4^2
Error for A	n_3	V_3	σ_3^2
Doubtful error$_1$	n_2	V_2	σ_2^2
Doubtful error$_2$	n_1	V_1	σ_1^2

V_1 lines. Thus, if V_2/V_1 were not significant, the two doubtful lines could be pooled; this pooled mean square will be called V_{12}. We might then test V_3 against V_{12}, pooling if this result were not significant. The F test of the A effect would then be V_4/V_{123}. It is also possible that V_2/V_1 might be significant, but V_3/V_2 might not be. Then, the treatment test would be V_4/V_{23}.

If the nominal significance level for the test of treatments is .05, the true probability of a Type I error will not exceed .10 under the sometimes pool procedure if $\alpha = .25$ for the preliminary tests described above and these relations hold among the various df:

(a) $n_3 = n_4$ and $n_1 + n_2 < 10$
(b) $n_3 = n_4 + 2$ and $n_1 + n_2 < 16$
(c) $n_3 = n_4 + 4$ and $n_1 + n_2 < 50$
(d) $n_3 = n_4 + 6$ and $n_1 + n_2 < 60$
(e) $n_3 = n_4 + 8$ and $n_1 + n_2 < 70$
(f) $n_3 = n_4 + 10$ and $n_1 + n_2 < 80$

Srivastava and Bozivich[*] also indicate some other rather complex conditions under which the Type I error rate will not be unreasonably inflated. If the cited conditions do not hold, $\alpha = .50$ should be used for preliminary tests in the sometimes pool procedure.

With regard to the question of the power of the sometimes pool procedure, it will be more powerful than the never pool procedure (test V_4 against V_3 without preliminary testing) when $\sigma_2^2/\sigma_1^2 < 1.5$ and $\sigma_3^2/\sigma_2^2 < 2$; it will be less powerful when $\sigma_2^2/\sigma_1^2 \geq 1.5$ and $\sigma_3^2/\sigma_2^2 > 3$. In other instances, either procedure might be more powerful, depending upon the exact pair of ratios involved.

As in the simpler situation described earlier, when only three lines were involved, no attempt to pool should be made unless the experimenter has good reason to believe, *prior to the analysis*, that σ_2^2/σ_1^2 and σ_3^2/σ_2^2 are small. If he has this expectation, he should then choose an α of .25 or .50 for the preliminary test, the actual level depending upon the relations among the df.

The entire preceding discussion is relevant if the lines which might be pooled contain only random effect variance components. There is at present no comparable investigation for the case in which one of the doubtful lines contains a fixed effect component. An illustration of this case would be a completely randomized design involving three fixed factors: one might consider pooling the ABC interaction with the S/ABC term on the assumption that $\theta_{ABC}^2 = 0$. However, in the absence of sufficient information on the consequences of this type of pooling, a never pool procedure is recommended. (This means that in practice the pooling illustrated in Table 11-4 would never be carried out.) In general, it is recommended that whenever possible the experimenter should design his research in the expectation that preliminary tests, even if carried out, will be significant. He will then ordinarily have sufficient df to obtain powerful F tests, using the usual ratios.

[*] S. R. Srivastava and H. Bozivich, "Power of Certain Analysis of Variance Test Procedures Involving Preliminary Tests," *Bulletin de L'Institute International Statistique*, 33d Session (1961).

11.3 ESTIMATION OF COMPONENTS OF VARIANCE

Thus far the discussion of the analysis of variance has been concerned solely with tests of significance, with the question, Do the different treatment levels (or treatment combinations) have different effects? However, as noted in Chapter 2, there is an equally important question: How greatly do the effects of different treatment levels (or treatment combinations) differ? Indeed, it may be argued that the first question is the less important; that given sufficient data, the variance of any set of treatment effects is significant. Furthermore, since the psychologist invariably deals with data that are quantitative in nature, it is reasonable to assume that he will profit by examining the magnitude of the quantity. Finally, it is only through the estimation of population effects that the relative influences of several variables can be assessed. In view of the desirability of examining the absolute and relative magnitudes of effects, we now turn to the estimation of components of variance which comprise our expected mean squares. We will first deal with point estimation, subsequently turning to the development of confidence intervals.

11.3.1 Point estimation

Consider Table 11-7, which contains the analysis of data from a hierarchical experiment in which $a = 4$, $g = 5$, $b = 2$, $c = 5$, $n = 6$. Suppose that we

TABLE 11-7

Analysis of variance for a hierarchical design

SV	df	MS	EMS	F
A	3	20.6	$\sigma_e^2 + 60\sigma_{G/A}^2 + 5\sigma_{S/GB/A}^2 + 300\theta_A^2$	4.6 *
G/A	16	4.5	$\sigma_e^2 + 60\sigma_{G/A}^2 + 5\sigma_{S/GB/A}^2$	
B	1	15.2	$\sigma_e^2 + 5\sigma_{S/GB/A}^2 + 30\sigma_{GB/A}^2 + 600\theta_B^2$	2.9
AB	3	12.4	$\sigma_e^2 + 5\sigma_{S/GB/A}^2 + 30\sigma_{GB/A}^2 + 150\theta_{AB}^2$	2.4
GB/A	16	5.2	$\sigma_e^2 + 5\sigma_{S/GB/A}^2 + 30\sigma_{GB/A}^2$	
$S/GB/A$	200	3.0	$\sigma_e^2 + 5\sigma_{S/GB/A}^2$	
C	4	35.2	$\sigma_e^2 + 12\sigma_{GC/A}^2 + \sigma_{SC/GB/A}^2 + 240\theta_C^2$	3.6 *
AC	12	7.6	$\sigma_e^2 + 12\sigma_{GC/A}^2 + \sigma_{SC/GB/A}^2 + 60\theta_{AC}^2$	.8
GC/A	64	9.8	$\sigma_e^2 + 12\sigma_{GC/A}^2 + \sigma_{SC/GB/A}^2$	
BC	4	4.1	$\sigma_e^2 + 6\sigma_{GBC/A}^2 + \sigma_{SC/GB/A}^2 + 120\theta_{BC}^2$	1.2
ABC	12	5.2	$\sigma_e^2 + 6\sigma_{GBC/A}^2 + \sigma_{SC/GB/A}^2 + 30\theta_{ABC}^2$	1.5
GBC/A	64	3.5	$\sigma_e^2 + 6\sigma_{GBC/A}^2 + \sigma_{SC/GB/A}^2$	
$SC/GB/A$	800	4.6	$\sigma_e^2 + \sigma_{SC/GB/A}^2$	

$*p < .025$

are interested in estimating θ_A^2, the variance of the means of the four treatment populations defined by the levels of A.   Referring to Table 11-7, we note that

$$E(MS_A) - E(MS_{G/A}) = (\sigma_e^2 + 60\sigma_{G/A}^2 + 5\sigma_{S/GB/A}^2 + 300\theta_A^2)$$
$$- (\sigma_e^2 + 60\sigma_{G/A}^2 + 5\sigma_{S/GB/A}^2)$$
$$= 300\theta_A^2$$

Then,

$$\frac{E(MS_A - MS_{G/A})}{300} = \theta_A^2$$

or, substituting numerical values from Table 11-7,

$$\hat{\theta}_A^2 = \frac{20.6 - 4.5}{300}$$
$$= .054$$

Note the use of ^ to denote "estimate of."

Some of our estimates will turn out to be negative.   For example, we find that

$$\hat{\theta}_{AC}^2 = \frac{MS_{AC} - MS_{GC/A}}{12}$$
$$= -.183$$

an unreasonable result, since variances cannot be negative.   We conclude that our best estimate of θ_{AC}^2 is zero; the negative result is a chance happening.

What has been gained from the estimation process?   Even the partial analysis just performed sheds some light beyond that provided by the F ratios.   The significant A effect is less impressive now. $\hat{\theta}_A^2$ is quite small, and its significance seems to testify more to the amount of data collected than to any inherent differences in the effects of the four treatment levels.   In contrast, note that $\hat{\theta}_C^2$ equals .106, and is two times as large as θ_A^2.   This sort of summary of effects is not provided by the F ratio, which does not tell us whether the effect is large or small but only (with some probability) that it is or is not zero.   Nor can F ratios be compared to provide knowledge of the relative effectiveness of variance sources unless the df are identical for the two ratios.   Moreover, estimates of the magnitude of the effect are prerequisite to the establishment of quantitative behavioral laws.

11.3.2   Interval estimation

As was pointed out in Chapter 2, we require not only an estimate of the population effect but some index of the reliability of the estimate as well. Confidence intervals provide such indices.   In this section, confidence intervals are considered for the entire *EMS* and then for the individual components which contribute to the expectation.   We begin by obtaining confidence intervals for σ^2, the variance of a single population from which a sample of

n scores has been obtained; the variance of the sample is denoted by S^2. If the scores are normally distributed, it can be shown that $(n-1)S^2/\sigma^2$ is distributed as χ^2 on $n-1$ df. That is, if samples of size n are repeatedly taken from a population with variance σ^2 and if the frequency with which various values of $(n-1)S^2/\sigma^2$ appear is noted, the frequency distribution would approximate the χ^2 on $n-1$ df. Therefore, we may assert that

$$(11.6) \qquad P\left[\chi^2_{1-\alpha,n-1} \leq \frac{(n-1)S^2}{\sigma^2} \leq \chi^2_{\alpha,n-1}\right] = 1 - 2\alpha$$

where χ^2_α is that value of χ^2 on $n-1$ df exceeded by 100α per cent of the population of χ^2 values. For example, suppose that there is a sample of size 5 and a 95 per cent confidence interval is desired. Then, $1 - 2\alpha = .95$ and $\alpha = .025$. We turn to Table A-4 in the Appendix and find that the χ^2 on 4 df required for significance at the .025 level is $\chi^2_{.025,4} = 11.1$; the χ^2 exceeded by 97.5 per cent of the population is $\chi^2_{.975,4} = .484$. Then, substituting in Equation (11.6),

$$(11.7) \qquad P\left(.484 \leq \frac{4S^2}{\sigma^2} \leq 11.1\right) = .95$$

At this point, we have a confidence interval containing $(n-1)S^2/\sigma^2$; what we want is a confidence interval containing σ^2. A little algebraic manipulation is required. We note that if $X < Y$, then $1/Y < 1/X$. Applying this knowledge to Equation (11.7), we have

$$(11.8) \qquad P\left(\frac{1}{11.1} \leq \frac{\sigma^2}{4S^2} \leq \frac{1}{.484}\right) = .95$$

Multiplying through by $4S^2$ provides the final result:

$$(11.9) \qquad P\left(\frac{4S^2}{11.1} \leq \sigma^2 \leq \frac{4S^2}{.484}\right) = .95$$

and, more generally,

$$(11.10) \qquad P\left[\frac{(n-1)S^2}{\chi^2_{\alpha,n-1}} \leq \sigma^2 \leq \frac{(n-1)S^2}{\chi^2_{1-\alpha,n-1}}\right] = .95$$

Equation (11.10) can be generalized to provide confidence intervals for any *EMS*. For example, suppose that we have

SV	df	MS	EMS
A	$a-1$	MS_A	$\sigma_e^2 + n\theta_A^2$
S/A	$a(n-1)$	$MS_{S/A}$	σ_e^2

The $1 - 2\alpha$ confidence limits for $\sigma_e^2 + n\theta_A^2$ are

$$(11.11) \qquad L_l = \frac{(a-1)MS_A}{\chi^2_{\alpha,a-1}} \qquad \text{(lower limit)}$$

and

(11.11′)
$$L_u = \frac{(a - 1)MS_A}{\chi^2_{1-\alpha, a-1}} \quad \text{(upper limit)}$$

For σ_e^2, we have the limits

(11.12)
$$L_l = \frac{a(n - 1)MS_{S/A}}{\chi^2_{\alpha, a(n-1)}}$$

and

(11.12′)
$$L_u = \frac{a(n - 1)MS_{S/A}}{\chi^2_{1-\alpha, a(n-1)}}$$

Confidence intervals for other expected mean squares follow the same pattern.

Thus far the development of confidence intervals has exactly followed the discussion of Chapter 2. Because of the difficulty of specifying the distribution of estimates, the problem becomes somewhat more complicated when one tries to develop limits on a single component such as θ_A^2. Numerous papers have been written presenting approximate intervals (i.e., intervals for which the probability is approximately $1 - 2\alpha$); one solution by Bross* will be considered which provides a reasonable approximation and is relatively simple to compute.

Before presenting Bross's technique, a notation designed for simplicity and generality will be introduced. Consider two lines of an analysis of variance table whose *EMS* differ by a single variance component. The notation indicated below will be used:

SV	df	MS	EMS
1	n_1	v_1	$\sigma_2^2 + n\theta_1^2$
2	n_2	v_2	σ_2^2

$$F = \frac{v_1}{v_2}$$

In terms of the above notation, the formulas derived by Bross are

(11.13)
$$L_l = \frac{F - F_{\alpha, n_1, n_2}}{FF_{\alpha, n_1, \infty} - F_{\alpha, n_1, n_2}} (F - 1) \frac{v_2}{n}$$

if $F \geq F_{\alpha, n_1, n_2}$; if $F < F_{\alpha, n_1, n_2}$, then $L_l = 0$.

For the upper limit, we have

(11.14)
$$L_u = \frac{F - F_{1-\alpha, n_1, n_2}}{FF_{1-\alpha, n_1, \infty} - F_{1-\alpha, n_1, n_2}} (F - 1) \frac{v_2}{n}$$

if $F \geq F_{1-\alpha, n_1, n_2}$; if $F < F_{1-\alpha, n_1, n_2}$, then $L_u = 0$.

Note that F is the observed F; F_{α, n_1, n_2} is the F required for significance at the α level on n_1 and n_2 df; and the other subscripted F's are similarly defined.

* I. Bross, "Fiducial Intervals for Variance Components," *Biometrics*, 6:136–144 (1950).

Furthermore, we note that $F_{1-\alpha,n_1,n_2}$ is rarely, if ever, tabled; only the upper end of the F distribution is generally available. Fortunately, the following relationship solves the problem: $F_{1-\alpha,n_1,n_2} = 1/F_{\alpha,n_2,n_1}$. Thus, if we require the F which is significant at the 95 per cent level on 3 and 10 df, we look for the F which is significant at the 5 per cent level on 10 and 3 df.

The point estimate of θ_1^2 is part of the interval estimate. Note that

$$(F - 1)\frac{\nu_2}{n} = \left(\frac{\nu_1}{\nu_2} - 1\right)\frac{\nu_2}{n}$$

(11.15)
$$= \frac{\nu_1}{n} - \frac{\nu_2}{n}$$

$$= \hat{\theta}_1^2$$

the point estimate of θ_1^2.

Tukey* has shown that if $1 < F < F_{1-\alpha,n_1,n_2}$, L_u may be negative. He suggests that whenever $F < F_{\alpha,n_1,n_2}$, i.e., *whenever F is not significant* by the usual criterion, the following formula should be used:

(11.16)
$$L_u = \left[\frac{F - F_{1-\alpha,n_1,n_2}}{F_{1-\alpha,n_1,\infty}}\right]\frac{\nu_2}{n}$$

As an example of the application of Bross's formulas for confidence limits, consider the analysis of variance of Table 11-8, which is for a simple

TABLE 11-8

Analysis of variance for a simple repeated measurements design

SV	df	MS	EMS	F
S	6	10.3	$\sigma_e^2 + 5\sigma_S^2$	
A	4	6.2	$\sigma_e^2 + \sigma_{SA}^2 + 7\theta_A^2$	4.13
$S \times A$	24	1.5	$\sigma_e^2 + \sigma_{SA}^2$	

repeated measurements design with seven subjects and five levels of A. Assuming that a 90 per cent confidence interval on θ_A^2 is desired, the following information is needed:

$$F_{.05,4,24} = 2.78$$

$$F_{.05,4,\infty} = 2.37$$

$$F_{.95,4,24} = \frac{1}{F_{.05,24,4}} = .17$$

$$F_{.95,4,\infty} = \frac{1}{F_{.05,\infty,4}} = .18$$

* J. W. Tukey, "Answer to Query No. 113," *Biometrics*, 11:111–113 (1955).

From Equation (11.15), we compute

$$\hat{\theta}_A^2 = (F - 1)\frac{v_2}{n}$$

$$= \frac{(3.13)(1.5)}{7}$$

$$= .67$$

Then,

$$L_l = .67\left[\frac{4.13 - 2.78}{(2.37)(4.13) - 2.78}\right]$$

$$= .13$$

and

$$L_u = .67\left[\frac{4.13 - .17}{(.18)(4.13) - .17}\right]$$

$$= 4.87$$

We have 90 per cent confidence that the true value of θ_A^2 falls between .13 and 4.87.

Suppose that in the above example, MS_A had been 3.0 with the result that the F was not significant at the .05 level. Since $F < F_{\alpha,n_1,n_2}$, we now take L_l to be zero. Furthermore, we use Tukey's expression for the upper bound:

$$L_u = \left(\frac{2.0 - .17}{.18}\right)\left(\frac{1.5}{7}\right)$$

$$= 2.7$$

The point estimate is

$$\hat{\theta}_A^2 = \frac{3.0 - 1.5}{7}$$

$$= .214$$

11.4 RELIABILITY AND THE ANALYSIS OF VARIANCE

Psychometricians generally assume that Y_{ij}, the score obtained from subject i on item j of a test, has two independent components: the true score, μ_i, and a component due to error of measurement, $\epsilon_{ij}\ (=\ Y_{ij} - \mu_i)$. More succinctly, we assume that

(11.17) $$Y_{ij} = \mu_i + \epsilon_{ij}$$

The true score, μ_i, may be viewed as the mean of an infinite population of measurements on subject i. The error may have many sources, such as the subject's set at the moment Y_{ij} was obtained. We can partition the variance of a population of scores into true and error variance. We subtract μ from both sides of Equation (11.17). Then, squaring both sides and taking the expectation over the population of subjects while noting that cross-product terms vanish on the right (since the two components are independent), we have

(11.18) $$E(Y_{ij} - \mu)^2 = E(\mu_i - \mu)^2 + F(\epsilon_{ij}^2)$$

or

(11.18′) $$\sigma_Y^2 = \sigma_S^2 + \sigma_e^2$$

We now have the basis for developing a formula for the reliability of a score. Reliability is defined as that proportion of the variance of scores which is true variance:

(11.19) $$\rho_{11} = \frac{\sigma_S^2}{\sigma_Y^2}$$
$$= \frac{\sigma_S^2}{\sigma_S^2 + \sigma_e^2}$$

If all the variability among scores of different subjects were due to individual differences in ability on the trait being measured, error variance would be zero and reliability would be 1. Since we have shown in Section 11.3.1 that components of variance such as σ_S^2 and σ_e^2 may be estimated from the mean squares of an analysis of variance, it seems sensible to use the same approach to obtain R_{11}, the sample estimate of ρ_{11}, the reliability of a score in the population. Our design is essentially a two-factor design, the factors being subjects (n randomly sampled levels) and items (a randomly sampled levels). Equation (11.17) suggests that the total variability in the data matrix has two sources: between subjects, and error (within subjects). The appropriate analysis of variance would appear to be that of Table 11-9.

TABLE 11-9

Partitioning of variance for a measure of R_{11}

SV	df	EMS
S	$n - 1$	$\sigma_e^2 + a\sigma_S^2$
Within S	$n(a - 1)$	σ_e^2

Our variance estimates are

(11.20) $$\hat{\sigma}_S^2 = \frac{MS_{\text{B.S}} - MS_{\text{W.S}}}{a}$$

and

(11.21) $$\hat{\sigma}_e^2 = MS_{\text{W.S}}$$

On the basis of Equation (11.19), it follows that

(11.22) $$R_{11} = \frac{\hat{\sigma}_S^2}{\hat{\sigma}_S^2 + \hat{\sigma}_e^2}$$

and substituting from Equations (11.20) and (11.21), we have

(11.23)
$$R_{11} = \frac{(MS_{B.s} - MS_{w.s})/a}{(MS_{B.s} - MS_{w.s})/a + MS_{w.s}}$$

$$= \frac{MS_{B.s} - MS_{w.s}}{MS_{B.s} + (a - 1)MS_{w.s}}$$

The reliability coefficient defined by Equation (11.23) may be thought of as a measure of the degree to which the a items are measuring the same trait. More specifically, R_{11} can be shown to be an average of the $[a(a - 1)]/2$ intercorrelations which can be computed among items when the average within-items variance is used as the denominator for all correlations.

Interest often centers on the reliability of the subject's average score, $\bar{Y}_{i..}$. Returning to Equation (11.17), we sum over j and divide by a to obtain

(11.24)
$$\bar{Y}_{i.} = \mu_i + \bar{\epsilon}_{i.}$$

Since μ_i is assumed to be independent of ϵ_{ij}, it can be shown that

(11.25)
$$\sigma^2_{\bar{Y}_{i.}} = \sigma^2_S + \sigma^2_{\bar{\epsilon}_{i.}}$$

The quantity $\sigma^2_{\bar{\epsilon}_{i.}}$ is the expectation over an infinite number of replications of the experiment of $(\sum_j \epsilon_{ij}/a)^2$. Since the ϵ_{ij} are independently distributed, $E(\epsilon_{ij}\epsilon_{ij'}) = 0$. Consequently,

$$E\left(\frac{\sum_j \epsilon_{ij}}{a}\right)^2 = E\left(\frac{\sum_j \epsilon^2_{ij}}{a^2}\right) = \frac{1}{a^2}\sum_j E(\epsilon^2_{ij}) = \frac{1}{a^2}\sum_j \sigma^2_{\epsilon_{ij}}$$

Since we assume homogeneity of variance (i.e., $\sigma^2_{\epsilon_{ij}} = \sigma^2_{\epsilon_{ij'}} = \sigma^2_e$),

$$E\left(\frac{\sum_j \epsilon_{ij}}{a}\right)^2 = \frac{\sigma^2_e}{a}$$

Then, Equation (11.25) becomes

(11.26)
$$\sigma^2_{\bar{Y}_{i.}} = \sigma^2_S + \frac{\sigma^2_e}{a}$$

Then the reliability of the mean, R_{aa}, is

(11.27)
$$R_{aa} = \frac{\hat{\sigma}^2_S}{\hat{\sigma}^2_S + \hat{\sigma}^2_e/a}$$

Substituting from the *EMS* column of Table 11-9, we have

(11.28)
$$R_{aa} = \frac{(MS_{B.s} - MS_{w.s})/a}{(MS_{B.s} - MS_{w.s})/a + MS_{w.s}/a}$$

$$= \frac{MS_{B.s} - MS_{w.s}}{MS_{B.s}}$$

$$= 1 - \frac{MS_{w.s}}{MS_{B.s}}$$

We may interpret R_{aa} as a measure of the correlation between the mean scores for two sets of a randomly sampled items administered at different times to the same sample of subjects. If R_{aa} were high, we could expect that a second sample of a items would provide a similar inference about the relative performance of our subjects.

Equation (11.17) implies that any differences among items are chance happenings. We have pooled the A and SA sources in the usual repeated measurements design (see Chapter 7) to give a single estimate of error. If there is reason to believe that systematic differences among items exist, the model represented by Equation (7.1) is more appropriate. This might be the case if the items had been intentionally selected at different levels of difficulty. As a second example, subjects might be rated by a raters, each of whom may be suspected to have a somewhat different set of standards. In any event, Equation (7.1), which is restated here, is now the basis for our reliability measure:

$$(7.1) \qquad Y_{ij} = \mu + \eta_i + \alpha_j + \epsilon_{ij}$$

The appropriate analysis of variance table is now Table 7-2; the estimate of error is $\hat{\sigma}_e^2 = MS_{SA}$. We merely substitute MS_{SA} for $MS_{\text{w.s}}$ in Equations (11.23) and (11.28) to arrive at the measures of R_{11} and R_{aa} under the revised model.

In order to obtain a confidence interval for R, we first relate the reliability measure to the F statistic. Dividing numerator and denominator of Equation (11.23) by $MS_{\text{w.s}}$, we obtain

$$(11.29) \qquad R_{11} = \frac{F - 1}{F + (a - 1)}$$

Now we obtain limits on F and substitute into Equation (11.29). If we desire a $1 - 2\alpha$ interval, the upper bound is FF_α and the lower bound is F/F_α, where F is the observed statistic and F_α is the F required for significance at the α level on $n - 1$ and $n(a - 1)$ df. Referring to Equation (11.29), we have

$$(11.30) \qquad P\left(\frac{F/F_\alpha - 1}{F/F_\alpha + a - 1} \le \rho_{11} \le \frac{FF_\alpha - 1}{FF_\alpha + a - 1}\right) = 1 - 2\alpha$$

The preceding developments will be illustrated using the analysis of variance of Table 11-8 as a point of departure. Assuming the model of Equation (11.17), the total variability of Table 11-8 is somewhat differently partitioned. Specifically, we view the levels of A as five items on which the seven subjects are rated; we assume that all variability is either between or within subjects; and we consequently pool SS_A and SS_{SA} $[4(6.2) + 24(1.5)]$. The result is Table 11-10.

Applying Equation (11.23) to the entries in Table 11-10,

$$R_{11} = \frac{10.30 - 2.17}{10.30 + 4(2.17)}$$

$$= \frac{8.13}{18.98}$$

$$= .43$$

TABLE 11-10

Analysis for a reliability example

SV	df	MS	EMS	F
S	6	10.30	$\sigma_e^2 + 5\sigma_S^2$	4.75
Within S	28	2.17	σ_e^2	

The reliability of the mean rating follows from the application of Equation (11.28):

$$R_{aa} = 1 - \frac{2.17}{10.30}$$

$$= .79$$

If we revise our model to include an A source of variance, we return to the breakdown of Table 11-8 and obtain:

$$R_{11} = \frac{10.30 - 1.50}{10.30 + 4(1.50)}$$

$$= .54$$

and

$$R_{aa} = 1 - \frac{1.50}{10.30}$$

$$= .86$$

It is not surprising that both R_{11} and R_{aa} are lower in the first analysis performed. In that instance, the A source of variance was pooled with the SA source, yielding a single estimate of error variability. If the A variability is large, this pooling procedure inflates the error estimate and lowers the estimate of reliability.

As an example of the development of confidence intervals, we apply Equation (11.30) to a 90 per cent interval for R_{11}, assuming the model of Equation (11.17). Then $F_\infty = 2.44$ and the lower bound is

$$L_l = \frac{4.75/2.44 - 1}{4.75/2.44 + 3}$$

$$= \frac{.54}{4.54}$$

$$= .12$$

The upper bound is

$$L_u = \frac{(4.75)(2.44) - 1}{(4.75)(2.44) + 3}$$

$$= \frac{10.59}{14.59}$$

$$= .73$$

The development of reliability estimates through the analysis of variance may go much further than the discussion of this section, which considered only the simplest possible repeated measurements design. The approach presented readily generalizes to more factors. For example, there might be b ratings from a raters on each of n subjects. All that is required is a clear statement of the model and a clear understanding of how to generate the *EMS*.

EXERCISES

11.1 Discuss in detail the implications of the expected mean square (*EMS*) for the design and analysis of experiments.

11.2 It is hypothesized that individual Marchant calculators vary greatly in performance. Five are chosen at random for an experiment. Ten operators do each of two problems (anova, correlation) on each of the five calculators. Give the *SV*, *df*, and error terms.

11.3 There are three levels of A (random variable), four levels of B (random), five levels of C (fixed), and ten scores in each cell.

SV	df	MS
A	2	3.8
B	3	14.0
C	4	10.0
AB	6	6.0
AC	8	3.6
BC	12	4.5
ABC	24	3.5
Within	540	2.0

Pool whenever possible. Provide point estimates for the remaining population variance components.

11.4 Consider a completely randomized two-factor design. Prove that $E(F)$, when testing main effects against an error term based on the pool of S/AB and AB, is less than 1 if $\theta_{AB}^2 > 0$.

11.5 Find point and interval estimates of θ_A^2, θ_B^2, and θ_{AB}^2.

SV	df	MS
A	2	18.5
B	4	16.6
AB	8	11.3
S/AB	75	5.2

SUPPLEMENTARY READINGS

The discussion of *EMS* in this and other chapters has been limited to the case in which random effects have been sampled from infinitely large populations. This will usually be a reasonable assumption in psychological research. In those rare instances in which the levels of a variable are a random sample from a finite number of levels, a more general set of rules for establishing *EMS* will be required. Such rules appear in

CORNFIELD, J. AND J. W. TUKEY, "Average Values of Mean Squares in Factorials," *Annals of Mathematical Statistics*, 27:907–949 (1956).

Our brief presentation of the role of analysis of variance in estimating reliability is considerably supplemented by the following book:

HAGGARD, ERNEST A., *Intraclass Correlation With the Analysis of Variance*. New York: Dryden Press, 1958.

Reliability estimation in a variety of designs is also considered in Chapter 16 of

LINDQUIST, E. F., *Design and Analysis of Experiments in Psychology and Education*. Boston: Houghton Mifflin, 1953.

ANALYSIS OF COVARIANCE

12

12.1 INTRODUCTION

As has been indicated, much of the error in experimentation may be traced to those characteristics of individual subjects that correlate highly with the dependent variable. For example, evaluation of the effects of different instructions on concept formation performance is made more difficult by the relationship between this performance and the intelligence of the subject. Variability in intelligence among subjects increases variability in performance within groups. Furthermore, if the average intelligence is higher for some groups than for others, the effects of the independent variable may be either obscured or spuriously enhanced.

Several experimental designs have been presented, each of which provides an alternative approach to this problem of experimental error. In this chapter we take a different tack: we consider a statistical adjustment of each dependent measure (e.g., number of errors in a concept formation task) for the contribution to that measure of a concomitant variable (e.g., intelligence test score). The technique that will be examined is the analysis of covariance. First its application to data obtained from the completely randomized one-factor design of Chapter 4 will be considered; more complex applications will be subsequently discussed. Finally, the covariance approach will be compared with the treatments × blocks design, which also uses a concomitant measure for the purpose of reducing the influences of error variance.

12.2 THE COMPLETELY RANDOMIZED ONE-FACTOR DESIGN

12.2.1 The covariance model

In Chapter 4 the following structural equation was presented for the simple one-factor design:

$$(12.1) \qquad\qquad Y_{ij} = \mu + \alpha_j + \epsilon_{ij}$$

We can conceptualize components of both α_j and ϵ_{ij} which are predictable on the basis of some dependent measures, X_{ij}. Thus, assuming that values of X_{ij} are available, we may restate Equation (12.1):

$$(12.2) \qquad Y_{ij} = \mu + [\alpha_j' + \beta(\overline{X}_{.j} - \overline{X}_{..})] + [\epsilon_{ij}' + \beta(X_{ij} - \overline{X}_{.j})]$$

where α_j' is the treatment effect of A_j adjusted for the effect of the concomitant variable, X_{ij}; ϵ_{ij}' is the error component of the ijth score adjusted for the contribution of the concomitant variable; and β is the regression coefficient (the "slope") for the straight line that best fits the plot of Y as a function of X in the population. The quantities α_j' and ϵ_{ij}' are those components of the treatment and error effects which cannot be predicted from a knowledge of the X data. The phrase "best fit" implies a least-squares criterion; a best fitting straight line is one about which the variability of data is minimal.

We assume that the ϵ_{ij}' are independently and normally distributed in each treatment population and that each such distribution has zero mean and variance $\sigma_{e'}^2$. These assumptions parallel those presented in Chapter 4 for the unadjusted error scores. In addition to these analogues of the usual assumptions, several others are required that are peculiar to the covariance analysis. We assume that the values of X are unaffected by the treatment, that the regression of Y on X is linear for all treatment populations, and that this regression is of the same magnitude for all treatment populations. These last two assumptions are equivalent to assuming that within the jth treatment population the data are adequately described by an equation of the form $Y_{ij} - \overline{Y}_{.j} = \beta_j(X_{ij} - \overline{X}_{.j})$ and that $\beta_{.1} = \cdots = \beta_{.j} = \cdots = \beta_a = \beta$.

The assumption that X is not affected by the treatments is not necessary for the ratio of adjusted mean squares to be distributed as F. However, if this assumption is violated, the inferential process may be complicated. For example, suppose that three methods of teaching arithmetic are to be compared. If the methods differentially affect study time, and if study time is the concomitant measure, the effects of treatments upon arithmetic performance may be obscured when adjustments for study time are made. We will consider this and related problems of interpretation in Section 12.4.

The linearity and homogeneity of regression assumptions are basic to the analysis of covariance, as will be seen shortly. Actually, it is possible to use nonlinear relationships between X and Y as a basis for adjusting X (e.g., $Y_{ij} = X_{ij}^k$), but the computations become much more involved. Since an analysis of covariance involves roughly three times the effort of the analysis of variance for the same design, it is desirable to adhere to the relatively simple linear model for adjustment.

12.2.2 Partitioning the sums of squares

In the ordinary analysis of variance for a one-factor design, it is sufficient to partition the total sum of squares into treatment and error variability. Equation (12.2) suggests a more complex partitioning in the analysis of covariance. We will first analyze the total sum of squares into a component predictable from the X data and a residual component, the adjusted total. This adjusted total will then be partitioned into treatment and error components. Partitioning a total variability adjusted for the contribution of the concomitant variable is an efficient procedure if the $\overline{X}_{.j}$ and $\overline{Y}_{.j}$ are not correlated while the X and Y scores within groups are highly correlated. Under these conditions, the adjustment will lead to a greatly decreased error mean square, with little decrease in the treatment mean square; therefore, the magnitude of the F ratio will increase.

We first ignore the treatment variable, considering the data as a set of an pairs of X and Y scores, for example, the data set of Figure 12-1. The

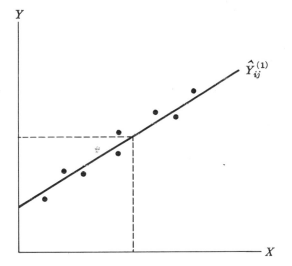

FIGURE 12-1   A least-squares regression line and an illustration of how it is used to predict a value of Y on the basis of a value of X

line labeled $\hat{Y}_{ij}^{(1)}$ is the line that minimizes $\sum_{j} \sum_{i} (Y_{ij} - \hat{Y}_{ij}^{(1)})^2$, the variability about the line. The equation for this line is

(12.3) $$\hat{Y}_{ij}^{(1)} = m + b^{(1)} X_{ij}$$

where the least-squares solutions of m and $b^{(1)}$ are

(12.4) $$m = \overline{Y}_{..} - b^{(1)} \overline{X}_{..}$$

and

(12.5) $$b^{(1)} = \frac{\sum_{i} \sum_{j} (X_{ij} - \overline{X}_{..})(Y_{ij} - \overline{Y}_{..})}{\sum_{i} \sum_{j} (X_{ij} - \overline{X}_{..})^2}$$

Substituting for m, Equation (12.3) may be rewritten as

$$(12.6) \qquad \hat{Y}_{ij}^{(1)} = \overline{Y}_{..} + b^{(1)}(X_{ij} - \overline{X}_{..})$$

$\hat{Y}_{ij}^{(1)}$ may be thought of as the Y score predicted for the ijth subject on the basis of his concomitant score, X_{ij}, assuming a linear relationship with regression coefficient $b^{(1)}$. Returning to Figure 12-1, the same prediction can be obtained by drawing a vertical line from X_{ij} to the best fitting straight line and then drawing a horizontal line to the Y axis. The point at which the horizontal line intersects the Y axis is the value predicted on the basis of X_{ij} and the regression line described by Equation (12.6). The process is illustrated by the dashed lines of Figure 12-1.

We next attempt to relate the variability about $\hat{Y}_{ij}^{(1)}$ to the total variability about the grand mean, which we usually partition in the analysis of variance. We begin with the identity

$$(12.7) \qquad Y_{ij} - \overline{Y}_{..} = (\hat{Y}_{ij}^{(1)} - \overline{Y}_{..}) + (Y_{ij} - \hat{Y}_{ij}^{(1)})$$

Equation (12.7) states that the deviation of a score from the grand mean can be partitioned into two parts, its deviation from the predicted value and the deviation of the predicted value from the grand mean.

Squaring both sides of Equation (12.7), summing over i and j, and noting that the cross-product terms equal zero, we obtain

$$(12.8) \qquad \underset{SS_{\text{tot}}}{\underbrace{\sum_i \sum_j (Y_{ij} - \overline{Y}_{..})^2}} = \underset{SS_{\text{lin}}}{\underbrace{\sum_i \sum_j (\hat{Y}_{ij}^{(1)} - \overline{Y}_{..})^2}} + \underset{SS_{\text{tot}\,(y')}}{\underbrace{\sum_i \sum_j (Y_{ij} - \hat{Y}_{ij}^{(1)})^2}}$$

The SS_{tot} is a familiar term. The SS_{lin} (sum of squares for linearity) is a measure of the difference between the best fitting line and a line with slope of zero; i.e., the variability of the predicted values about the grand mean. The $SS_{\text{tot}\,(y')}$ is a measure of the variability of the observed data about the regression line, the very quantity that our selection of the line minimized. It is this quantity that we will further partition in the course of the analysis of covariance. In order to analyze this adjusted total variability, we must introduce several additional regression equations and for each one define an additional regression coefficient. The reader is reminded that $\hat{Y}_{ij}^{(1)}$ and $b^{(1)}$ are defined by Equations (12.6) and (12.5), respectively, and that $\hat{Y}_{ij}^{(1)}$ is the value of Y_{ij} predicted on the basis of X_{ij}, using a regression coefficient based on all an scores without regard to levels of A. The remaining three pairs of regression lines and coefficients follow:

$$(12.9) \qquad \hat{Y}_{ij}^{(2)} = \overline{Y}_{.j} + b_j^{(2)}(X_{ij} - \overline{X}_{.j})$$

$$(12.9') \qquad b_j^{(2)} = \frac{\sum_i (X_{ij} - \overline{X}_{.j})(Y_{ij} - \overline{Y}_{.j})}{\sum_i (X_{ij} - \overline{X}_{.j})^2}$$

$$(12.10) \qquad \hat{Y}_{ij}^{(3)} = \overline{Y}_{.j} + b^{(3)}(X_{ij} - \overline{X}_{.j})$$

$$(12.10') \qquad b^{(3)} = \frac{\sum_i \sum_j (X_{ij} - \overline{X}_{\cdot j})(Y_{ij} - \overline{Y}_{\cdot j})}{\sum_i \sum_j (X_{ij} - \overline{X}_{\cdot j})^2}$$

$$(12.11) \qquad \hat{Y}_{\cdot j} = \overline{Y}_{\cdot \cdot} + \overline{b}(\overline{X}_{\cdot j} - \overline{X}_{\cdot \cdot})$$

$$(12.11') \qquad \overline{b} = \frac{\sum_j (\overline{X}_{\cdot j} - \overline{X}_{\cdot \cdot})(\overline{Y}_{\cdot j} - \overline{Y}_{\cdot \cdot})}{\sum_j (\overline{X}_{\cdot j} - \overline{X}_{\cdot \cdot})^2}$$

Equations (12.9) and (12.10) both describe the regression of Y on X. They differ because $\hat{Y}_{ij}^{(2)}$ is predicted using a regression coefficient based only on the data of the jth group, while $\hat{Y}_{ij}^{(3)}$ uses a regression coefficient which results from a pooling of all the b_j. Equation (12.11) describes the regression of the $\overline{Y}_{\cdot j}$ on the $\overline{X}_{\cdot j}$. It is as if there were only a pairs of scores, the X and Y means for each treatment group. Then Equation (12.11) describes the linear function which relates the means, and $\overline{b}$ defines the slope of that line. The three predictions of $Y_{\cdot j}$ and the prediction of $\overline{Y}_j$ may be related by the following identity:

$$(12.12) \quad Y_{ij} - \hat{Y}_{ij}^{(1)} = (\hat{Y}_{ij}^{(2)} - \hat{Y}_{ij}^{(3)}) + (Y_{ij} - \hat{Y}_{ij}^{(2)}) + (\overline{Y}_{\cdot j} - \hat{Y}_{\cdot j})$$
$$+ [(\hat{Y}_{ij}^{(3)} - \hat{Y}_{ij}^{(1)}) - (\overline{Y}_{\cdot j} - \hat{Y}_{\cdot j})]$$

Squaring both sides, and summing over i and j, we finally arrive at the partitioning of the adjusted total sum of squares:

$$\sum_i \sum_j (Y_{ij} - \hat{Y}_{ij}^{(1)})^2 = \sum_i \sum_j (\hat{Y}_{ij}^{(2)} - \hat{Y}_{ij}^{(3)})^2 + \sum_i \sum_j (Y_{ij} - \hat{Y}_{ij}^{(2)})^2$$

$$(12.13) \qquad SS_{\text{tot } (y')} \qquad\qquad SS_1 \qquad\qquad SS_2$$

$$+ n \sum_j (\overline{Y}_{\cdot j} - \hat{Y}_{\cdot j})^2$$
$$SS_3$$

$$+ \sum_i \sum_j [(\hat{Y}_{ij}^{(3)} - \hat{Y}_{ij}^{(1)}) - (\overline{Y}_{\cdot j} - \hat{Y}_{\cdot j})]^2$$
$$SS_4$$

SS_1 is a measure of the variability of the $b_j^{(2)}$ defined by Equation (12.9'). If the slopes were identical for all a groups, i.e., if $b_1^{(2)} = b_2^{(2)} = \cdots = b_a^{(2)}$, these coefficients would all equal the average coefficient, $b^{(3)}$. In that case, upon subtracting Equation (12.10) from (12.9) with $b_j^{(2)} = b^{(3)}$, we have $\hat{Y}_{ij}^{(2)} - \hat{Y}_{ij}^{(3)} = 0$, and consequently $SS_1 = 0$. Obviously, the b_j will vary to some extent due to sampling error; the question is whether they vary sufficiently to indicate that the β_j, the regression coefficients for the treatment populations, actually differ. In order to answer this question, we require a measure of error variance. A mean square based on SS_2 provides this measure. Note that SS_2 is a pooled within-groups variability, analogous to $SS_{S/A}$ in Chapter 4. The difference is that we are now considering variability about a group regression line, rather than about a group mean.

The quantities SS_1 and SS_2 provide a basis for testing the assumption that the best fitting regression line has the same slope in all treatment populations. If the F ratio, MS_1/MS_2, is not significant, then it may be concluded that the β_j are essentially homogeneous and that the observed variability in the b_j is attributable to sampling error. In this case, MS_1 and MS_2 are both estimates of error variance, and the two components may be pooled to provide an error term for the test of the adjusted treatment effects.

We next consider the interpretation of SS_3 and SS_4. If the adjusted treatment effects were all zero, then the plot of $\overline{Y}_{.j}$ as a function of $\overline{X}_{.j}$ should resemble the plot of the Y_{ij} as a function of the X_{ij}; in both cases error variance is the only factor contributing to the variability of data points about the best fitting linear function. In deciding that the two plots resemble each other, we are particularly concerned with two aspects of the plots. If the null hypothesis is true, (a) variability of the $\overline{Y}_{.j}$ about $\hat{Y}_{.j}$ should be the same as the variability of the Y_{ij} about $\hat{Y}_{ij}^{(3)}$; and (b) $\overline{b}$, which represents the regression of the $\overline{Y}_{.j}$ on $\overline{X}_{.j}$, should not differ significantly from $b^{(3)}$, which represents the regression of individual scores about the average group regression line. SS_3 seems to indicate clearly the extent of variability of the $\overline{Y}_{.j}$ about $\hat{Y}_{.j}$. It is not as clear that SS_4 is a function of $(\overline{b} - b^{(3)})$, but this can be proved. Since the proof is somewhat tedious, it is omitted.

Generally, SS_3 and SS_4 are pooled and divided by their pooled df to provide the numerator of the F test for the adjusted treatment effects. The denominator is the pooled error term based on the first two components of the adjusted total sum of squares.

To summarize the previous discussion, the usual total variability among the Y measures, $SS_{\text{tot} (y)}$, can be divided into two components: a variability due to the deviation of the best fitting straight line from the grand mean, SS_{lin}, and an adjusted total, $SS_{\text{tot} (y')}$, which measures the total variability about the best fitting line. In the analysis of variance, the total sum of squares is partitioned; in the analysis of covariance, the adjusted total sum of squares is partitioned. The first component resulting from this partitioning, SS_1, measures the variability of the group regression coefficients about an average coefficient. The second term, SS_2, measures the variability of scores about each group regression line. The hypothesis of homogeneity of regression may be tested by a ratio of mean squares based on the two terms just described. If the F statistic is not significant, the two terms may be pooled to form a single estimate of error which will be subsequently used in testing treatment effects. The third component of $SS_{\text{tot} (y')}$, SS_3, reflects the variability of treatment means about the line which gives the predicted value of $\overline{Y}_{.j}$. The fourth component, SS_4, measures the difference between the slope of that line and the slope of the average within-groups regression line. If variability of the means about this best fitting line is significant, then variation among the $\overline{Y}_{.j}$ is attributable to something more than the variation in $\overline{X}_{.j}$ and error variance; the "something more" is presumably treatment effects. If SS_4 is significantly large, the rate of change of $\overline{Y}_{.j}$ as a function of $\overline{X}_{.j}$ is not the same as the rate of change within groups, and again we conclude that the treatments are playing a role. The point is that if either SS_3 or SS_4 is significantly large, then the same function that describes the plot within a group does not adequately describe the plot of group means, and we conclude that the difference is attributable to the presence of treatment effects.

12.2.3 Computational formulas for the analysis of covariance

In order to carry out the analysis of covariance as efficiently as possible, it is desirable to provide raw score computational formulas for the four components of $SS_{\text{tot }(y')}$ which we have just discussed. These four expressions may be obtained by appropriately combining entries in Table 12-1. The entries

TABLE 12-1

Computational formulas for the analysis of covariance

	Sums of Squares (SS)		Sums of Products (SP)
	Y	X	
Total	$\displaystyle\sum_i \sum_j Y_{ij}^2 - C_y$	$\displaystyle\sum_i \sum_j X_{ij}^2 - C_x$	$\displaystyle\sum_i \sum_j X_{ij}Y_{ij} - C_{xy}$
A	$\displaystyle\frac{\sum_j \left(\sum_i Y_{ij}\right)^2}{n} - C_y$	$\displaystyle\frac{\sum_j \left(\sum_i X_{ij}\right)^2}{n} - C_x$	$\displaystyle\frac{\sum_j \left(\sum_i X_{ij}\right)\left(\sum_i Y_{ij}\right)}{n} - C_{xy}$
S/A	$SS_{\text{tot}} - SS_A$	$SS_{\text{tot}} - SS_A$	$SP_{\text{tot}} - SP_A$
Group j	$\displaystyle\sum_i Y_{ij}^2 - \frac{\left(\sum_i Y_{ij}\right)^2}{n}$	$\displaystyle\sum_i X_{ij}^2 - \frac{\left(\sum_i X_{ij}\right)^2}{n}$	$\displaystyle\sum_i X_{ij}Y_{ij} - \frac{\left(\sum_i X_{ij}\right)\left(\sum_i Y_{ij}\right)}{n}$
	$C_y = \dfrac{\left(\sum_i \sum_j Y_{ij}\right)^2}{an}$	$C_x = \dfrac{\left(\sum_i \sum_j X_{ij}\right)^2}{an}$	$C_{xy} = \dfrac{\left(\sum_i \sum_j X_{ij}\right)\left(\sum_i \sum_j Y_{ij}\right)}{an}$

in the first two columns are simply the usual formulas for the analysis of variance of a completely randomized one-factor design with the addition of formulas for group j; their role will shortly become clearer. The SP (sums of cross-products) terms can be arrived at by analogy to the SS terms. For example,

$$SS_{A(x)} = \frac{\sum_j \left(\sum_i X_{ij}\right)^2}{n} - \frac{\left(\sum_i \sum_j X_{ij}\right)^2}{an}$$

$$= \frac{\sum_j \left(\sum_i X_{ij}\right)\left(\sum_i X_{ij}\right)}{n} - \frac{\left(\sum_i \sum_j X_{ij}\right)\left(\sum_i \sum_j X_{ij}\right)}{an}$$

Then, replacing one X by Y,

$$SP_A = \frac{\sum_j \left(\sum_i X_{ij}\right)\left(\sum_i Y_{ij}\right)}{n} - \frac{\left(\sum_i \sum_j X_{ij}\right)\left(\sum_i \sum_j Y_{ij}\right)}{an}$$

Computation of the entries in Table 12-1 is the first step in the analysis of covariance. They will be combined to yield raw score expressions for the four components of $SS_{\text{tot } (y)}$. SS_1 and SS_2 will then be used to provide a test of the homogeneity of regression assumption stated in Section 12.2.1. If this assumption appears tenable, SS_1 and SS_2 will provide a pooled error term against which treatment effects SS_3 and SS_4 are tested.

Before presenting the raw score formulas for the four sum of squares components, the method of obtaining them from earlier expressions will be exhibited, beginning with SS_1. According to Equation (12.13),

$$SS_1 = \sum_i \sum_j (\hat{Y}_{ij}^{(2)} - \hat{Y}_{ij}^{(3)})^2$$

From Equations (12.9) and (12.10), we have

(12.14) $\quad SS_1 = \sum_i \sum_j \{[\bar{Y}_{.j} + b_j^{(2)}(X_{ij} - \bar{X}_{.j})] - [\bar{Y}_{.j} + b^{(3)}(X_{ij} - \bar{X}_{.j})]\}^2$

Simplifying,

$$SS_1 = \sum_i \sum_j (b_j^{(2)} - b^{(3)})^2 (X_{ij} - \bar{X}_{.j})^2$$

(12.15) $\qquad = \sum_j [(b_j^{(2)} - b^{(3)})^2 \sum_i (X_{ij} - \bar{X}_{.j})^2]$

Substituting raw scores for the means of Equations (12.9′) and (12.10′), in the manner exemplified in Chapter 3, we have

(12.16) $\quad b_j^{(2)} = \dfrac{\sum\limits_i X_{ij}Y_{ij} - \left(\sum\limits_i X_{ij}\right)\left(\sum\limits_i Y_{ij}\right)/n}{\sum\limits_i X_{ij}^2 - \left(\sum\limits_i X_{ij}\right)^2/n}$

$$= \frac{SP_j}{SS_{j(x)}}$$

and

(12.17) $\quad b^{(3)} = \dfrac{\sum\limits_i \sum\limits_j X_{ij}Y_{ij} - \sum\limits_j \left(\sum\limits_i X_{ij}\right)\left(\sum\limits_i Y_{ij}\right)/n}{\sum\limits_i \sum\limits_j X_{ij}^2 - \sum\limits_j \left(\sum\limits_i X_{ij}\right)^2/n}$

$$= \frac{SP_{S/A}}{SS_{S/A(x)}}$$

Note also that

(12.18) $\qquad \sum_i (X_{ij} - \bar{X}_{.j})^2 = \sum_i X_{ij}^2 - \dfrac{\left(\sum\limits_i X_{ij}\right)^2}{n}$

$$= SS_{j(x)}$$

Substituting from Equations (12.16) to (12.18) into Equation (12.15), we have

$$SS_1 = \sum_j \left(\frac{SP_j}{SS_{j(x)}} - \frac{SP_{S/A}}{SS_{S/A(x)}} \right)^2 SS_{j(x)}$$

$$= \sum_j \left[\left(\frac{SP_j^2}{SS_{j(x}^2} + \frac{SP_{S/A}^2}{SS_{S/A(x)}^2} - 2 \frac{SP_j SP_{S/A}}{SS_{j(x)} SS_{S/A(x)}} \right) SS_{j(x)} \right]$$

(12.19)

$$= \sum_j \left(\frac{SP_j^2}{SS_{j(x)}} + \frac{SP_{S/A}^2 SS_{j(x)}}{SS_{S/A(x)}^2} - 2 \frac{SP_j SP_{S/A}}{SS_{S/A(x)}} \right)$$

$$= \sum_j \frac{SP_j^2}{SS_{j(x)}} + \frac{SP_{S/A}^2}{SS_{S/A(x)}^2} \sum_j SS_{j(x)} - 2 \frac{SP_{S/A}}{SS_{S/A(x)}} \sum_j SP_j$$

Noting that $\sum_j SS_{j(x)} = SS_{S/A(x)}$ and $\sum_j SP_j = SP_{S/A}$, we have the final result:

(12.20)
$$SS_1 = \sum_j \frac{SP_j^2}{SS_{j(x)}} - \frac{SP_{S/A}^2}{SS_{S/A(x)}}$$

The remaining derivations are left as exercises for the reader. The procedure always involves starting with Equation (12.13); then the regression formulas are substituted for predicted values, and using Equations (12.8) to (12.11), formulas are obtained for the regression coefficients in terms of the entries in Table 12-1. Finally, the expressions are simplified. The results are

(12.21)
$$SS_2 = SS_{S/A(y)} - \sum_j \frac{SP_j^2}{SS_{j(x)}}$$

(12.22)
$$SS_3 = SS_{A(y)} - \frac{SP_A^2}{SS_{A(x)}}$$

(12.23)
$$SS_4 = \frac{SP_A^2}{SS_{A(x)}} + \frac{SP_{S/A}^2}{SS_{S/A(x)}} - \frac{SP_{tot}^2}{SS_{tot(x)}}$$

To complete the analysis of covariance it is also helpful to note that

(12.24)
$$SS_{tot(y')} = SS_1 + SS_2 + SS_3 + SS_4$$
$$= SS_{tot(y)} - SS_{lin}$$
$$= SS_{tot(y)} - \frac{SP_{tot}^2}{SS_{tot(x)}}$$

The SS_1 is distributed on $a - 1$ df, since we are concerned with the variability of a regression coefficients about the pooled coefficient, $b^{(3)}$. Note that this is consistent with Equation (12.20), in which one squared quantity is subtracted from the sum of a squared quantities. The df for SS_2 are $a(n - 2)$; the explanation lies in a closer examination of the meaning of this variability. In each group, the variance of n scores is taken about a group regression line. The estimation of this line involves the loss of two df, one for estimating β_j, the regression coefficient, and the other for estimating $\overline{Y} - \beta \overline{X}$, the slope intercept. Thus there are $n - 2$ df pooled over a groups. Referring to Equation (12.21), we note that the relationship of squared quantities to df still holds; we have $a(n-1) - a$ $[= a(n-2)]$ squared quantities on the right-hand side. The SS_3 measures the variability of a means about a regression line; again the estimation of the line involves the loss of two df, so that SS_3 is distributed on $a - 2$ df. Alternatively, we refer to Equation (12.22) and note that we have $a - 1$ df for $SS_{A(y)}$, and that one more is lost for the squared cross-product term. Since SS_4 measures the difference between two regression coefficients, it is on 1 df. The computational formula is again consistent with the conclusion.

Before testing treatment effects, we must consider the null hypothesis that

$$\beta_1 = \beta_2 = \cdots = \beta_a$$

The appropriate statistic is

$$F = \frac{SS_1/(a-1)}{SS_2/a(n-2)}$$

The logic of this F test should be apparent. The question is whether the variability among treatment regression coefficients is significantly greater than the pooled variability about the group regression lines.

We are now ready to test the adjusted treatment effects. The null hypothesis is that

$$\alpha_1' = \alpha_2' = \cdots = \alpha_a'$$

i.e., the adjusted treatment effects are homogeneous. The appropriate statistic is

$$F = \frac{(SS_3 + SS_4)/(a-1)}{(SS_1 + SS_2)/[a(n-1)-1]}$$

The pool of SS_1 and SS_2 requires that the test of homogeneity of regression coefficients does not have a significant result. Table 12-2 summarizes the analysis of covariance and includes the adjusted (adj) sources, their df, the SS formulas for the adjusted terms, the EMS and the F ratios. Note that we obtain the sums of squares for the adjusted A source by subtraction: $SS_{\text{tot}(y')} - SS_{S/A(y')}$. This is equivalent to adding $SS_3 + SS_4$, since

$$SS_{A(y')} = SS_{\text{tot}(y')} - SS_{S/A(y')}$$

$$= \left(SS_{\text{tot}(y)} - \frac{SP_{\text{tot}}^2}{SS_{\text{tot}(x)}}\right) - \left(SS_{S/A(y)} - \frac{SP_{S/A}^2}{SS_{S/A(x)}}\right)$$

$$= SS_{\text{tot}(y)} - SS_{S/A(y)} - \frac{SP_{\text{tot}}^2}{SS_{\text{tot}(x)}} + \frac{SP_{S/A}^2}{SS_{S/A(x)}}$$

and since $SS_{A(y)} = SS_{\text{tot}(y)} - SS_{S/A(y)}$,

(12.25)
$$SS_{A(y')} = SS_{A(y)} - \frac{SP_{\text{tot}}^2}{SS_{\text{tot}(x)}} + \frac{SP_{S/A}^2}{SS_{S/A(x)}}$$

$$= SS_3 + SS_4$$

summing Equations (12.22) and (12.23).

To summarize the computations briefly:

TABLE 12-2

Analysis of covariance for a completely randomized one-factor design

SV	df	SS	EMS	F
Total(adj)	$an - 2$	$SS_{\text{tot}\,(y')} = SS_{\text{tot}\,(y)} - \dfrac{SP_{\text{tot}}^2}{SS_{\text{tot}\,(x)}}$		
A(adj)	$a - 1$	$SS_{A(y')} = SS_{\text{tot}\,(y')} - SS_{S/A(y')}$	$\sigma_{e'}^2 + n\theta_{A'}^2$	$\dfrac{MS_{A(\text{adj})}}{MS_{S/A\,(\text{adj})}}$
S/A(adj)	$a(n - 1) - 1$	$SS_{S/A(y')} = SS_{S/A(y)} - \dfrac{SP_{S/A}^2}{SS_{S/A(x)}}$	$\sigma_{e'}^2$	

(a) The total sums of squares for the X and for the Y data are separately analyzed as in the usual analysis of variance; the cross-products sums are similarly treated. The formulas are in Table 12-1.

(b) Substituting into Equations (12.20) and (12.21), a test of homogeneity of regression is carried out.

(c) Assuming the population regression coefficients to be homogeneous, the adjusted sums of squares of Table 12-2 can be calculated, and the F tests of that table carried through.

Relationships between the adjusted sums of squares and correlation coefficients are illuminating; it is important to note that a squared correlation coefficient may be interpreted as a proportion of variance. Consider the adjusted error sum of squares:

$$SS_{S/A(y')} = SS_1 + SS_2$$

$$= SS_{S/A(y)} - \frac{SP_{S/A}^2}{SS_{S/A(x)}}$$

(12.26)
$$= SS_{S/A(y)} - \frac{SP_{S/A}^2}{SS_{S/A(x)}}\left(\frac{SS_{S/A(y)}}{SS_{S/A(y)}}\right)$$

$$= SS_{S/A(y)}\left(1 - \frac{SP_{S/A}^2}{SS_{S/A(x)}SS_{S/A(y)}}\right)$$

$$= SS_{S/A(y)}(1 - r_{xy/A}^2)$$

where $r_{xy/A}$ is the correlation of X and Y scores, pooled over the a treatment groups. Therefore, our adjusted error sum of squares is that proportion of the unadjusted error sum of squares not attributable to the linear relationship between X and Y. It is clear from Equation (12.26) that the efficiency of covariance relative to the usual analysis will depend on the magnitude of the correlation between X and Y; the larger the correlation, the smaller the adjusted error term will be and the greater the profit from performing the covariance analysis.

Manipulations similar to those performed above show that

(12.27) $$SS_{A(y')} = SS_{A(y)} - [SS_{\text{tot}(y)}r_{xy/\text{tot}}^2 - SS_{S/A(y)}r_{xy/A}^2]$$

where $r_{xy/\text{tot}}$ is the correlation of the an X and Y scores, disregarding treatment classifications. Equation (12.27) thus provides an interpretation of the adjusted treatment variability. The adjustment is the difference between the total variability predicted from X and the variability within groups predicted from X.

12.2.4 A numerical example

An analysis of covariance will now be applied to the data of Table 12-3. We first partition the X variability. The total is

$$SS_{tot\ (x)} = (12)^2 + (10)^2 + \cdots + (7)^2 + (9)^2$$
$$- \frac{(12 + 10 + 7 + \cdots + 7 + 9)^2}{18}$$

$$= 2{,}385 - 2{,}200.06$$

$$= 184.94$$

TABLE 12-3

Data for the analysis of covariance for a one-factor design

	A_1		A_2		A_3
X	Y	X	Y	X	Y
12	26	11	32	6	23
10	22	12	31	13	35
7	20	6	20	15	44
14	34	18	41	15	41
12	28	10	29	7	28
11	26	11	31	9	30

Then,

$$SS_{A(x)} = \frac{(12 + 10 + \cdots + 11)^2 + (11 + 12 + \cdots + 11)^2}{6}$$
$$+ \frac{(6 + 13 + \cdots + 9)^2}{6} - C_x$$

$$= 2{,}200.83 - 2{,}200.06$$

$$= .77$$

and

$$SS_{S/A(x)} = 184.94 - .77$$
$$= 184.17$$

We next turn to the Y data:

$$SS_{tot\ (y)} = (26)^2 + (22)^2 + \cdots + (30)^2 - \frac{(26 + 22 + \cdots + 30)^2}{18}$$

$$= 17{,}099 - 16{,}260.06$$

$$= 838.94$$

The components are

$$SS_{A(y)} = (26 + 22 + \cdots + 26)^2 + (32 + 31 + \cdots + 31)^2$$
$$+ (23 + 35 + \cdots + 30)^2 - C_y$$

$$= 16{,}432.17 - 16{,}260.06$$

$$= 172.11$$

and

$$SS_{S/A(y)} = 838.94 - 172.11$$
$$= 666.83$$

Next we obtain the cross-product terms. The total is

$$SP_{tot} = (12)(26) + (10)(22) + \cdots + (9)(30)$$

$$- \frac{(12 + 10 + \cdots + 9)(26 + 22 + \cdots + 30)}{18}$$

$$= 6{,}317 - 5{,}981.06$$

$$= 335.94$$

The treatment term is

$$SP_A = \frac{(12 + 10 + \cdots + 11)(26 + 22 + \cdots + 26)}{6}$$

$$+ \frac{(11 + 12 + \cdots + 11)(32 + 31 + \cdots + 31)}{6}$$

$$+ \frac{(6 + 13 + \cdots + 9)(23 + 35 + \cdots + 30)}{6} - C_{xy}$$

$$= 5{,}978.83 - 5{,}981.06$$

$$= -2.23$$

Note that it is possible to obtain negative SP terms (but not SS), since the SP term is the numerator of a correlation coefficient. The $SP_{S/A}$ is

$$SP_{S/A} = SP_{tot} - SP_A$$
$$= 335.94 - (-2.23)$$
$$= 338.17$$

Table 12-4 summarizes the analysis thus far. The remainder of the

TABLE 12-4

Preliminary computations for the covariance analysis for a one-factor design

	$SS_{(x)}$	$SS_{(y)}$	SP
Total	184.94	838.94	335.94
A	.77	172.11	−2.23
S/A	184.17	666.83	338.17

analysis of covariance involves the manipulation of the quantities in Table 12-4 according to the formulas of Table 12-2. The adjusted total variability is

$$SS_{tot\ (y')} = SS_{tot\ (y)} - \frac{SP_{tot}^2}{SS_{tot\ (x)}}$$

$$= 838.94 - \frac{(335.94)^2}{184.94}$$

$$= 228.71$$

The error variability is computed next:

$$SS_{S/A(y')} = SS_{S/A(y)} - \frac{SP^2_{S/A}}{SS_{S/A(x)}}$$

$$= 666.83 - \frac{(338.17)^2}{184.17}$$

$$= 47.89$$

The residual variability accounts for the treatment effects:

$$SS_{A(y')} = SS_{\text{tot}(y')} - SS_{S/A(y')}$$

$$= 228.71 - 47.89$$

$$= 180.82$$

TABLE 12-5

Analysis of covariance for a one-factor design

SV	df	SS	MS	F
Total	16	228.71		
A	2	180.82	90.41	26.43 *
S/A	14	47.89	3.42	
				*p < .001

Table 12-5 presents the final results of the analysis of covariance. The A main effect is a highly significant source of variance. If the covariance adjustment had not been made, F would have had a lower value:

$$F = \frac{SS_{A(y)}/2}{SS_{S/A(y)}/15}$$

$$= \frac{172.11/2}{666.83/15}$$

$$= \frac{86.06}{44.46}$$

$$= 1.94$$

It is clear that the covariance adjustment has resulted in a marked change in the results of the F test.

12.3 THE ANALYSIS OF COVARIANCE FOR MULTI-FACTOR DESIGNS

12.3.1 The completely randomized two-factor design

We will first consider a completely randomized two-factor design; the techniques of this section and Section 12.3.2 generalize readily to designs involving more treatment variables.

Calculations of the usual sums of squares for both X and Y are presented in Chapter 4, and therefore $SS_{A(x)}$, $SS_{A(y)}$, $\cdots$, $SS_{AB(y)}$, $SS_{S/AB(x)}$, and $SS_{S/AB(y)}$ require no further comment. We will need calculations of sums of cross-products. The appropriate formulas are

$$(12.28) \qquad C_{xy} = \frac{\left(\sum\limits_{i}^{n}\sum\limits_{j}^{a}\sum\limits_{k}^{b} X_{ijk}\right)\left(\sum\limits_{i}^{n}\sum\limits_{j}^{a}\sum\limits_{k}^{b} Y_{ijk}\right)}{abn}$$

$$(12.29) \qquad SP_{\text{tot}} = \sum\limits_{i}^{n}\sum\limits_{j}^{a}\sum\limits_{k}^{b} X_{ijk}Y_{ijk} - C_{xy}$$

$$(12.30) \qquad SP_A = \frac{\sum\limits_{j}^{a}\left(\sum\limits_{i}^{n}\sum\limits_{k}^{b} X_{ijk}\right)\left(\sum\limits_{i}^{n}\sum\limits_{k}^{b} Y_{ijk}\right)}{bn} - C_{xy}$$

$$(12.31) \qquad SP_B = \frac{\sum\limits_{k}^{b}\left(\sum\limits_{i}^{n}\sum\limits_{j}^{a} X_{ijk}\right)\left(\sum\limits_{i}^{n}\sum\limits_{j}^{a} Y_{ijk}\right)}{an} - C_{xy}$$

$$(12.32) \qquad SP_{AB} = \frac{\sum\limits_{j}^{a}\sum\limits_{k}^{b}\left(\sum\limits_{i}^{n} X_{ijk}\right)\left(\sum\limits_{i}^{n} Y_{ijk}\right)}{n} - C_{xy} - SP_A - SP_B$$

$$(12.33) \qquad SP_{S/AB} = SP_{\text{tot}} - SP_A - SP_B - SP_{AB}$$

Again note the correspondence between the SP and SS terms. For example,

$$SS_{A(y)} = \frac{\sum\limits_{j}\left(\sum\limits_{i}\sum\limits_{k} Y_{ijk}\right)^2}{bn} - C = \frac{\sum\limits_{j}\left(\sum\limits_{i}\sum\limits_{k} Y_{ijk}\right)\left(\sum\limits_{i}\sum\limits_{k} Y_{ijk}\right)}{bn} - C$$

and

$$SP_A = \frac{\sum\limits_{j}\left(\sum\limits_{i}\sum\limits_{k} X_{ijk}\right)\left(\sum\limits_{i}\sum\limits_{k} Y_{ijk}\right)}{bn} - C_{xy}$$

We are now ready to present exact computational formulas for the adjusted sums of squares. Considering $SS_{A(y')}$, we begin by computing an adjusted pooled sum of squares for A and S/AB:

$$(12.34) \qquad SS_{(A+S/AB)(y')} = (SS_{A(y)} + SS_{S/AB(y)}) - \frac{(SP_A + SP_{S/AB})^2}{SS_{A(x)} + SS_{S/AB(x)}}$$

Next, we obtain the adjusted error sum of squares:

$$(12.35) \qquad SS_{S/AB(y')} = SS_{S/AB(y)} - \frac{SP^2_{S/AB}}{SS_{S/AB(x)}}$$

The adjusted sum of squares for the treatment variable A is

$$SS_{A(y')} = SS_{(A+S/AB)(y')} - SS_{S/AB(y')}$$

$$(12.36) \qquad = SS_{A(y)} - \frac{(SP_A + SP_{S/AB})^2}{SS_{A(x)} + SS_{S/AB(x)}} + \frac{SP^2_{S/AB}}{SS_{S/AB(x)}}$$

Corresponding to Equation (12.35), we have

$$df_{A(\text{adj})} = (a - 1) - 1 + 1 = a - 1$$

The above calculations can be better understood by comparing Equation (12.36) with Equation (12.25). Rewrite Equation (12.25), making the following substitutions:

$$SS_{\text{tot }(x)} = SS_{A(x)} + SS_{S/A(x)}$$

and

$$SP_{\text{tot}} = SP_A + SP_{S/A}$$

It is now clear that Equation (12.25) and Equation (12.36) are of identical form. Equation (12.36) also describes the pool of two sums of squares quantities, analogous to SS_3 and SS_4 of the preceding section.

The $SS_{B(y')}$ and $SS_{AB(y')}$ are computed in similar manner to $SS_{A(y')}$. We have

(12.37) $$SS_{B(y')} = SS_{B(y)} - \frac{(SP_B + SP_{S/AB})^2}{SS_{B(x)} + SS_{S/AB(x)}} + \frac{SP^2_{S/AB}}{SS_{S/AB(x)}}$$

and

(12.38) $$SS_{AB(y')} = SS_{AB(y)} - \frac{(SP_{AB} + SP_{S/AB})^2}{SS_{AB(x)} + SS_{S/AB(x)}} + \frac{SP^2_{S/AB}}{SS_{S/AB(x)}}$$

The test for homogeneity of regression coefficients also follows that for the one-factor design. We compute

(12.39) $$SS_1 = \sum_j \sum_k \frac{SP^2_j}{SS_{j(x)}} - \frac{SP^2_{S/AB}}{SS_{S/AB(x)}}$$

and

(12.40) $$SS_2 = SS_{S/AB(y)} - \sum_j \sum_k \frac{SP^2_j}{SS_{j(x)}}$$

To test the null hypothesis that

$$\beta_{11} = \beta_{12} = \cdots = \beta_{ab}$$

we compute

(12.41) $$F = \frac{SS_1/(ab - 1)}{SS_2/ab(n - 2)}$$

The procedures of this section are readily extended to designs involving a greater number of factors and to designs other than the completely randomized design. All that is necessary is that the transition from SS formulas to SP formulas be understood, and that the general form for the sum of squares for any main or interaction effect be recognized:

(12.42) $$SS_{\text{effect }(y')} = SS_{\text{effect }(y)} - \frac{(SP_{\text{effect}} + SP_{\text{error}})^2}{SS_{\text{effect }(x)} + SS_{\text{error }(x)}} + \frac{SP^2_{\text{error}}}{SS_{\text{error }(x)}}$$

In the next section, the application of Equation (12.42) to a design involving between- and within-subjects variability will be illustrated. Following that is a numerical example.

12.3.2 A mixed design

Consider a groups of n subjects who are given b trials on a paired-associate task. The groups differ with respect to the meaningfulness of the material. All an subjects have previously been tested for b trials on one list of associates which is not included among the a experimental lists. Thus, there are b pretest scores (X) as well as b dependent measures (Y) for each of the an subjects. We may readily apply Equation (12.42) to this experimental design, which involves one between- and one within-subjects variable. The "error" of Equation (12.42) depends upon which treatment effect the adjusted sum of squares is being computed for. Thus, in our example,

$$SS_{A(y')} = SS_{A(y)} - \frac{(SP_A + SP_{S/A})^2}{SS_{A(x)} + SS_{S/A(x)}} + \frac{SP_{S/A}^2}{SS_{S/A(x)}}$$

$$SS_{B(y')} = SS_{B(y)} - \frac{(SP_B + SP_{SB/A})^2}{SS_{B(x)} + SS_{SB/A(x)}} + \frac{SP_{SB/A}^2}{SS_{SB/A(x)}}$$

$$SS_{AB(y')} = SS_{AB(y)} - \frac{(SP_{AB} + SP_{SB/A})^2}{SS_{AB(x)} + SS_{SB/A(x)}} + \frac{SP_{SB/A}^2}{SS_{SB/A(x)}}$$

The error term calculations are

$$SS_{S/A(y')} = SS_{S/A(y)} - \frac{SP_{S/A}^2}{SS_{S/A(x)}}$$

and

$$SS_{SB/A(y')} = SS_{SB/A(y)} - \frac{SP_{SB/A}^2}{SS_{SB/A(x)}}$$

The sum of squares calculations have been previously presented in Chapter 8. The SP calculations follow readily as in the past. For example,

$$SS_{S/A(y)} = \frac{\sum_{j=1}^{a} \sum_{i=1}^{n} \left(\sum_{k=1}^{b} Y_{ijk} \right)^2}{b} - \frac{\sum_{j=1}^{a} \left(\sum_{i=1}^{n} \sum_{k=1}^{b} Y_{ijk} \right)^2}{bn}$$

$$= \frac{\sum_{j} \sum_{i} \left(\sum_{k} Y_{ijk} \right) \left(\sum_{k} Y_{ijk} \right)}{b} - \frac{\sum_{j} \left(\sum_{i} \sum_{k} Y_{ijk} \right) \left(\sum_{i} \sum_{k} Y_{ijk} \right)}{bn}$$

and

$$SP_{S/A} = \frac{\sum_{j} \sum_{i} \left(\sum_{k} Y_{ijk} \right) \left(\sum_{k} X_{ijk} \right)}{b} - \frac{\sum_{j} \left(\sum_{i} \sum_{k} Y_{ijk} \right) \left(\sum_{i} \sum_{k} X_{ijk} \right)}{bn}$$

12.3.3 A numerical example

Table 12-6 presents X and Y data for an experiment involving four subjects, two at A_1 and two at A_2; all four are tested at all levels of B. The sums of

TABLE 12-6

Data for the covariance of a mixed design

		X Data				Y Data		
		B_1	B_2	B_3		B_1	B_2	B_3
A_1	S_{11}	22	23	20	A_1 S_{11}	14	17	22
	S_{21}	23	18	26	S_{21}	16	20	24
A_2	S_{12}	22	18	21	A_2 S_{12}	6	23	33
	S_{22}	19	26	28	S_{22}	8	27	35

squares for X and for Y are computed as in Chapter 8. Therefore, computational details are omitted and results are merely listed in Table 12-7. The

TABLE 12-7

Preliminary computations for the analysis of covariance for a mixed design

	$SS_{(x)}$	$SS_{(y)}$	SP
Total	115.67	870.92	133.17
Between S	25.00	48.92	21.50
A	.34	30.09	3.17
S/A	24.66	18.83	18.33
Within S	90.67	822.00	111.67
B	15.17	623.17	71.42
AB	8.16	197.16	39.08
SB/A	67.34	1.67	1.17.

cross-product (SP) calculations parallel those for sums of squares. The total is given by

$$SP_{tot} = (22)(14) + (23)(17) + \cdots + (28)(35)$$

$$- \frac{(22 + 23 + \cdots + 28)(14 + 17 + \cdots + 35)}{12}$$

$$= 5,564.00 - 5,430.83$$

$$= 133.17$$

As with the sums of squares, the total may be partitioned into a between- and a within-subjects component. Thus, we have

$$SP_{\text{B.s}} = \frac{(22 + .23 + 20)(14 + 17 + 22)}{3} + \cdots$$

$$+ \frac{(19 + 26 + 28)(8 + 27 + 35)}{3} - C_{xy}$$

$$= 5{,}452.33 - 5{,}430.83$$

$$= 21.50$$

This, in turn, can be partitioned:

$$SP_A = \frac{(22 + 23 + \cdots + 26)(14 + 16 + \cdots + 24)}{6}$$

$$+ \frac{(22 + 19 + \cdots + 28)(6 + 8 + \cdots + 35)}{6} - C_{xy}$$

$$= 5{,}434.00 - 5{,}430.83$$

$$= 3.17$$

and

$$SP_{S/A} = SP_{\text{B.s}} - SP_A$$
$$= 21.50 - 3.17$$
$$= 18.33$$

The within-subjects component is obtained by subtraction:

$$SP_{\text{w.s}} = SP_{\text{tot}} - SP_{\text{B.s}}$$
$$= 133.17 - 21.50$$
$$= 111.67$$

This is now partitioned into SP_B, SP_{AB}, and $SP_{SB/A}$. First,

$$SP_B = \frac{(22 + \cdots + 19)(14 + \cdots + 8)}{4} + \cdots$$

$$+ \frac{(20 + \cdots + 28)(22 + \cdots + 35)}{4} - C_{xy}$$

$$= 5{,}502.25 - 5{,}430.83$$

$$= 71.42$$

Next,

$$SP_{AB} = \frac{(22 + 23)(14 + 16) + \cdots + (21 + 28)(33 + 35)}{2}$$

$$- C_{xy} - SP_A - SP_B$$

$$= 5{,}544.50 - 5{,}430.83 - 3.17 - 71.42$$

$$= 39.08$$

Finally,

$$SP_{SB/A} = SP_{\text{w.s}} - SP_B - SP_{AB}$$
$$= 111.67 - 71.42 - 39.08$$
$$= 1.17$$

These results are also included in Table 12-7.

Using the entries in Table 12-7, we may now proceed to obtain the adjusted sums of squares. The key is the correct application of Equation (12.42). Thus, we have

$$SS_{A(y')} = SS_{A(y)} - \frac{(SP_A + SP_{S/A})^2}{SS_{A(x)} + SS_{S/A(x)}} + \frac{SP^2_{S/A}}{SS_{S/A(x)}}$$

$$= 30.09 - \frac{(3.17 + 18.33)^2}{.34 + 24.66} + \frac{(18.33)^2}{24.66}$$

$$= 25.22$$

The error term is straightforward:

$$SS_{S/A(y')} = SS_{S/A(y)} - \frac{SP^2_{S/A}}{SS_{S/A(x)}}$$

$$= 18.83 - \frac{(18.33)^2}{24.66}$$

$$= 5.21$$

Turning to the within-subjects effects, we have

$$SS_{B(y')} = SS_{B(y)} - \frac{(SP_B + SP_{SB/A})^2}{SS_{B(x)} + SS_{SB/A(x)}} + \frac{SP^2_{SB/A}}{SS_{SB/A(x)}}$$

$$= 623.17 - \frac{(71.42 + 1.17)^2}{15.17 + 67.34} + \frac{(1.17)^2}{67.34}$$

$$= 559.33$$

and

$$SS_{AB(y')} = SS_{AB(y)} - \frac{(SP_{AB} + SP_{SB/A})^2}{SS_{AB(x)} + SS_{SB/A(x)}} + \frac{SP^2_{SB/A}}{SS_{SB/A(x)}}$$

$$= 197.16 - \frac{(39.08 + 1.17)^2}{8.16 + 67.34} + \frac{(1.17)^2}{67.34}$$

$$= 175.72$$

For the error term, we have

$$SS_{SB/A(y')} = SS_{SB/A(y)} - \frac{SP^2_{SB/A}}{SS_{SB/A(x)}}$$

$$= 1.67 - \frac{(1.17)^2}{67.34}$$

$$= 1.65$$

The final analysis is summarized in Table 12-8.

TABLE 12-8

Analysis of covariance for a mixed design

SV	df	SS	MS	F
Total	11	767.13		
Between S	3	30.43		
A	1	25.22	25.22	9.66 *
S/A	2	5.21	2.61	
Within S	8	736.70		
B	2	559.33	279.67	682.12 *
AB	2	175.72	87.86	214.29 *
SB/A	4	1.65	.41	

$*p < .001$

12.4 INTERPRETATION OF COVARIANCE TESTS

In many instances of the use of covariance by psychologists, the $\overline{X}_j$ differ sufficiently to suggest a systematic difference among the groups with respect to the concomitant variable. In such situations, the experimenter is prone to interpret the results of an analysis of covariance as indicative of the treatment effects on Y when X is held constant. For example, three methods of teaching arithmetic are compared; Y is a performance measure and X is amount of study time. Method 1 is significantly superior to the other two when an analysis of variance test is carried out. However, after adjustment for study time, the effect due to methods is no longer significant. The experimenter concludes that the originally obtained difference in performance was due to differences in study time, and that when study time is held constant, the three methods are equally effective. This interpretation is not necessarily correct. Variation in performance may not be due to variation in study time, but, instead, variability in both measures may be due to a third factor, e.g., differences in motivation resulting from the three methods. If this were the case, and if study time were actually held constant (all subjects were required to study for a set time period), methods might have a significant effect, since the degree of motivation is still free to vary. Another reason why the experimental control of study time may have different results than the statistical control is that the experimental environment has changed. For example, subjects instructed to study for a given amount of time may have a different set from subjects in the covariance experiment, who were given no particular instructions with regard to study time. The point is that *statistically* adjusting for study time is not the same as *experimentally* holding study time constant.

H. Fairfield Smith* very clearly makes the point of the above discussion. Smith notes that the heights of mountains and the density of air surrounding them are correlated. Therefore, adjustment for air density would result in apparently negligible differences among the heights of mountains. However, it is hard to believe that if we could find a way to thin the air around Pike's Peak, the result would be to increase its height to that of Mt. Everest.

In view of the preceding discussion, how are we to deal with situations in which systematic variation in $\overline{X}_j$ is likely? If X is an integral part of the treatment, adjustment for variation in X should not be undertaken. Returning to the example of study time and performance, suppose that our interest is solely in deciding which method is best. How this method achieves its success is irrelevant. In this case, it is of no interest to adjust the mean performances for variability among the mean study times. On the other hand, suppose the interest lies in the influence of study time upon performance. In this case, study time should be systematically manipulated as one independent variable in a factorial design.

12.5 COMPARISON WITH THE TREATMENTS × BLOCKS DESIGN

The preceding section suggests that one should generally be interested in covariance as a technique for reducing error variance. In this regard, it is important to compare the analysis with the use of the treatments × blocks design, since both use a concomitant variable to increase precision. Three advantages of the covariance approach are discernible:

(a) The concomitant data may be used after the fact, if the covariance analysis is applied. For example, if problem-solving scores prove to be highly variable, intelligence test data can be collected and an analysis of covariance carried out even though this had not been planned prior to the collection of data.

(b) The establishment of blocks is often impractical. For example, we are interested in the problem-solving behavior of high and low socially cohesive groups. It is most efficient, and possibly more interesting, to work with already established groups, such as Boy Scout troops. However, it may be impossible to find an equal number of high and low intelligence groups at each level of cohesiveness. It is more practical merely to measure intelligence and use it as a covariate rather than as a factor in the design.

(c) The analysis of covariance is more precise than the treatments ×

---

* H. Fairfield Smith, "Interpretation of Adjusted Treatment Means and Regressions in Analysis of Covariance," *Biometrics*, 13:282–308 (September 1957).

blocks design when the true correlation between X and Y is greater than .6.*

Although the covariance approach has the advantages just cited, the treatments × blocks design is superior in several other respects:

(a) The computational labor involved in an analysis of variance performed on treatments × blocks data is approximately one-third to one-half that involved in the covariance analysis, thus partly compensating for the increased experimental labor resulting from establishing blocks of subjects.

(b) The treatments × blocks approach (assuming the optimal number of levels) is more precise than the covariance approach when the true correlation between X and Y is less than .4. This is important, since correlations of less than .4 are more frequent in psychological research than correlations greater than .6.

(c) The treatments × blocks interaction may be of interest. Furthermore, if there is reason to expect such an interaction to be significant, covariance should be avoided. If the block means differ more at one treatment level than at another, then the values of Y_{ij} are changing more rapidly as a function of X_{ij} at one treatment level than at another. In short, if a treatments × blocks interaction is significant, the assumption of homogeneity of regression coefficients is not correct, and the covariance model presented earlier in this chapter is not appropriate to the data.

(d) Perhaps the most important advantage of the experimental over the statistical approach lies in the relative complexity of the covariance model. There are more assumptions, more things that can go wrong, and statisticians have not yet adequately assessed the consequences of violating the model.

Add to the points just cited the inferential problems raised in the preceding section, and one begins to understand why most biometricians and statisticians recommend the experimental over the statistical approach. The author does not feel that covariance should never be used but recommends that the experimenter consider the estimated correlation of X and Y, the probable validity of the covariance model for the data to be collected, and any possible inferential problems. If the choice is approached this way, more often than not the treatments × blocks design will be used.

* L. S. Feldt, "A Comparison of the Precision of Three Experimental Designs Employing a Concomitant Variable," *Psychometrika*, 23:335–353 (1958).

EXERCISES

12.1 Do the following analysis of covariance:

		A_1		A_2	
	X	Y	X	Y
	23.8	7.9	28.5	25.1
	23.8	7.1	18.5	20.7
B_1	22.6	7.7	20.3	20.3
	22.8	11.2	26.6	18.9
	22.0	6.4	21.2	25.4
	19.6	10.0	24.0	30.0
	27.5	20.1	22.9	19.9
	28.1	17.7	25.2	28.2
B_2	35.7	16.8	20.8	18.1
	27.7	30.5	13.5	13.5⁻
	25.9	21.0	19.1	19.3
	27.9	29.3	32.2	35.1

12.2 A study is designed to test the effects of two training methods upon lathe performance. Each of 72 subjects is assigned at random to one of three machines and to one of the two methods. The machines have been randomly selected from a large number of the same type. An analysis of covariance is performed using productivity as the dependent variable (Y) and a machinist-proficiency test (X) as the concomitant variable. Give the SV, df, and sum of squares formula for the analysis.

12.3 The following 3 × 3 Latin square has one S in each sequence and an X (covariate) and Y (dependent) measure in each cell. Compute the adjusted F test for treatments.

	A_1	A_2	A_3
X	4	1	5
Y	3	4	6

	A_2	A_3	A_1
X	3	2	4
Y	5	8	2

	A_3	A_1	A_2
X	1	3	4
Y	10	2	4

SUPPLEMENTARY READINGS

The following issue of *Biometrics* was devoted to the analysis of covariance:
Biometrics, 13, No. 3 (September 1957).

Some comments on the difficulty of interpretation of covariance results may be found, together with some alternative approaches, in the following article:
ANDERSON, NORMAN H., "Comparison of Different Populations: Resistance to Extinction and Transfer," *Psychological Review*, 70:162–179 (March 1963).

FURTHER DATA ANALYSES:

QUALITATIVE INDEPENDENT VARIABLES

13

13.1 INTRODUCTION

Chapters 4 to 12 have been concerned with the total variability among treatment population means. The null hypothesis that the variance of the entire set of means is zero has been tested, and estimates, point and interval, of the variance of the entire set of means have been established. This is often only the beginning of a complete analysis of the data. It leaves unanswered questions about the slope and shape of performance curves, and it leaves unexplored differences among means within subsets smaller than the entire treatment set.

If the independent variable is quantitative (e.g., amount of reward, length of time in therapy), the overall F test is often only a preliminary test, useful in determining whether or not to proceed further with the analysis. Knowing that there is significant variability among the means, we may ask whether performance shows a general improvement over the levels of the independent variable, and whether several apparent changes in the direction of the function are significant. In short, the overall F indicates that the means do not fall on a straight line with slope of zero. We then wish to know more about the slope and shape of the best fitting function.

In the case of a qualitative variable (e.g., type of reward, type of therapy), the F test is again only a first step. For example, consider an experiment in which motivation is manipulated. There is one group in which correct responses are rewarded, but errors are not punished (group R), a second group which is punished for errors but not rewarded for correct responses (group P), a third group which is both rewarded for correct responses and punished for incorrect responses (group RP), and a fourth group which receives neither reward for correct responses nor punishment for incorrect responses (*NRP*). A significant overall F shows that differences exist among the treatment population means. Why? Are reward and punishment different in effect? Is their combination (*RP*) more effective than either alone? Does the *RP* effect differ from the average effect for the *R* and *P* groups? Is the effect of the *NRP* treatment significantly different from that of the average of the three incentive groups? These are all reasonable questions, and others could be asked.

Analyses relevant to quantitative independent variables will be considered in the next chapter. For the present, the discussion is restricted to the sorts of comparisons among means indicated in the preceding paragraph. These comparisons can also be made with quantitative variables (e.g., Do the effects of one and two food pellets of reward differ?), but for these variables the analyses of Chapter 14 will generally be more fruitful.

To clarify the analyses that follow, we return to the example of the experiment on reward and punishment. Consider each of the questions raised: Are reward and punishment different in effect? implies the null hypothesis

$$(13.1) \qquad \mu_R - \mu_P = 0$$

Is their combination (*RP*) more effective than either alone? implies the null hypotheses

$$(13.2) \qquad \mu_{RP} - \mu_R = 0$$

and

$$(13.3) \qquad \mu_{RP} - \mu_P = 0$$

Does the *RP* effect differ from the average effect for the *R* and *P* groups? implies the null hypothesis

$$(13.4) \qquad \mu_{RP} - \tfrac{1}{2}(\mu_R + \mu_P) = 0$$

Is the effect of the *NRP* treatment significantly different from that of the average of the three incentive groups? implies the null hypothesis

$$(13.5) \qquad \mu_{NRP} - \tfrac{1}{3}(\mu_R + \mu_P + \mu_{RP}) = 0$$

We may rewrite the five null hypotheses:

$$(13.1') \qquad (1)\mu_R + (-1)\mu_P + (0)\mu_{RP} + (0)\mu_{NRP} = 0$$

$$(13.2') \qquad (-1)\mu_R + (0)\mu_P + (1)\mu_{RP} + (0)\mu_{NRP} = 0$$

$$(13.3') \qquad (0)\mu_R + (-1)\mu_P + (1)\mu_{RP} + (0)\mu_{NRP} = 0$$

$$(13.4') \qquad (-\tfrac{1}{2})\mu_R + (-\tfrac{1}{2})\mu_P + (1)\mu_{RP} + (0)\mu_{NRP} = 0$$

$$(13.5') \qquad (-\tfrac{1}{3})\mu_R + (-\tfrac{1}{3})\mu_P + (-\tfrac{1}{3})\mu_{RP} + (1)\mu_{NRP} = 0$$

A close examination of Equations (13.1') to (13.5') indicates the general form of the null hypotheses to be considered in this chapter (and, in fact, in the next chapter as well; the difference is in the rationale for selecting the multipliers of the μ's). The general null hypothesis is

$$\psi = 0$$

where $\psi = \sum_j w_j \mu_j$, and the w_j are the coefficients which multiply the μ_j; they vary as a function of the specific hypotheses being tested. The sum of these coefficients is always zero for any contrast. It is helpful to note that the analyses will be unchanged if both sides of any of the above equations are multiplied by a constant. Thus, all w_j in Equation (13.5′) may be translated into integers by multiplying by 3:

$$(13.5'') \qquad -\mu_R - \mu_P - \mu_{RP} + 3\mu_{NRP} = 0$$

The problem of estimation is, in general, the problem of estimating ψ or of obtaining a confidence interval for ψ.

In the next section, we will present a general computational formula for sums of squares for contrasts of the type exemplified by Equations (13.1) to (13.5). Following this, we will examine the inferential problem that exists when several contrasts are simultaneously investigated, and consider some proposed solutions to the problem. The first of these solutions will utilize the computational formulas which are developed below.

13.2   SUMS OF SQUARES FOR MULTIPLE COMPARISONS

13.2.1   Computations

The sum of squares for any estimate of the population contrast, ψ, is given by

$$(13.6) \qquad SS_{\hat{\psi}} = \frac{\left(\sum\limits_j w_j \overline{Y}_{.j}\right)^2}{\sum\limits_j (w_j^2 / n_j)}$$

To clarify the meaning of this sum of squares, consider the contrast in Equation (13.5″). The $SS_{\hat{\psi}}$ is a measure of the variability of two means about the grand mean; one mean is the mean of the combined R, P, and RP groups, and the second mean is the mean of the NRP group. The calculations of Equation (13.6) are equivalent to the calculations involved in comparing two treatment groups, where one group consists of $n_R + n_P + n_{RP}$ scores and the second consists of n_{NRP} scores. If each of the individual treatment means are based on the same n, we have the alternative calculation:

$$(13.6') \qquad SS_{\hat{\psi}} = \frac{\left[\sum\limits_j^a (w_j/n)\left(\sum\limits_i^n Y_{ij}\right)\right]^2}{(1/n)\sum\limits_j w_j^2}$$

$$= \frac{\left[\sum\limits_j w_j \left(\sum\limits_i Y_{ij}\right)\right]^2}{n\sum\limits_j w_j^2}$$

As an example of the application of Equation (13.6′), consider the reward and punishment experiment. Assume ten subjects in each of the four treatment groups. The total number of errors in 20 trials for each group is

R	P	RP	NRP
42	34	25	88

To determine whether the average effect of the R and P treatments differs from that of the RP treatment, we compute

$$SS_{\hat{\psi}} = \frac{[42 + 34 - 2(25)]^2}{(10)(6)}$$

$$= \frac{676}{60}$$

$$= 11.27$$

Using Equation (13.6), which would also apply if the cell frequencies were unequal, we have

$$SS_{\hat{\psi}} = \frac{[4.2 + 3.4 - 2(2.5)]^2}{.1 + .1 + .4}$$

$$= \frac{6.76}{.6}$$

$$= 11.27$$

The computation of $SS_{\hat{\psi}}$ is not more complicated for the designs other than the completely randomized one-factor design. It is only necessary to replace n of Equation (13.6′) by the total number of measurements on which each treatment mean is based. For example, if there is a three-factor design with a, b, and c levels of the variables A, B, and C, and if the interest lies in some contrast among the $\bar{Y}_{...m}$ (the means at the levels of C), each mean is based on nab scores:

$$SS_{\hat{\psi}} = \frac{\left[\sum\limits_{m=1}^{c} \left(w_m \sum\limits_{i=1}^{n} \sum\limits_{j=1}^{a} \sum\limits_{k=1}^{b} Y_{ijkm} \right) \right]^2}{nab \sum\limits_{m=1}^{c} w_m^2}$$

That is to say, we find the sum at each level of C, multiply by the appropriate coefficient, add these cross-products (coefficient × sum) together, and square the resulting total; we then divide by the total number of measures in a level of C times the sum of squared coefficients.

13.2.2 A general single *df* formula

It may help the reader to note the relationship between the calculations just presented and other calculations previously encountered in this text. The quantity

$$\frac{\left[\sum_j w_j \left(\sum_i Y_{ij}\right)\right]^2}{n \sum_j w_j^2}$$

and its equivalent for unequal n [Equation (13.6)] are general formulas for any sum of squares distributed on 1 df. For example, there is no real difference between the above formula and the quantity on the right of Equation (5.65). In Chapter 5 we had a 2×2 design, and we provided a shortcut formula for SS_{AB}:

$$SS_{AB} = \frac{(T_{11} + T_{22} - T_{12} - T_{21})^2}{4n}$$

This can be rewritten

$$SS_{AB} = \frac{\left[(1)\left(\sum_i Y_{i11}\right) + (1)\left(\sum_i Y_{i22}\right) + (-1)\left(\sum_i Y_{i12}\right) + (-1)\left(\sum_i Y_{i21}\right)\right]^2}{[(1)^2 + (1)^2 + (-1)^2 + (-1)^2]n}$$

which is clearly of the form of the right-hand quantity of Equation (13.6). In general, the formula for any sum of squares on 1 df may be represented by

$$(13.7) \quad SS_{1df} = \frac{\text{(sum of the weighted cell totals)}^2}{\text{(sum of the squared weights)} \times \text{(cell frequencies)}}$$

and if the n's are unequal,

$$(13.8) \quad SS_{1df} = \frac{\text{(sum of the weighted cell means)}^2}{\text{sum of the ratios of squared weights to cell frequencies}}$$

13.2.3   Orthogonality

It was noted in the introduction that there are many possible contrasts, that the five listed for a set of four treatments were only some of those that could be investigated. Not all of these possible contrasts will be independent of each other. However, sets of independent contrasts can be obtained; these are called *orthogonal sets*. Assuming a treatment means are contrasted, each set of orthogonal contrasts will have $a - 1$ members. The sum of squares for each term will be distributed on 1 df, and the total of the $a - 1$ sums of squares will equal the SS_A distributed on $a - 1$ df.

Two contrasts, ψ_p and $\psi_{p'}$, are independent if (a) the sum of the coefficients for each contrast is zero, i.e., $\sum_j w_{jp} = 0$ and $\sum_j w_{jp'} = 0$, and (b) the sum of cross-products of coefficients is zero, i.e., $\sum_j w_{jp} w_{jp'} = 0$. To illustrate the concept of orthogonality, we again return to the example of the experiment on reward and punishment. One possible set of three orthogonal contrasts is

	R	P	RP	NRP
w_{j1}	-1	$+1$	0	0
w_{j2}	-1	-1	$+2$	0
w_{j3}	-1	-1	-1	$+3$

To verify that the three contrasts are independent, we note that

$$\sum_j w_{j1}w_{j2} = (-1)(-1) + (+1)(-1) + (0)(+2) + (0)(0) = 0$$

$$\sum_j w_{j1}w_{j3} = (-1)(-1) + (+1)(-1) + (0)(-1) + (0)(+3) = 0$$

$$\sum_j w_{j2}w_{j3} = (-1)(-1) + (-1)(-1) + (+2)(-1) + (0)(+3) = 0$$

Using the data of Section 13.2.1,

$$SS_A = \frac{(42)^2 + (34)^2 + (25)^2 + (88)^2}{10} - \frac{(189)^2}{40}$$

$$= 1,128.9 - 893.025$$

$$= 235.875$$

For the three contrasts, we have

$$SS_{\hat{\psi}_1} = \frac{(42 - 34)^2}{(2)(10)}$$

$$= 3.2$$

$$SS_{\hat{\psi}_2} = \frac{[42 + 34 - (2)(25)]^2}{(6)(10)}$$

$$= 11.267$$

$$SS_{\hat{\psi}_3} = \frac{[42 + 34 + 25 - (3)(88)]^2}{(12)(10)}$$

$$= \frac{26,569}{120}$$

$$= 221.408$$

Adding,

$$\sum_p SS_{\hat{\psi}_p} = 3.2 + 11.267 + 221.408$$

$$= 235.875$$

$$= SS_A$$

Many orthogonal sets other than the one just investigated could be obtained. Generally, contrasts are tested because they are of psychological interest, not because they are independent of each other. However, in Chapter 14 we will discuss sets of contrasts which are of psychological import and are also independent of each other. Therefore the concept of orthogonality has been discussed here.

13.3 NULL HYPOTHESIS TESTS AND CONFIDENCE INTERVALS FOR MULTIPLE COMPARISONS

Consider a completely randomized one-factor design. The contrast $\psi = \sum_j w_j \mu_j$ $(\sum_j w_j = 0)$ has the unbiased estimate

$$(13.9) \qquad \hat{\psi} = \sum_j w_j \overline{Y}_{.j}$$

The sampling variance of $\hat{\psi}$ is

$$\sigma_{\hat{\psi}}^2 = \sum_j w_j^2 \, \text{var} \, \overline{Y}_{.j}$$

$$(13.10) \qquad = \frac{\sum_j w_j^2 \, \text{var} \, (Y_{ij})}{n_j}$$

$$= \hat{\sigma}^2 \sum_j \frac{w_j^2}{n_j}$$

where n_j is the number of scores under treatment A_j. The estimate of $\sigma_{\hat{\psi}}^2$ is

$$S_{\hat{\psi}}^2 = S^2 \sum_j \frac{w_j^2}{n_j}$$

$$(13.11) \qquad = (MS_{S/A}) \sum_j \frac{w_j^2}{n_j}$$

The t statistic is the deviation of a quantity from its expected value (assuming H_0 to be true), divided by the sampling error of the quantity. Thus, a reasonable first step in assessing ψ would seem to be the calculation

$$(13.12) \qquad t = \frac{\sum_j w_j \overline{Y}_{.j}}{\sqrt{MS_{S/A}} \sqrt{\sum_j (w_j^2/n_j)}}$$

Alternatively, noting that an F with a single df quantity in the numerator is equal to t^2, we might calculate

$$(13.13) \qquad F = \frac{\left(\sum_j w_j \overline{Y}_{.j}\right)^2 \Big/ \sum_j (w_j^2/n_j)}{MS_{S/A}}$$

where the numerator is the $SS_{\hat{\psi}}$ of the preceding section.

How are we to assess the significance of the F presented above? Presumably, our obtained F is evaluated just as any other F on 1 and $\sum_j n_j - a$ df; the α level would be that used in assessing the F statistic for the test of the overall main effect. The problem with this intuitively reasonable approach is best illustrated by considering a series of tosses of a coin. Although the probability of a head on any one toss is .5, the probability of *at least one head* in a series of tosses is greater than .5, and the magnitude of this probability is a direct function of the total number of tosses. Similarly, any single test of a comparison has probability α of a Type I error.   However, as the number of comparisons made increases, the probability of *at least one Type I error increases*.   Note that the same problem exists if the largest observed contrast is selected for testing.   This is equivalent to testing all contrasts, since the probability that the largest observed contrast is significant is the probability that at least one contrast is significant.

The usual α level, the probability that a single comparison results in a Type I error, will be referred to as the *error rate per comparison* (*EC*).   The probability that an entire set of comparisons contains at least one Type I error will be referred to as the *error rate experimentwise* (*EW*).   The problem with holding the *EC* constant, regardless of the number of comparisons made, is not that this results in a high *EW*.   If the *EC* is very small, the *EW* will not be overly high.   The real problem lies in the difficulty of interpreting significance results independently of the size of the experiment.   Ideally, we want a criterion for significance such that the *EW* is constant regardless of the number of treatment groups.   Only in this way can we adequately compare the results of the same comparison in different experiments.   In effect, a rule is required for adjusting the *EC* downwards as the total number of comparisons increases, and adjusting in such a way that the change in the number of comparisons does not alter the *EW*.   Two such rules will be considered in the remainder of this section.

13.3.1   Scheffé's multiple comparison method

Assume a levels of the treatment variable A.   To test the null hypothesis that the pth contrast is zero, i.e., $\sum_j w_{jp}\mu_j = 0$, Scheffé* proposes that the F statistic of Equation (13.13) be evaluated against $(a-1)F_{\alpha;a-1,a(n-1)}$, where the criterion F is that required for significance at the α level on $a-1$ and $a(n-1)$ df.   (With unequal n, the denominator df are $\sum n_j - a$.)   The basis for this null hypothesis test is the following theorem (proved by Scheffé in Section 3.5 of his text): the probability is $1 - \alpha$ that the values of all contrasts simultaneously lie within the confidence intervals of the form,

$$(13.14) \qquad \hat{\psi}_p - S\hat{\sigma}_{\hat{\psi}_p} \leqq \psi_p \leqq \hat{\psi}_p + S\hat{\sigma}_{\hat{\psi}_p}$$

where $S^2 = (a-1)F_{\alpha;a-1,a(n-1)}$, $\hat{\psi}_p = \sum_j w_{jp}\bar{Y}_{.j}$, and $\hat{\sigma}_{\hat{\psi}_p}$ is the square root of the error term for the test of the overall main effect; e.g., $\hat{\sigma}_{\hat{\psi}_p} = \sqrt{MS_{S/A}}$ in a completely randomized one-factor design.   In previous chapters we were concerned with the interval estimation of a single parameter, and confidence was interpreted as the proportion of intervals containing the true parameter value.   Now each experiment involves the simultaneous estimation of several intervals, one for each possible contrast; confidence is the proportion of experiments in which all the contrasts are contained within their intervals.

If the probability that all contrasts are contained within their intervals

* See Supplementary Readings at the end of this chapter.

is $1 - \alpha$, the probability that at least one population contrast is not contained in its interval is α. In view of the discussion of confidence intervals and null hypothesis tests in Chapter 2, it follows that the probability of at least one Type I error within the set of possible contrasts is α. Thus, from the theorem preceding Equation (13.14), it follows that Scheffé's method holds the *EW* (rather than the *EC*) at α.

Experimenters who have used the Scheffé procedure (or, for that matter, the Tukey procedure which will be considered next), have sometimes been perplexed to find that a significant test of the overall main effect has not been followed by at least one significant contrast. If there is some difference within the set of μ_j, why is this difference not reflected within one of the subsets of μ_j which are subsequently considered? The answer lies in the fact that if the overall test is significant at the α level, at least the maximum possible contrast will also be significant at the α level. Unfortunately, the maximum possible contrast may have been of little interest, and therefore may not have been computed. There is no guarantee that the obvious contrasts (e.g., differences within pairs of means) or the contrasts most interesting for the psychologist will be significant when the overall F test is.

Related to the point just discussed is the fact that the power of the Scheffé test is equal to that of the overall F test only when the detection of the maximum possible contrast is at issue. The power to detect the significance of other contrasts is lower than that for the main effect test because the *EW* is held constant over the entire set of possible contrasts. Scheffé, recognizing the power problem, suggests that the *EW* be set at 10 per cent. This may strike some as heresy, but it should be noted that *EW* and *EC* are different concepts, and there is no reason to demand that traditional *EC* levels of significance be applied to the *EW*. Even with the *EW* at 10 per cent, the *EC* will generally be quite low.

13.3.2 Tukey's multiple comparison method

The statistical literature contains an overabundance of proposals for dealing with the multiple comparison-error rate problem. Of this variety of approaches, only the Scheffé and the Tukey *HSD* (honestly significant difference)* approaches hold the *EW* at α for the entire possible set of contrasts. Tukey's method is based on the distribution of q, the studentized range. This distribution is defined by first taking the range (R) for a set of a independent, normally distributed values. R is then divided by S, the estimate of the standard deviation of the values whose range is being considered. The sampling distribution of q is the sampling distribution of R/S and de-

---

* The Tukey method described in the text was presented in an unpublished talk. It is a slight modification of that presented in J. W. Tukey, "Quick and Dirty Methods in Statistics: Part II. Simple Analyses for Standard Designs," *Proceedings of the Fifth Annual Convention, American Society for Quality Control*, pp. 189–197 (1951).

pends upon a (the number of values ranged over) and upon the df associated with S. Significant values are presented in Table A-9 in the Appendix. Assuming a completely randomized one-factor design and assuming that the estimates of the treatment population means are independent and normally distributed and have homogeneous variances, the probability is $1 - \alpha$ that

$$(13.15) \quad \hat{\psi}_p - qS_{\bar{Y}}\left(\tfrac{1}{2}\sum_j |w_{jp}|\right) \leq \psi_p \leq \hat{\psi}_p + qS_{\bar{Y}}\left(\tfrac{1}{2}\sum_j |w_{jp}|\right)$$

for all values of p (i.e., for all possible contrasts), where $q = q_{\alpha;a,a(n-1)}$, the q required for significance at the α level when there are a means within the range and the error df are $a(n-1)$, $S_{\bar{Y}} = \sqrt{MS_{S/A}/n}$, and $|w_{jp}|$ is the absolute value of the jth weight for the pth contrast. To test the null hypothesis that

$$\psi = 0$$

we note whether

$$(13.16) \qquad \frac{\hat{\psi}}{S_{\bar{Y}}\left(\tfrac{1}{2}\sum_j |w_j|\right)} > q$$

or, as is more commonly done, whether

$$(13.17) \qquad \hat{\psi} > S_{\bar{Y}}\left(\tfrac{1}{2}\sum_j |w_j|\right)q$$

13.3.3 Comparison of the Scheffé and Tukey methods

Consider the contrast $\psi_3 = \mu_R + \mu_P + \mu_{RP} - 3\mu_{NRP}$, based on the illustrative experiment previously presented in this chapter. For the sample data of Section 13.2.3, $SS_{\psi_3} = 221.408$. Assuming that $MS_{S/A} = 15.00$, the F statistic to test the significance of ψ is $F = 221.408/15.00 = 14.76$. According to Scheffé, this statistic is evaluated against $a - 1$ (3, in our example) times the F required for significance at the α level, df equaling $a - 1$ and $a(n - 1)$. Letting $EW = 10$ per cent, and assuming $n = 10$, the criterion F is 6.75. The contrast is clearly significant at the 10 per cent level.

Next, we illustrate the Tukey test for the same contrast.

$$\hat{\psi}_3 = 3(8.8) - (4.2 + 3.4 + 2.5)$$

$$= 16.3$$

When $a = 4$, $df = 36$, and $\alpha = .10$, the q required for significance is 3.36. Therefore, we compute

$$S_{\bar{Y}}\left(\tfrac{1}{2}\sum_j |w_j|\right)q = \sqrt{\frac{15}{10}}\,(\tfrac{1}{2})(6)(3.36)$$

$$= 12.30$$

Since $16.30 > 12.30$, we again conclude that the contrast is significant at the 10 per cent level.

A comparison of the Scheffé and Tukey confidence intervals for the contrast just tested will clarify the relationship between these two approaches to the control of error rate. From Equation (13.14), we have the Scheffé 90 per cent interval:

$$16.30 - \sqrt{6.75}\,\sqrt{15.00} \leq \psi_p \leq 16.30 + \sqrt{6.75}\,\sqrt{15.00}$$

which reduces to $6.24 \leq \psi_p \leq 26.36$. From Equation (13.15), we have the Tukey 90 per cent interval:

$$16.30 - \sqrt{\frac{15}{10}}\,(\tfrac{1}{2})(6)(3.36) \leq \psi_p \leq 16.30 + \sqrt{\frac{15}{10}}\,(\tfrac{1}{2})(6)(3.36)$$

which reduces to $4.00 \leq \psi_p \leq 28.60$. Note that the Scheffé interval is narrower. In view of our discussion of confidence intervals and hypothesis tests (Section 2.5), it follows that the Scheffé procedure also provides a more powerful significance test. This will generally be true of contrasts involving more than two treatment means. The situation is somewhat different when each side of the contrast involves exactly one treatment. For example, suppose we contrast the R and NRP treatments. Then, $\hat{\psi}_p = 8.8 - 4.2 = 4.6$. The Scheffé 90 per cent interval is

$$4.60 - \sqrt{6.75}\,\sqrt{15.00} \leq \psi_p \leq 4.60 + \sqrt{6.75}\,\sqrt{15.00}$$

or $-5.46 \leq \psi_p \leq 14.66$. The Tukey 90 per cent interval is

$$4.60 - \sqrt{\frac{15}{10}}\,(\tfrac{1}{2})(2)(3.36) \leq \psi_p \leq 4.60 + \sqrt{\frac{15}{10}}\,(\tfrac{1}{2})(2)(3.36)$$

or $.50 \leq \psi_p \leq 8.70$. The Tukey approach provides a much narrower interval and consequently a more powerful test of the contrast. This will generally be true when the contrast involves only two treatments.

In attempting to evaluate the merits of the Scheffé and Tukey procedures, we note the following:

(a) The Scheffé procedure is less sensitive to violations of normality and homogeneity of variance assumptions.

(b) The Tukey procedure requires equal n, while the Scheffé procedure does not.

(c) Tables of the F statistic are more widely available than tables of the q statistic.

(d) As noted above, the Tukey procedure is more powerful for contrasts of the type, $\mu_j - \mu_{j'}$, while the Scheffé procedure is more powerful for more complex contrasts involving more than two treatment means.

If the n's are equal, and if the normality and homogeneity of variance assumptions appear reasonable, (d) should determine the choice of approach. When the experimenter is only interested in comparing two means at a time, the

Tukey procedure is preferred; if more complex processes are also to be investigated, the Scheffé procedure should be used.

13.3.4 Dunnett's test: comparing a control group with experimental groups

If one of the a groups is a control group, there are $a - 1$ nonindependent comparisons which may be of interest. In order to keep the error rate at α for the entire set of comparisons, the statistic,

$$\frac{\overline{Y}_{.j} - \overline{Y}_{c}}{\sqrt{MS_{S/A}[(1/n_j) + (1/n_c)]}}$$

is evaluated against the statistic d, whose distribution depends upon the value of a and the error df. Significant values of d are presented in Table A-10 in the Appendix. The null hypothesis test can also be carried out by determining whether

$$(13.18) \qquad \overline{Y}_{.j} - \overline{Y}_{c} > \left[\sqrt{MS_{S/A}\left(\frac{1}{n_j} + \frac{1}{n_c}\right)} \right] d_{\alpha;a,a(n-1)}$$

where $\overline{Y}_{c}$ is the mean of the control group, n_j and n_c are the numbers of observations in the jth experimental group and the control group, and $d_{\alpha;a,a(n-1)}$ is the value of d required for significance at the α level when there are a groups (including group C), with n measurements in a group. For designs other than the completely randomized one-factor, $MS_{S/A}$ and $a(n - 1)$ are replaced by the appropriate error term and error df, and the n's are always the numbers of observations on which the two means are based.

The probability is $1 - \alpha$ that all $a - 1$ confidence intervals include the true difference $(\mu_{.j} - \mu_c)$ if the confidence interval is computed as

$$(13.19) \quad (\overline{Y}_{.j} - \overline{Y}_{c}) - ds\sqrt{\frac{1}{n_j} + \frac{1}{n_c}} \leq \mu_j - \mu_c \leq (\overline{Y}_{.j} - \overline{Y}_{c}) + ds\sqrt{\frac{1}{n_j} + \frac{1}{n_c}}$$

where $s = MS_{\text{error}}$ and d is the d required for significance at the α level.

13.4 THE ANALYSIS OF INTERACTION

Suppose that we have selected a group of subjects who score high on the MMPI obsessive-compulsive scale (OC), a group that scores high on the psychopathic deviant (PD) scale, and a control (C) group consisting of subjects who are close to the mean on both measures. A second variable in the study is the type of motivation: gains and losses of money following correct and incorrect decisions in a gambling task (GL), gains for correct decisions but no losses for incorrect decisions (G), and losses for incorrect decisions but no gains for correct ones (L). We might attempt to determine whether the difference between the GL mean and the average of the combined G and L data varies with personality type. That is, we are interested in variability in the contrast $2\mu_{GL} - \mu_G - \mu_L$ as a function of personality type. This suggests that the interaction of personality and motivation is of interest, which is true but not sufficient to describe our goal. A significant interaction merely suggests that the spread among motivation effects is a function of personality; we want to know if the particular motivational contrast cited varies with personality. We might push our inquiry into the nature of the interaction still further. For example, it is possible to ask whether the contrast cited above is different for the PD population as compared to the same contrast for the OC population. In this case, we are interested in a contrast among contrasts, specifically,

$$(2\mu_{GL,OC} - \mu_{G,OC} - \mu_{L,OC}) - (2\mu_{GL,PD} - \mu_{G,PD} - \mu_{L,PD})$$

The first question involves the interaction of personality type with the pth component of motivation; i.e., pers $\times$ p(mot). The general form of the null hypothesis when we are considering contrasts among the means at the levels of A as a function of level of B (in our example, *motivation* would be A, *personality*, B) is

$$H_0: \sum_j w_j\mu_{j1} = \sum_j w_j\mu_{j2} = \cdots = \sum_j w_j\mu_{jb}$$

That is, the null hypothesis is that the pth contrast among the a treatment means is the same at all levels of B.

The second question raised above involves the interaction of the qth component of personality with the pth component of motivation; i.e., q(pers) $\times$ p(mot). The general form of the null hypothesis is

$$H_0: \sum_j \sum_k w_{j.}w_{.k}\mu_{jk} = 0$$

In this section we will present computations for significance tests of the two types of null hypotheses.

13.4.1 Calculations for $SS_{p(A) \times B}$ and its error terms

We are interested in whether the magnitude of the pth contrast among the means of the various levels of A changes as a function of the level of B. Computations for this sort of contrast are very similar to those for the sum of squares for a main effect. In the present case, we measure the variability of b contrasts about an average contrast; in the case of the main effect, we measure the variability of b means about a grand mean. This analogy suggests that the computations for $SS_{p(A) \times B}$ should involve $b - 1$ squared quantities, and that this sum of squares will be distributed on $b - 1$ df. We can develop a set of rules for establishing computational formulas for contrasts on the basis of df, just as we did with main and interaction effects in previous chapters. Knowing that there are $b - 1$ squared quantities, we begin with

$$\sum_k^b (\quad)^2 - (\quad)^2$$

Next, we place all summation signs which are not outside the parentheses inside them, yielding

$$\sum_k^b \left(\sum_i^n \sum_j^a \quad \right)^2 - \left(\sum_i^n \sum_j^a \sum_k^b \quad \right)^2$$

The weights and the data values are next considered, yielding

$$\sum_k^b \left(\sum_i^n \sum_j^a w_{jp} Y_{ijk} \right)^2 - \left(\sum_i^n \sum_j^a \sum_k^b w_{jp} Y_{ijk} \right)^2$$

We divide by the product of the sum of the squared weights times the number of scores that are summed at a level of A prior to squaring. Thus, the final result is

$$(13.20) \qquad SS_{p(A) \times B} = \frac{\sum_k^b \left(\sum_i^n \sum_j^a w_{jp} Y_{ijk} \right)^2}{n \sum_j w_{jp}^2} - \frac{\left(\sum_i^n \sum_j^a \sum_k^b w_{jp} Y_{ijk} \right)^2}{nb \sum_j w_{jp}^2}$$

Note that the "correction term" is actually $SS_{p(A)}$.

The application of Equation (13.20) is illustrated using the data of Table 13-1. The sum of squares will be calculated for $p(A) \times B$, where 2, -1,

TABLE 13-1

Data for a numerical example

		A_1	A_2	A_3	$\sum_j Y_{ijk}$	
		4	6	12	22	
B_1		5	9	14	28	$w_{1q} = 0$
		6	8	13	27	
		8	8	16	32	
$\sum_i Y_{ij1} = 23$			31	55	$\sum_i \sum_j Y_{ij1} = 109$	
		5	14	15	34	
B_2		7	12	18	37	$w_{2q} = +1$
		6	16	15	37	
		4	16	17	37	
$\sum_i Y_{ij2} = 22$			58	65	$\sum_i \sum_j Y_{ij2} = 145$	
		6	14	24	44	
B_3		4	14	22	40	$w_{3q} = -1$
		5	17	20	42	
		8	15	28	51	
$\sum_i Y_{ij3} = 23$			60	94	$\sum_i \sum_j Y_{ij3} = 177$	
$w_{jp} =$		2	-1	-1		

and -1 are the coefficients for A_1, A_2, and A_3, respectively. We first calculate $SS_{p(A)}$, multiplying the sum of all A_1 scores by 2, the sum of all A_2 scores by -1, and the sum of all A_3 scores by -1, squaring the sum of these three cross-products, and dividing by 72 ($= bn \sum_j w_j^2$):

$$SS_{p(A)} = [(2)(4 + 5 + \cdots + 5 + 8) - (6 + 9 + \cdots + 17 + 15)$$
$$- (12 + 14 + \cdots + 20 + 28)]^2/(12)(6)$$
$$= 715.68$$

To complete the sum of squares calculations, we carry out the above calculations at each level of B, and then sum the results:

$$\sum_k^b \frac{\left(\sum_i^n \sum_j^a w_{jp} Y_{ijk} \right)^2}{n} = \frac{[(2)(4 + \cdots + 8) - (6 + \cdots + 8) - (12 + \cdots + 16)]^2}{(4)(6)}$$
$$+ \cdots$$
$$+ \frac{[(2)(6 + \cdots + 8) - (14 + \cdots + 15) - (24 + \cdots + 28)]^2}{(4)(6)}$$
$$= 812.71$$

Combining terms,

$$SS_{p(A) \times B} = 812.71 - 715.68$$
$$= 97.03$$

In order to test the significance of the $p(A) \times B$ term, we form an F ratio, dividing the sum of squares by the associated df ($b - 1$, in our example), and then dividing this by an error mean square. The answer to the question of what is the appropriate error term depends upon the design and the structural model. We will consider several cases in turn.

(a) *Completely randomized; repeated measurements, additive model.* The appropriate error term for $p(A) \times B$ is the error term for the AB interaction effect. This would be $MS_{S/AB}$ in the completely randomized design and MS_{ABS} in the repeated measurements design, assuming no interactions involving subjects in the population.

(b) *Repeated measurements, nonadditive model.* Assuming the existence of σ_{ABS}^2, we have

$$E(MS_{p(A) \times B}) = \sigma_e^2 + \sigma_{S \times p(A) \times B}^2 + \theta_{p(A) \times B}^2$$

which would be tested against a mean square with expectation,

$$E(MS_{S \times p(A) \times B}) = \sigma_e^2 + \sigma_{S \times p(A) \times B}^2$$

We require a computational formula for $MS_{S \times p(A) \times B}$. The nature of the computations will be clearer if we better understand the nature of the interaction. What is involved is the variability of the contrasts among the a treatment means over the nb combinations of S and B, adjusting for the variability in the contrast that is due to S ($p(A) \times S$) and the variability in the contrast as a function of B ($p(A) \times B$). This is quite similar to the SB interaction effect; there our concern is with variability among means; here, it is with variability among contrasts. This analogy suggests $(n - 1)(b - 1)$ df. Using the df approach suggested earlier, we arrive at the formula

$$(13.21) \quad SS_{S \times p(A) \times B} = \frac{\sum\limits_{k}^{b} \sum\limits_{i}^{n} \left(\sum\limits_{j}^{a} w_{jp} Y_{ijk} \right)^2}{\sum\limits_{j}^{a} w_{jp}^2} - SS_{p(A)} - SS_{p(A) \times B}$$

$$- SS_{p(A) \times S}$$

We have already presented formulas for the $p(A) \times B$ and $p(A)$ terms. For the subject interaction, we have

$$(13.22) \quad SS_{p(A) \times S} = \frac{\sum\limits_{i}^{n} \left(\sum\limits_{j}^{a} \sum\limits_{k}^{b} w_{jp} Y_{ijk} \right)^2}{b \sum\limits_{j}^{a} w_{jp}^2} - SS_{p(A)}$$

Let us assume for Table 13-1 that the scores $\langle 4, 6, 12; 5, 14, 15; 6, 14, 24 \rangle$ all come from one subject, $\langle 5, 9, \cdots, 14, 22 \rangle$ from a second, and so on. Then we have scores under all nine treatment combinations for each of four subjects. Then,

$$SS_{p(A) \times S} = \frac{[2(4 + 5 + 6) - (6 + 14 + 14) - (12 + 15 + 24)]^2}{(3)(6)} + \cdots$$

$$+ \frac{[2(8 + 4 + 8) - (8 + 16 + 15) - (16 + 17 + 28)]^2}{(3)(6)} - SS_{p(A)}$$

$$= 720.61 - 715.68$$

$$= 4.93$$

In order to complete the calculations for $S \times p(A) \times B$, we require a measure of the variability in $p(A)$ over SB combinations, which is

$$SS_{\overline{S \times p(A) \times B}} = \frac{[(2)(4) - 6 - 12]^2 + \cdots + [(2)(8) - 15 - 28]^2}{6} - SS_{p(A)}$$

$$= 826.50 - 715.68$$

$$= 110.82$$

Finally, we have

$$SS_{S \times p(A) \times B} = SS_{\overline{S \times p(A) \times B}} - SS_{p(A) \times B} - SS_{p(A) \times S}$$
$$= 110.82 - 97.03 - 4.93$$
$$= 8.86$$

Suppose we desire an F test of the $p(A) \times B$ effect. Then,

$$MS_{p(A) \times B} = \frac{SS_{p(A) \times B}}{b - 1}$$

$$= \frac{97.03}{2}$$

$$= 48.52$$

and

$$MS_{S \times p(A) \times B} = \frac{SS_{S \times p(A) \times B}}{(n - 1)(b - 1)}$$

$$= \frac{8.86}{6}$$

$$= 1.48$$

Then,

$$F = \frac{48.52}{1.48}$$

$$= 32.78$$

(c) *One between- and one within-subjects variable.* Suppose B is a between-subjects variable and A is a within-subjects variable. (If A, the variable whose means are contrasted, is a between-subjects variable, the error term is just $MS_{S/A}$; partitioning of the overall error term is sensible only when there are repeated measurements on the variable whose means are contrasted.) Reasoning similar to that for the repeated measurements design leads us to

$$E(MS_{p(A) \times B}) = \sigma_e^2 + \sigma_{S \times p(A)/B}^2 + n\theta_{p(A) \times B}^2$$

and

$$E(MS_{S \times p(A)/B}) = \sigma_e^2 + \sigma_{S \times p(A)/B}^2$$

Essentially, we want to measure the variability of the contrast among subjects in a particular level of B, do this for each level of B, and then pool the results. Thus, there will be n contrasts corrected for their average contrast within a level of B. In short, there are $b(n - 1)$ squared quantities in the formula for $SS_{S \times p(A)/B}$, and this sum of squares is distributed on $b(n - 1)$ *df*. According to the approach to sums of squares developed earlier in this section, we begin with

$$\sum_k^b \sum_i^n (\quad)^2 - \sum_k^b (\quad)^2$$

Next, we place the remaining summations within the parentheses:

$$\sum_k^b \sum_i^n \left(\sum_j^a Y_{ijk} \right)^2 - \sum_k^b \left(\sum_i^n \sum_j^a Y_{ijk} \right)^2$$

The weights are still missing within the parentheses. Therefore, we have

$$\sum_k^b \sum_i^n \left(\sum_j^a w_{jp} Y_{ijk} \right)^2 - \sum_k^b \left(\sum_i^n \sum_j^a w_{jp} Y_{ijk} \right)^2$$

Division by $\sum_j^a w_{jp}^2$ times the number of scores within the parentheses at a level of j (the index of the weights) yields the final result:

$$(13.23) \quad SS_{S \times p(A)/B} = \frac{\sum\limits_k^b \sum\limits_i^n \left(\sum\limits_j^a w_{jp} Y_{ijk} \right)^2}{\sum\limits_j w_{jp}^2} - \frac{\sum\limits_k^b \left(\sum\limits_i^n \sum\limits_j^a w_{jp} Y_{ijk} \right)^2}{n \sum\limits_j w_{jp}^2}$$

The application of Equation (13.23) is illustrated by calculations on the data of Table 13-1, again assuming that we wish to contrast the effect of A_1 with the average A_2 and A_3 effect. In this case, we assume that there is a total of 12 subjects, four at each level of B. We have

$$SS_{S \times p(A)/B} = \frac{[(2)(4) - 6 - 12]^2 + \cdots + [(2)(8) - 15 - 28]^2}{6}$$

$$- \left\{ \frac{[(2)(4 + \cdots + 8) - (6 + \cdots + 8) - (12 + \cdots + 16)]^2}{(4)(6)} + \cdots \right.$$

$$+ \left. \frac{[(2)(6 + \cdots + 8) - (14 + \cdots + 15) - (24 + \cdots + 28)]^2}{(4)(6)} \right\}$$

$$= 826.50 - 812.71$$

$$= 13.79$$

To test the $p(A) \times B$ effect, we have

$$F = \frac{SS_{p(A) \times B}/(b - 1)}{SS_{p(A) \times S/B}/[b(n - 1)]}$$

$$= \frac{48.52}{13.79/9}$$

$$= 31.71$$

13.4.2 Single df components of interaction and their error terms

It was suggested earlier that contrasts among contrasts might be of interest in some studies. For example, does

$$(2\mu_{GL,OS} - \mu_{G,OS} - \mu_{L,OS}) - (2\mu_{GL,PD} - \mu_{G,PD} - \mu_{L,PD})$$

equal zero? We might speak of the pth contrast among motivation levels and the qth contrast among personality types, where

$$w_{1p} = 2, \qquad w_{2p} = -1, \qquad w_{3p} = -1$$
$$w_{1q} = 0, \qquad w_{2q} = 1, \qquad w_{3q} = -1$$

In general, the null hypothesis is

$$H_0 : \sum_j^a \sum_k^b w_{jp} w_{kq} \mu_{jk} = 0$$

The appropriate sum of squares is

$$(13.24) \qquad SS_{p(A) \times q(B)} = \frac{\left(\sum_{j}^{a} \sum_{k}^{b} \sum_{i}^{n} w_{jp} w_{kq} Y_{ijk} \right)^2}{n \sum_{j} \sum_{k} (w_{jp} w_{kq})^2}$$

This formula conforms to our dicussion of computational formulas in the preceding section. To see this, consider the product of $w_{jp} w_{kq}$ as a single weight, i.e., $w'_{jk,pq} = w_{jp} w_{kq}$. Then, since the quantity is on 1 df, we have first

$$(\quad)^2$$

All summations not outside the parentheses should be within the parentheses, yielding

$$\left(\sum_{j}^{a} \sum_{k}^{b} \sum_{i}^{n} \quad \right)^2$$

As before, we insert the weight and the score within the parentheses, yielding

$$\left(\sum_{j}^{a} \sum_{k}^{b} \sum_{i}^{n} w'_{jp,kq} Y_{ijk} \right)^2$$

We divide by the sum of the squared weights times the number of scores at each level of the index, jk. The final result is

$$(13.25) \qquad SS_{p(A) \times q(B)} = \frac{\left(\sum_{j}^{a} \sum_{k}^{b} \sum_{i}^{n} w'_{jp,kq} Y_{ijk} \right)^2}{n \sum_{j} \sum_{k} w'^2_{jp,kq}}$$

which is algebraically identical to that of Equation (13.24).

As an illustrative example, we apply Equation (13.24) to the data of Table 13-1:

$$SS_{p(A) \times q(B)} = \frac{[(0)(2)(23) + (0)(-1)(31) + \cdots + (-1)(-1)(94)]^2}{(4)(12)}$$
$$= 17.52$$

We next consider the error terms for this contrast among contrasts. If there are n different subjects in each of the ab cells, $MS_{S/AB}$ is the appropriate error term. If there are n subjects at each level of b, all of whom go through all levels of A, the error SS is given by Equation (13.23). If A is the between-subjects variable and B is the within-subjects variable, we modify Equation (13.23) by interchanging $\sum_{j}^{a}$ and $\sum_{k}^{b}$. Thus,

$$(13.23') \quad SS_{S \times q(B)/A} = \frac{\sum_{j}^{a} \sum_{i}^{n} \left(\sum_{k}^{b} w_{kq} Y_{ijk} \right)^2}{\sum_{k} w_{kq}^2} - \frac{\sum_{j}^{a} \left(\sum_{i}^{n} \sum_{k}^{b} w_{kq} Y_{ijk} \right)^2}{n \sum_{k} w_{kq}^2}$$

If all subjects go through all ab combinations, we require $SS_{S \times p(A) \times q(B)}$ for the error sum of squares. This is a measure of the variability of the $p(A) \times q(B)$ contrast over subjects. Then, we have n contrasts, one for each subject, deviated about their average. The result is

$$(13.26) \quad SS_{S \times p(A) \times q(B)} = \frac{\sum\limits_{i}^{n} \left(\sum\limits_{j}^{a} \sum\limits_{k}^{b} w_{jp} w_{kq} Y_{ijk} \right)^2}{\sum\limits_{j} \sum\limits_{k} (w_{jp} w_{kq})^2} - SS_{p(A) \times q(B)}$$

We apply this formula to the data of Table 13-1, again assuming four subjects with nine scores on each; e.g., $\langle 4, 6, 12; 5, 14, 15; 6, 14, 24 \rangle$ are assumed to come from S_1. We have

$$SS_{S \times p(A) \times q(B)} = \frac{[(0)(2)(4) + (0)(-1)(6) + \cdots + (-1)(-1)(24)]^2}{12} + \cdots$$

$$+ \frac{[(0)(2)(8) + (0)(-1)(8) + \cdots + (-1)(-1)(28)]^2}{12}$$

$$- 17.52$$

$$= 21.75 - 17.52$$

$$= 4.23$$

The F test of $p(A) \times q(B)$ would be

$$F = \frac{17.52}{4.23/3}$$

$$= \frac{17.52}{1.41}$$

$$= 12.43$$

13.5 CONCLUDING REMARKS

Much time and space has been devoted to some rather complex analyses of interaction which provide inferences about highly specific null hypotheses. This was done because it is felt that the fact that the AB interaction is significant is only a first step toward understanding the interaction. A significant F for a main effect merely tells us that some treatment population means differ, not which ones; similarly, a precise understanding of the nature of interaction only *begins* with the overall test.

The analysis of interaction involves the same error rate problems which were discussed in Section 13.3. The approach of that section generalizes readily to tests for null hypotheses of the form,

$$H_0: \sum_{j} \sum_{k} w_{jp} w_{kq} \mu_{jk} = 0$$

The criterion F will be $(a - 1)(b - 1)$ times the F required for significance at the α level, distributed on $(a - 1)(b - 1)$ and the error df. We do not have a specific solution when the null hypothesis is of the form

$$H_0: \sum_{j} w_j \mu_{j1} = \cdots = \sum_{j} w_j \mu_{jb} = 0$$

We can only note that such contrasts should be regarded with even more than the usual caution until further data are available.

EXERCISES

13.1 Consider the following anova table and group means (each mean is the sum of scores for the group divided by 75—15 subjects, five measurements each).

SV	df	SS	MS	F
Total	374	32,086.80		
Between S	74	27,938.15		
Groups	4	7,117.16	1,779.29	5.98*
S/G	70	20,820.99	297.44	
Within S	300	4,148.65		
Time	4	1,846.20	461.55	60.49*
$T \times G$	16	166.24	10.39	1.36
$S \times T/G$	280	2,136.21	7.63	

$$*p < .001$$

A	B	C	D	E
20.546	14.560	13.332	11.160	7.200

Perform both the Scheffé and Tukey tests, making all comparisons of the form A versus B, A versus C, etc.

13.2 (a) *GSR* measures are taken on parachutists. Measures are obtained on groups two weeks before the jump (*BJ*-2), one week before (*BJ*-1), on the day of the jump prior to jumping (*DJ*-*P*), and on the day of the jump after jumping (*DJ*-*A*). In addition, a control group of normal (nonparachuting) cowards is tested (*C*). The mean scores for the groups are:

BJ-2	BJ-1	DJ-A	DJ-P	C
5	5	7	9	2

One hypothesis is that parachutists two weeks before the jump behave similarly to the controls. Determine whether these two groups differ significantly from the other three groups. There are six subjects in each group, and the MS_W was 4.0.

(b) Suppose the above contrast was one of a number being tested. What would your criterion of significance then be? Find both the Scheffé and Tukey confidence intervals.

13.3 (a) Five groups of rats were run in a study on the effects of drugs upon performance. There were two levels of a depressant, two levels of a stimulant, and one no-drug group. The experimenter obtained a significant F on 4 df. He then desired to compare the two types of drugs. Give the formula for the sum of squares. What other orthogonal contrasts may now be made? Give *SS*. Supposing the experimenter desired to make some non-orthogonal contrasts. Give three contrasts which are not orthogonal to the first one. Describe a procedure for determining the significance level of each of a number of contrasts.

(b) Suppose equal concentrations of four different drugs and a control group were used. Now what tests should follow the initial F?

13.4 Compute the SS for numerator and denominator of each of the following contrasts, assuming that all subjects go through all levels of B:

(a) the mean for treatments B_1 and B_2 versus the mean for treatment B_3,

(b) the variability in the above contrast over the levels of A.

		B_1	B_2	B_3
A_1	S_{11}	4	5	3
	S_{21}	1	6	2
A_2	S_{12}	5	4	2
	S_{22}	3	7	4

SUPPLEMENTARY READINGS

A presentation of the derivation of the Scheffé test may be found in

SCHEFFÉ, HENRY, *The Analysis of Variance*. New York: Wiley, 1959.

Ryan has discussed the rationale underlying multiple comparison tests and has suggested some extensions of available tests in the following two articles:

RYAN, T. A., "Multiple Comparisons in Psychological Research," *Psychological Bulletin*, 56:26–47 (1959).

RYAN, T. A., "Significance Tests for Multiple Comparison of Proportions, Variances, and Other Statistics," *Psychological Bulletin*, 57:318–328 (1960).

Wilson has criticized Ryan's approach. Ryan expanded his original discussion in a reply to Wilson. The references are

WILSON, W., "A Note on the Inconsistency Inherent in the Necessity to Perform Multiple Comparisons," *Psychological Bulletin*, 59:296–300 (1962).

RYAN, T. A., "The Experiment as the Unit for Computing Rate of Error," *Psychological Bulletin*, 59:301–305 (1962).

FURTHER DATA ANALYSES:

QUANTITATIVE INDEPENDENT VARIABLES

14

14.1 INTRODUCTION

In Chapter 13 various procedures for comparing the means of treatment groups were discussed. The primary concern was answering questions which seem most appropriate when the independent variable is qualitative. Certainly it is possible to investigate the contrasts of the previous chapter even when the independent variable is quantitative; however, with quantitative variables it will usually be more interesting to consider the overall trend in the treatment group means rather than to make the specific comparisons among means which were the chief concern in Chapter 13. The formulas are basically the same for quantitative and qualitative contrasts. This being the case, the main topic of the present chapter will be development of the rationale for the evaluation of trend.

In order to illustrate more precisely the purposes of trend analysis and the types of questions that it can answer, we consider an experiment on signal detection. A subject sits a fixed distance from a 25-sq. ft. screen. Every ten seconds, a small circle of light appears on the screen, and the subject must report the location of this target. Detection time is recorded by the experimenter. One independent variable is the intensity of the target illumination. A second variable is the structure of the screen, which may be one open area, or which may be divided by a vertical line into two equal segments or by two vertical lines into three equal segments, and so on. The experimenter hypothesizes that a certain amount of segmenting of the screen facilitates the search. However, there will be some point at which further segmenting will actually result in deterioration of performance; the subject will become confused and will repeatedly search the same segment, thus losing time.   It is further hypothesized that this optimal number of segments will be a function of intensity of illumination.   The higher the illumination, the higher will be the optimal number of segments.   Figure 14-1 illustrates one way the data might look if the experimenter's hypotheses were correct.

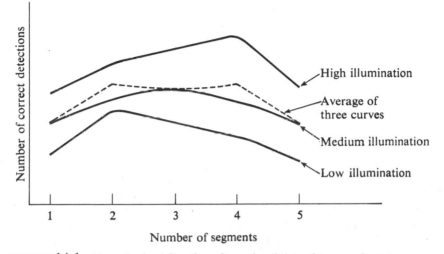

FIGURE 14-1   Hypothesized functions for a signal detection experiment

In Figure 14-1 the behavioral hypotheses mentioned above have been translated into hypotheses about performance trends over numbers of segments.   With regard to the average curve—the plot of the main effect, segments—one might note that (a) if a straight line were fitted to this curve, its slope would be zero, and (b) the function appears to be better fitted by a curved than by a straight line.   The behavioral hypotheses also lead to definite inferences about the three intensity curves.   If a straight line were fitted to each, the three lines would have different slopes.   Furthermore, it appears that the three functions differ in their shapes.

In view of the initial hypotheses, and of Figure 14-1, which provides one plausible representation of the hypotheses, it seems that tests are required to answer such questions as

(a) Does the plot of mean detection time as a function of number of segments have a slope other than zero?

(b) Is the plot of mean detection time as a function of segments adequately fitted by a straight line?

(c) Do the three plots of detection time against segments differ in slope?

(d) Do the three plots of detection time against segments differ in shape?

The computations involved in answering questions such as these about the shapes and slopes of functions come under the general heading of trend analysis. In the succeeding sections, a detailed consideration of the rationale and mechanics of trend analysis will be presented.

14.2 THE COMPLETELY RANDOMIZED ONE-FACTOR DESIGN

14.2.1 Partial analysis

We begin with a very simple trend analysis: an subjects are randomly distributed among a treatment groups, the treatment levels are equally spaced along some quantitative continuum (e.g., 2, 4, 6, or 8 food pellets), and the variability among the treatment means is partially analyzed into two components, one of which is distributed on 1 df and the other on $a - 2$ df. In Section 14.2.2 we will present a complete analysis of the SS_A into $a - 1$ components, each distributed on a single df. In Section 14.3 the complete analysis will be extended to multi-factor designs, and in Section 14.4, computations will be presented for the case when the levels are not equally spaced.

In broad terms, there are two possible sources of significant variability among treatment means: linearity and deviations from linearity. Linearity describes the condition in which the means differ because there is some overall improvement or impairment of performance with increases in the independent variable; the slope of the line of best fit is not zero. This situation is depicted in the upper panel of Figure 14-2. The treatment means may also differ significantly because the best fitting function deviates from a straight line. This is the case in the middle panel of Figure 14-2. Significant variability among treatment means may reflect both linearity and deviations from linearity as in the bottom panel of Figure 14-2. As indicated in the signal detection example presented in Section 14.1, knowing whether either or both sources are significant may be important to an evaluation of the experimenter's hypotheses. In any event, it is only through the further analysis of a main effect that a precise quantitative description of the effects of quantitative independent variables can be obtained.

The test for linearity is a test to determine whether the best fitting straight line has a slope significantly different from zero. (It is important to understand that the best fitting straight line may not be a good fit, as is the case in the bottom panel of Figure 14-2; it is that line about which the sums of squared deviations of treatment means are minimal.) Letting X_j be the level of the independent variable (e.g., X_j might be two food pellets), the null hypothesis in question is

H_0: The regression of the μ_j on X_j is zero.

From Chapter 12 on covariance, we know that the appropriate regression coefficient is

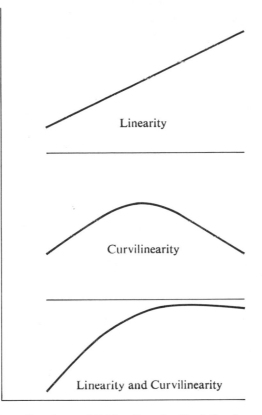

FIGURE 14-2   Some functions exhibiting linearity (deviation from a slope of zero) and curvilinearity (deviation from a straight line)

$$b = \frac{\sum\limits_{j} (\mu_j - \mu)(X_j - \overline{X}.)}{\sum\limits_{j} (X_j - \overline{X}.)^2}$$

the numerator of which must be zero if the null hypothesis is true.   Thus the null hypothesis that the slope of the best fitting line is zero is restated as

$$H_0: \sum_{j} (\mu_j - \mu)(X_j - \overline{X}.) = 0$$

If $X_j - \overline{X}.$ is relabeled as w_j, the null hypothesis is identical in form to the contrasts introduced in Section 13.1.   It therefore follows that Equation (13.6) provides the SS_{lin}, which is distributed on 1 df and is the numerator of the F test of the null hypothesis stated above.

As an example of the calculations, assume that there are four delays of reward in an experiment in discrimination learning.   The delays are 5, 10, 15, and 20 sec.   The group error totals, each based on ten subjects, are 22,

28, 36, and 48, respectively.   The values of $X_j - \overline{X}_.$ are $-7.5, -2.5, 2.5$, and 7.5.   We know from Chapter 13 that the multiplication or division of all weights by a constant does not change the sum of squares, and we therefore divide by 2.5, obtaining

$$w_1 = -3 \qquad w_2 = -1 \qquad w_3 = 1 \qquad w_4 = 3$$

Applying Equation (13.6), we have

$$SS_{\text{lin}} = \frac{[(-3)(22) + (-1)(28) + (1)(36) + (3)(48)]^2}{(10)(20)}$$

$$= \frac{(86)^2}{200}$$

$$= 36.98$$

Dividing SS_{lin} by $MS_{S/A}$, we have an F test to determine whether the slope of the best fitting straight line deviates significantly from zero.

The variability of the treatment means about the best fitting straight line may be chance variability or it may represent a curvilinear trend in the population.   To determine whether or not the deviations from linearity are significant, we compute $SS_{\text{dev lin}} = SS_A - SS_{\text{lin}}$; this quantity is distributed on $(a - 1) - 1$, or $a - 2$, df.   Dividing by the df and then by the $MS_{S/A}$, we have an F test to determine whether the data points are best fitted by a straight line or a curved function.   The latter inference would be drawn if the deviations from linearity proved to be significant.

14.2.2 Complete analysis

In the preceding section, the SS_A was partitioned into two components, one distributed on a single df (SS_{lin}) and one distributed on $a - 2$ df ($SS_{\text{dev lin}}$). The developments of Chapter 13 suggest that the $SS_{\text{dev lin}}$ can be further analyzed into $a - 2$ single df components, which are distributed independently of each other and of SS_{lin}. This further analysis will be carried out in the present section, but first some understanding of the nature of the orthogonal (independent) components is necessary.

We begin our discussion of the complete trend analysis by noting that any a data points may be described by an equation having the general form

(14.1) $\qquad Y = b_0 + b_1 X + b_2 X^2 + \cdots + b_p X^p + \cdots + b_{a-1} X^{a-1}$

Equations of this form are referred to as *polynomial functions of order a* − 1. Figure 14-3 presents several such functions, each labeled by the appropriate equation.   Note the restriction that if there are a points, the order of the polynomial is at most $a - 1$ (it can be less, since b_{a-1}, b_{a-2}, etc., can be zero). To understand why this is so, consider a first order polynomial, the straight line

(14.2) $\qquad\qquad\qquad Y = b_0 + b_1 X$

At least two data points are required in order to estimate the parameters, b_0 and b_1. Similarly, three data points are required in order to fit a second-order polynomial, otherwise known as a quadratic function,

(14.3) $$Y = b_0 + b_1X + b_2X^2$$

since three parameters are to be estimated. In general, a polynomial of order

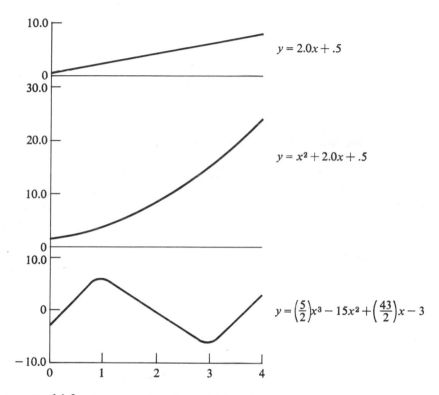

FIGURE 14-3 Some sample polynomial functions

$a - 1$ involves the estimation of a parameters, and at least that many data points are required.

For the purpose of the complete trend analysis, it is important to know that any polynomial function may be analyzed into $a - 1$ orthogonal polynomial functions of order 1, 2, $\cdots$, $a - 1$, respectively. This view of a polynomial as a sum of orthogonal polynomials involves replacing Equation (14.1) by

(14.4) $$Y = b_0' + b_1'\xi_1 + b_2'\xi_2 + \cdots + b_p'\xi_p + \cdots + b_{a-1}'\xi_{a-1}$$

where the ξ_p's are *orthogonal coefficients* such that

$$\xi_1 = \alpha_1 + X$$

$$\xi_2 = \alpha_2 + \beta_2 X + X^2$$

(14.5)
$$\vdots$$
$$\xi_p = \alpha_p + \beta_p X + \gamma_p X^2 + \cdots + X^p$$
$$\vdots$$

$$\xi_{a-1} = \alpha_{a-1} + \beta_{a-1} X + \gamma_{a-1} X^2 + \cdots + X^{a-1}$$

An independent sum of squares can be computed for each of the ξ_p. Such quantities permit testing of the null hypothesis that the pth component does not contribute to the true (population) function; i.e., we test the null hypothesis that $b'_p = 0$. Before considering calculations for $SS_{p(A)}$ (the sum of squares for the pth orthogonal component of the A main effect; this is the same notation used in Chapter 13), we will further explore the meaning of the orthogonal components.

Returning to the example of the signal detection experiment, we find that the experimenter's concern with the segment main effect is essentially a matter of determining whether b'_1 and b'_2 are significantly different from zero; i.e., are either the linear or quadratic components significant? Suppose that the segment means fell as in Figure 14-4. If the linear component is signifi-

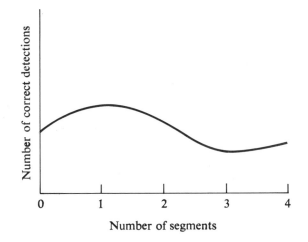

FIGURE 14-4 Possible outcome of a signal detection experiment

cant, we conclude that there is an overall deterioration in performance. If the quadratic component is also significant, we conclude that some type of inverted U-shaped function is contributing to the true performance curve. Suppose that the cubic (third order) component is also significant. The conclusion would be that the curve contains both a maxima and a minima point; the upturn from the fourth to the fifth level of segments is not just chance variation. Such an occurrence would be a signal to the investigator to re-examine the theoretical position which has led him to postulate only a linear and quadratic component.

If the levels of the quantitative independent variable are equally spaced, numerical values of ξ' can be obtained from Table A-11 in the Appendix (we speak of ξ' rather than ξ because non-integer values of ξ have been multiplied by a constant to yield integer values, i.e., the ξ'). In Section 14.4 we shall illustrate a method for deriving values of ξ' for any set of levels of the independent variable, whether equally spaced or not. For the present, we will assume equal spacing and use the ξ' values in Table A-11.

As an example of the calculations, assume that we have the following treatment totals:

A_1	A_2	A_3	A_4
22	22	20	36

Further assume that $n = 10$ and $MS_{S/A} = 1.2$. We have

$$SS_A = \frac{(22)^2 + \cdots + (36)^2}{10} - \frac{(22 + \cdots + 36)^2}{40}$$

$$= 16.4$$

Applying Equation (13.6) with w_{jp} first equal to the ξ'_{j1}, we have

$$SS_{\text{lin} (A)} = \frac{[(-3)(22) + (-1)(22) + (1)(20) + (3)(36)]^2}{(10)(20)}$$

$$= 8.0$$

Using the ξ'_2 next, we have

$$SS_{\text{quad} (A)} = \frac{(-22 + 22 + 20 - 36)^2}{(10)(4)}$$

$$= 6.4$$

The cubic contrast yields

$$SS_{\text{cub} (A)} = \frac{[-22 + (3)(22) + (-3)(20) + 36]^2}{(10)(20)}$$

$$= 2.0$$

Note that

$$SS_A = SS_{\text{lin} (A)} + SS_{\text{quad} (A)} + SS_{\text{cub} (A)}$$

which must be true if our calculations are correct. Only the linear and quadratic components are significant; we conclude that the cubic sum of squares reflects chance variability.

The upper panel of Figure 14-5 contains plots of b'_0, $b'_1 \xi'_1$ and $b'_2 \xi'_2$ for the data set just analyzed. The parameter b'_0 is merely $\overline{Y}_{..}$; other coefficients are obtained from the general expression

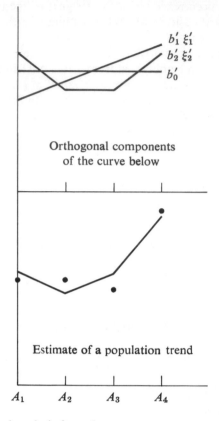

FIGURE 14-5   Trend analysis for a data set

$$(14.6) \qquad b'_p = \frac{\sum_j \xi_{jp} \overline{Y}_{.j}}{\sum_j (\xi_{jp}^2/n_j)}$$

Our numerical coefficients are

$$b'_0 = \frac{22 + 22 + 20 + 36}{40} = 2.5$$

$$b'_1 = \frac{(-3)(2.2) - 2.2 + 2.0 + (3)(3.6)}{2} = 2.0$$

$$b'_2 = \frac{2.2 - 2.2 - 2.0 + 3.6}{.4} = 4.0$$

Since the cubic coefficient was not significant, we assume the population value of b'_3 to be zero and consequently do not estimate a cubic component. As required by Equation (14.4), we literally sum the orthogonal components plotted in the upper panel of Figure 14-5. The result is the second-order polynomial plotted in the bottom panel. This function is not the function which best fits the data points; a perfect fit could be obtained by adding in $b'_3\xi'_3$. However, we do not wish to fit the data points (the $\overline{Y}_{.j}$); our goal is to describe the plot of the population values (the μ_j). Since our analysis has led us to conclude that the cubic component is not significant, the curve in the lower panel of Figure 14-5 is our estimate of the population function. The variability of data points about that function is assumed to be error variability, rather than the result of a cubic component in the population function.

14.3 MULTI-FACTOR DESIGNS

14.3.1 The analysis of interaction

We have thus far considered the orthogonal components of a main effect. This analysis enables us to answer several specific questions, such as, Is the slope of the best fitting straight line significantly different from zero? Is there quadratic curvature? Other questions arise when the design involves more than one independent variable. If there is a significant interaction between the variables A and B, and if A is a quantitative variable, we might wish to investigate further the source of the interaction. Why are the b curves not parallel? Do they differ in their slopes? In their quadratic components? In their cubic components? These questions imply tests of the null hypothesis that the b'_p are the same for all values of k (levels of B). For example, the comparison of slopes involves testing the null hypothesis

$$H_0: b'_{11} = b'_{21} = \cdots = b'_{k1} = \cdots b'_{b1}$$

Consider carefully what is implied. There are b curves, each plotted over the levels of A. We wish to compare the b linear components of A, then the b quadratic components of A, and so on. There are $a - 1$ possible comparisons of this type, i.e., as many as there are orthogonal components of the A effect. In general, we are interested in testing the interaction of the pth component of A with the levels of B, in determining whether the pth component of A varies as a function of the level of B. The relevant source of variance is labeled $p(A) \times B$, following our practice in Section 13.4.1. The calculations and df are exactly those presented in Chapter 13, with the w_{jp} of the sum of squares formula replaced by the appropriate ξ'_{jp}. The error terms are also those presented in Section 13.4.1 and are dictated by the design and analysis of variance model.

In Section 13.4.2 we considered the complete analysis of interaction into $(a - 1)(b - 1)$ components, each distributed on a single df. Replacing the w's by ξ's, the same breakdowns are possible in trend analysis. For example, suppose that there are four performance curves, each obtained under a different training method (A), plotted over five blocks of trials (B). In our analysis of the interaction of trend components, we would first test the source, lin $(B) \times A$, which represents the variability of the slopes of the four curves. If this is significant, the slopes differ as a function of training method. Additional hypotheses may now be considered. For example, the average slope of the A_1 and A_2 curves may differ from the average slope of the A_3 and A_4 curves. In this case, we are concerned with lin $(B) \times p(A)$ (p represents the contrast of A_1 and A_2 against A_3 and A_4), whose sum of squares is distributed on a single df. Two sets of weights are involved:

$$
\begin{array}{lll}
\xi_{11} = -2 & & w_{1p} = +1 \\
\xi_{21} = -1 & & w_{2p} = +1 \\
\xi_{31} = 0 & \text{and} & w_{3p} = -1 \\
\xi_{41} = +1 & & w_{4p} = -1 \\
\xi_{51} = +2 & &
\end{array}
$$

Given these weights, we proceed to calculate $SS_{\text{lin } (B) \times p(A)}$ as we calculated $SS_{q(B) \times p(A)}$ in Section 13.4.2. Calculation of error terms again follows directly from the developments in Chapter 13.

Suppose that in the experiment just described, A is also a quantitative variable, for example, amount of practice. Then, there are two sets of ξ's, enabling us to obtain such terms as lin $(A) \times$ lin (B) and quad $(A) \times$ cub (B). The calculations are the same as for any single df component of interaction. The interpretation is somewhat more complicated than before. Let us consider the specific case of the lin $(A) \times$ lin (B) source. In the upper panel of Figure 14-6 are plotted the cell means for a two-factor experiment (solid lines). Furthermore, the linear component, the best fitting straight line (dashed lines), is plotted for each curve. The magnitude of the variability among the slopes of the linear components will be reflected in the magnitude of $SS_{\text{lin } (B) \times A}$. The a linear regression coefficients have themselves been plotted as a function of the level of A in the bottom panel of Figure 14-6. The $SS_{\text{lin } (A) \times \text{lin } (B)}$ reflects the extent to which the best fitting straight line in the bottom panel deviates from a slope of zero. It enables us to measure the extent to which the plot of the linear coefficients exhibits a linear trend. The $SS_{\text{quad } (A) \times \text{lin } (B)}$ would reflect the quadratic curvature in the plot of the linear coefficients in the bottom panel of Figure 14-6. The $SS_{\text{lin } (A) \times \text{quad } (B)}$ would imply a plot of the b quadratic coefficients and would reflect the extent to which they exhibited a trend away from a slope of zero. As an illustration of the application of these analyses, suppose that we are interested in determining the function which describes the relation of dark adaptation rate (i.e., the slope of the dark adaptation curve over time) to the intensity of a pre-adapting light. If we let A represent intensity and B time, the $SS_{\text{lin } (B) \times A}$ would permit us to test the hypothesis that dark adaptation rate varied as a function of pre-adapting intensity. A significant lin $(A) \times$ lin (B) source might indicate that the rate decreased as pre-adapting intensity increased.

Investigation of the interaction of other components of A with lin (B) would provide further information about changes in dark adaptation rate as a function of pre-adapting intensity.

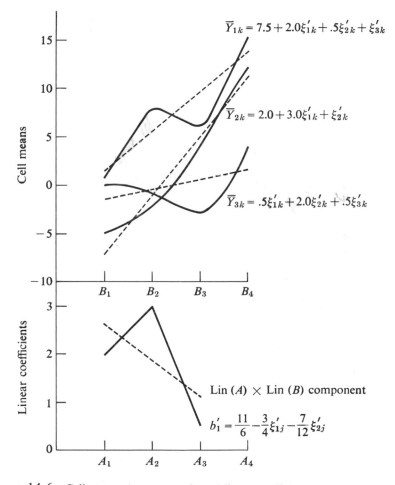

FIGURE 14-6 Cell means (upper panel) and linear coefficients (lower panel) of a two-factor experiment

Before proceeding to a numerical example, it may be wise to summarize the analysis of the interaction source. Assuming that B is a quantitative scaled variable, we may examine the variation in the qth component of B as a function of the levels of A. Therefore, our first breakdown of the AB source yields

SV	df
AB	$(a-1)(b-1)$
lin $(B) \times A$	$a-1$
quad $(B) \times A$	$a-1$
.	.
.	.
.	.
$q(B) \times A$	$a-1$
.	.
.	.
.	.
$(b-1)(B) \times A$	$a-1$

Each of the above sources may be further analyzed by assigning weights to the levels of A.   If A is also a quantitative variable, we obtain

SV	df
AB	$(a-1)(b-1)$
lin $(B) \times A$	$a-1$
lin $(B) \times$ lin (A)	1
lin $(B) \times$ quad (A)	1
.	.
.	.
.	.
lin $(B) \times p(A)$	1
.	.
.	.
.	.
lin $(B) \times (a-1)(A)$	1
quad $(B) \times A$	$a-1$
quad $(B) \times$ lin (A)	1
.	.
.	.
.	.
quad $(B) \times p(A)$	1
.	.
.	.
.	.
quad $(B) \times (a-1)(A)$	1
$q(B) \times A$	$a-1$
$q(B) \times$ lin (A)	1
.	.
.	.
.	.
$q(B) \times p(A)$	1
.	.
.	.
.	.
$q(B) \times (a-1)(A)$	1

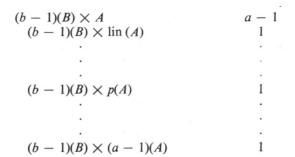

$(b - 1)(B) \times A$	$a - 1$
$(b - 1)(B) \times \lin (A)$	1
.	.
.	.
.	.
$(b - 1)(B) \times p(A)$	1
.	.
.	.
.	.
$(b - 1)(B) \times (a - 1)(A)$	1

The sum of squares formulas and error terms follow from Chapter 13. However, to ensure that the application is clear, we proceed to a numerical example involving two quantitative variables.

14.3.2 A numerical example

We assume three equally spaced levels of the independent variable A and five equally spaced levels of the independent variable B with four scores in each cell. The data, together with various totals and sub-totals, are presented in Table 14-1. The appropriate sets of orthogonal coefficients, taken from Table A-11 are also present. The total variability is calculated in the usual way:

$$SS_{tot} = (20)^2 + (18)^2 + \cdots + (7)^2 - \frac{(802)^2}{60}$$

$$= 11{,}792.000 - 10{,}720.067$$

$$= 1{,}071.933$$

For the A main effect, we have

$$SS_A = \frac{(344)^2 + (233)^2 + (225)^2}{20} - 10{,}720.067$$

$$= 442.433$$

and for B,

$$SS_B = \frac{(205)^2 + \cdots + (132)^2}{12} - 10{,}720.067$$

$$= 405.433$$

We next compute the variability due to polynomial components according to Equation (13.6):

$$SS_{\lin (A)} = \frac{[-344 + (0)(233) + 225]^2}{(20)(2)}$$

$$= 354.025$$

and

$$SS_{\quad (A)} = \frac{[344 + (-2)(233) + 225]^2}{(20)(6)}$$

$$= 88.408$$

TABLE 14-1

Data for a trend analysis

		A_1	A_2	A_3	$\sum_j Y_{ijk}$	ξ'_{k1}	ξ'_{k2}	ξ'_{k3}	ξ'_{k4}
		20	18	16	54				
B_1		18	17	15	50				
		19	18	17	54	-2	2	-1	1
		16	16	15	47				
$\sum_i Y_{ij1} =$		73	69	63	$\sum_i \sum_j Y_{ij1} = 205$				
		18	15	14	47				
B_2		18	16	13	47				
		17	14	14	45	-1	-1	2	-4
		16	13	13	42				
$\sum_i Y_{ij2} =$		69	58	54	$\sum_i \sum_j Y_{ij2} = 181$				
		16	12	11	39				
B_3		18	13	14	45				
		17	12	13	42	0	-2	0	6
		16	10	12	38				
$\sum_i Y_{ij3} =$		67	47	50	$\sum_i \sum_j Y_{ij3} = 164$				
		15	5	6	26				
B_4		18	8	8	34				
		17	7	9	33	1	-1	-2	-4
		17	5	5	27				
$\sum_i Y_{ij4} =$		67	25	28	$\sum_i \sum_j Y_{ij4} = 120$				
		17	7	6	30				
B_5		18	10	9	37				
		18	9	8	35	2	2	1	1
		15	8	7	30				
$\sum_i Y_{ij5} =$		68	34	30	$\sum_i \sum_j Y_{ij5} = 132$				
$\sum_i \sum_k Y_{ijk} =$		344	233	225	$\sum_i \sum_j \sum_k Y_{ijk} = 802$				
	ξ_{j1}	-1	0	1					
	ξ_{j2}	1	-2	1					

The sum of the above two terms is 442.433, which equals SS_A, as it should. Partitioning SS_B, we obtain

$$SS_{\text{lin }(B)} = \frac{[(-2)(205) - 181 + (0)(164) + 120 + (2)(132)]^2}{(12)(10)}$$

$$= \frac{(207)^2}{120}$$

$$= 357.075$$

$$SS_{\text{quad }(B)} = \frac{[(2)(205) - 181 + (-2)(164) - 120 + (2)(132)]^2}{(12)(14)}$$

$$= \frac{(45)^2}{168}$$

$$= 12.054$$

$$SS_{\text{cub }(B)} = \frac{[-205 + (2)(181) \mid (0)(164) + (-2)(120) + 132]^2}{(12)(10)}$$

$$= \frac{(49)^2}{120}$$

$$= 20.008$$

and

$$SS_{\text{quart }(B)} = \frac{[205 + (-4)(181) + (6)(164) + (-4)(120) + 132]^2}{(12)(70)}$$

$$= \frac{(117)^2}{840}$$

$$= 16.296$$

Summing the four components, we obtain SS_B.

The interaction sum of squares is obtained as in previous chapters; thus

$$SS_{AB} = \frac{(73)^2 + (69)^2 + \cdots (30)^2}{4} - C - SS_A - SS_B$$

$$= 151.067$$

There are two ways to partition the AB variability; the choice depends on the questions that are asked of the data. We may compare the five curves (one at each level of B) with respect to the linear and quadratic components of A; then we are concerned with $SS_{p(A) \times B}$. Alternatively, we may compare the three curves (one at each level of A) with respect to each of the four components of B; then we are concerned with $SS_{q(B) \times A}$. The choice of approach does not affect the subsequent further analysis of interaction into $(a - 1)(b - 1)$ single df components of the form $p(A) \times q(B)$. For simplicity, we will assume that our primary interest lies in plotting a curve for each level of A over the five B_k data points and, therefore, in assessing $q(B) \times A$. Then, according to Equation (13.20),

$$SS_{\text{lin} (B)\times A} = \frac{[(-2)(73) - 69 + (0)(67) + 67 + (2)(68)]^2}{(4)(10)}$$

$$+ \frac{[(-2)(69) - 58 + (0)(47) + 25 + (2)(34)]^2}{(4)(10)}$$

$$+ \frac{[(-2)(63) - 54 + (0)(50) + 28 + (2)(30)]^2}{(4)(10)} - SS_{\text{lin} (B)}$$

$$= 123.350$$

Calculations of $SS_{\text{quad} (B)\times A}$, $SS_{\text{cub} (B)\times A}$, and $SS_{\text{quart} (B)\times A}$ are parallel to the above. We merely use a different set of ξ'. For example,

$$SS_{\text{quad} (B)\times A} = \frac{[(2)(73) - 69 + (-2)(67) - 67 + (2)(68)]^2}{(4)(14)}$$

$$+ \frac{[(2)(69) - 58 + (-2)(47) - 25 + (2)(34)]^2}{(4)(14)}$$

$$+ \frac{[(2)(63) - 54 + (-2)(50) - 28 + (2)(30)]^2}{(4)(14)} - SS_{\text{quad} (B)}$$

$$= 5.821$$

Similar manipulations yield

$$SS_{\text{cub} (B)\times A} = 13.067$$

and

$$SS_{\text{quart} (B)\times A} = 8.829$$

Each of the above four sum of squares components is distributed on 2 *df*, indicating the possibility of further partitioning. For example,

$$SS_{\text{lin} (B)\times A} = SS_{\text{lin} (B)\times \text{lin} (A)} + SS_{\text{lin} (B)\times \text{quad} (A)}$$

We compute these single *df* components as follows:

$$SS_{\text{lin} (B)\times \text{lin} (A)} = \frac{[(-2)(-1)(73) + (-2)(0)(69) + \cdots + (2)(1)(30)]^2}{(4)(20)}$$

$$= 80$$

and

$$SS_{\text{lin} (B)\times \text{quad} (A)} = \frac{[(-2)(1)(73) + (-2)(-2)(69) + \cdots + (2)(1)(30)]^2}{(4)(60)}$$

$$= 43.350$$

The complete breakdown of the interaction sum of squares is presented in Table 14-2.

We will now consider appropriate error terms for three experimental designs: completely randomized, repeated measurements ($S \times A \times B$), and a mixed design in which B is a between-subjects variable.

Completely randomized. Assume that each of the 60 scores in Table

14-1 represents a different subject. Then, all terms in the analysis of variance are tested against $MS_{S/AB}$. The results are presented in Table 14-2.

Repeated measurements. Assume that the first row at each level of B in Table 14-1 represents the performance of a single subject, that the second

TABLE 14-2*

Trend analyses for three two-factor designs

SV	df	SS
A	2	442.433
lin (A)	1	354.025
quad (A)	1	88.408
B	4	405.433
lin (B)	1	357.075
quad (B)	1	12.054
cub (B)	1	20.008
quart (B)	1	16.296
AB	8	151.067
lin $(B) \times A$	2	123.350
lin $(B) \times$ lin (A)	1	80.000
lin $(B) \times$ quad (A)	1	43.350
quad $(B) \times A$	2	5.821
quad $(B) \times$ lin (A)	1	.571
quad $(B) \times$ quad (A)	1	5.250
cub $(B) \times A$	2	13.067
cub $(B) \times$ lin (A)	1	5.000
cub $(B) \times$ quad (A)	1	8.067
quart $(B) \times A$	2	8.829
quart $(B) \times$ lin (A)	1	7.779
quart $(B) \times$ quad (A)	1	1.050

* Table 14-2 is continued on the following page.

row represents a second subject, etc. Then we have four subjects going through 15 combinations of levels of A and B. Assuming a nonadditive model, the selection of error terms follows the developments of Chapters 7 and 13. The A and B main effects are tested against the $S \times A$ and $S \times B$ terms, respectively. The $p(A)$ term is tested against the $S \times p(A)$ term. For example, if we wish to test whether there is a significant linear component in the plot of the A main effect, we compute $SS_{S \times \text{lin} (A)}$, which is distributed on 3 df. Calculation of this error term is aided if we pool the data over levels of B, establishing a table containing totals for each $S \times A$ combination. Table 14-3 accomplishes this for the data of Table 14-1. Then we calculate

Error Terms

Design	SV	df	SS	Error Term for
Completely randomized	S/AB	45	73.000	all sources
Repeated measurements	S × A	6	3.567	A
	S × lin (A)	3	2.275	lin (A)
	S × quad (A)	3	1.292	quad (A)
	S × B	12	21.767	B
	S × lin (B)	3	15.692	lin (B)
	S × quad (B)	3	3.065	quad (B)
	S × cub (B)	3	2.892	cub (B)
	S × quart (B)	3	.118	quart (B)
	S × A × B	24	12.912	AB
	S × A × lin (B)	6	1.183	A × lin (B)
	S × lin (A) × lin (B)	3	1.000	lin (A) × lin (B)
	S × quad (A) × lin (B)	3	.183	quad (A) × lin (B)
	S × A × quad (B)	6	5.418	A × quad (B)
	S × lin (A) × quad (B)	3	3.000	lin (A) × quad (B)
	S × quad (A) × quad (B)	3	2.418	quad (A) × quad (B)
	S × A × cub (B)	6	2.734	A × cub (B)
	S × lin (A) × cub (B)	3	2.500	lin (A) × cub (B)
	S × quad (A) × cub (B)	3	.234	quad (A) × cub (B)
	S × A × quart (B)	6	3.600	A × quart (B)
	S × lin (A) × quart (B)	3	2.349	lin (A) × quart (B)
	S × quad (A) × quart (B)	3	1.251	quad (A) × quart (B)
Mixed	S/B	15	56.500	B and all q(B)
	S × A/B	30	16.500	AB, all q(B) × A
	S × lin (A)/B	15	11.130	all q(B) × lin (A)
	S × quad (A)/B	15	5.370	all q(B) × quad (A)

$$SS_{S \times \text{lin} (A)} = \frac{[-86 + (0)(57) + 53]^2 + \cdots + [-80 + (0)(52) + 52]^2}{(5)(2)}$$

$$- SS_{\text{lin} (A)}$$

$$= 356.300 - 354.025$$

$$= 2.275$$

The calculations of $SS_{S \times \text{quad} (A)}$ and $SS_{S \times q(B)}$ ($q = \text{lin, quad, cub, quart}$) are left as an exercise for the reader. The results which should be obtained are presented in Table 14-2.

TABLE 14-3

Reorganization of Table 14-1 to facilitate calculations of interaction effects involving subjects

		A_1	A_2	A_3	$\sum_j \xi'_{j1} Y_{ijk}$	$\sum_j \xi'_{j2} Y_{ijk}$
	B_1	20	18	16	-4	0
	B_2	18	15	14	-4	2
S_1	B_3	16	12	11	-5	3
	B_4	15	5	6	-9	11
	B_5	17	7	6	-11	9
	$\sum_k Y_{1jk} = 86$		57	53	$\sum_k \sum_j \xi'_{j1} Y_{1jk} = -33$	$\sum_k \sum_j \xi'_{j2} Y_{1jk} = 25$
	B_1	18	17	15	-3	-1
	B_2	18	16	13	-5	-1
S_2	B_3	18	13	14	-4	6
	B_4	18	8	8	-10	10
	B_5	18	10	9	-9	7
	$\sum_k Y_{2jk} = 90$		64	59	$\sum_k \sum_j \xi'_{j1} Y_{2jk} = -31$	$\sum_k \sum_j \xi'_{j2} Y_{2jk} = 21$
	B_1	19	18	17	-2	0
	B_2	17	14	14	-3	3
S_3	B_3	17	12	13	-4	6
	B_4	17	7	9	-8	12
	B_5	18	9	8	-10	8
	$\sum_k Y_{3jk} = 88$		60	61	$\sum_k \sum_j \xi'_{j1} Y_{3jk} = -27$	$\sum_k \sum_j \xi'_{j2} Y_{3jk} = 29$
	B_1	16	16	15	-1	-1
	B_2	16	13	13	-3	3
S_4	B_3	16	10	12	-4	8
	B_4	17	5	5	-12	12
	B_5	15	8	7	-8	6
	$\sum_k Y_{4jk} = 80$		52	52	$\sum_k \sum_j \xi'_{j1} Y_{4jk} = -28$	$\sum_k \sum_j \xi'_{j2} Y_{4jk} = 28$

We next consider an error term for the F test of the significance of the general interaction component, $q(B) \times A$. The appropriate error sum of squares, $SS_{S \times q(B) \times A}$, which is distributed on $(n-1)(a-1)$ df, will be most easily calculated if the data are regrouped into four (in general, n) $S \times A$ tables, as has been done in Table 14-3. Then, for the specific test of lin $(B) \times A$, we require

$$SS_{S \times \text{lin } (B) \times A} = \frac{[(-2)(20) - 18 + (0)(16) + 15 + (2)(17)]^2}{10} + \cdots$$

$$+ \frac{[(-2)(15) - 13 + (0)(12) + 5 + (2)(7)]^2}{10}$$

$$- SS_{\text{lin } (B)} - SS_{S \times \text{lin } (B)} - SS_{A \times \text{lin } (B)}$$

$$= 1.182$$

Values for sums of squares for other error terms of the form $S \times q(B) \times A$ are presented in Table 14-2.

To test $p(A) \times q(B)$ we require $SS_{S \times p(A) \times q(B)}$, which is distributed on $n-1$ df. For example, if we are interested in testing lin $(A) \times$ lin (B), we compute

$$SS_{S \times \text{lin } (A) \times \text{lin } (B)}$$

$$= \frac{[(-2)(-1)(20) + (-2)(0)(18) + \cdots + (2)(0)(7) + (2)(1)(6)]^2}{20} + \cdots$$

$$+ \frac{[(-2)(-1)(16) + (-2)(0)(16) + \cdots + (2)(0)(8) + (2)(1)(7)]^2}{20}$$

$$- SS_{\text{lin } (A) \times \text{lin } (B)}$$

$$= 1.00$$

The general expression is provided by Equation (13.26).

Mixed design. Suppose that there are different subjects at each level of B, but all subjects are tested at all levels of A. Then each row of scores in Table 14-1 represents a different subject. The qth component of the B main effect is tested against $MS_{S/B}$, the between-subjects error term. To test the pth component of A, we require $SS_{S \times p(A)/B}$, which is distributed on $b(n-1)$ df. For example, if we wish to test lin (A), we compute

$$SS_{S \times \text{lin } (A)/B} = \frac{[-20 + (0)(18) + 16]^2 + \cdots + [(-15) + (0)(8) + 7]^2}{2}$$

$$- SS_{\text{lin } (A)} - SS_{\text{lin } (A) \times B}$$

$$= 11.130$$

The $MS_{S \times p(A)/B}$ is also the appropriate error term for testing all terms of the form $p(A) \times q(B)$. Thus $S \times$ lin $(A)/B$ would be the appropriate component for a test of either lin $(A) \times$ lin (B) or lin $(A) \times$ quad (B) or lin $(A) \times$ cub (B) or lin $(A) \times$ quart (B). This is analogous to the test of the interaction of a between-subjects and a within-subjects variable; the error term is the error term for testing the within-subjects main effect. In the present instance, the error term for the interaction of a between- and a within-subjects polynomial component is the error term for testing the within-subjects component.

14.4 UNEQUAL INTERVALS

The values of ξ' found in Table A-11 have been derived under the assumption that the levels of the quantitative variable are equally spaced. When this is untrue, other procedures for obtaining values of ξ' must be employed.

One approach which can be used to derive ξ' values for any spacing of the levels of the independent variable will now be illustrated. As an example, a design involving the following levels of delay of reward will be used: 0 sec., 5 sec., 15 sec., and 30 sec. We may divide by a constant to obtain the smallest possible integers. Dividing by five, the values of X_j are 0, 1, 3, and 6. We consider the ξ'_{j1} (the linear coefficients) first. Since $\xi_{j1} = \alpha_1 + X_j$, we have

$$\xi_{11} = \alpha_1$$

(14.7)
$$\xi_{21} = \alpha_1 + 1$$

$$\xi_{31} = \alpha_1 + 3$$

$$\xi_{41} = \alpha_1 + 6$$

Then, $\sum_j \xi_{j1} = 4\alpha_1 + 10$. However, $\sum_j \xi_{j1} = 0$, since the ξ are orthogonal coefficients. Therefore, $4\alpha_1 = -10$ and $\alpha_1 = -2.5$, and substituting into Equation (14.7),

$$\xi_{11} = -2.5$$

$$\xi_{21} = -1.5$$

$$\xi_{31} = .5$$

$$\xi_{41} = 3.5$$

Multiplying by 2 in order to obtain integers yields

$$\xi'_{11} = -5$$

$$\xi'_{21} = -3$$

$$\xi'_{31} = 1$$

$$\xi'_{41} = 7$$

The quadratic coefficients are considered next. Since $\xi_{j2} = \alpha_2 + \beta_2 X_j + X_j^2$,

$$\xi_{12} = \alpha_2$$

(14.8)
$$\xi_{22} = \alpha_2 + \beta_2 + 1$$

$$\xi_{32} = \alpha_2 + 3\beta_2 + 9$$

$$\xi_{42} = \alpha_2 + 6\beta_2 + 36$$

Then,

(14.9) $$\sum_{j} \xi_{j2} = 4\alpha_2 + 10\beta_2 + 46 = 0$$

We also know that $\sum_j \xi_{j1}\xi_{j2} = 0$. Therefore,

$$(-5)(\alpha_2) + (-3)(\alpha_2 + \beta_2 + 1) + (1)(\alpha_2 + 3\beta_2 + 9) + 7(\alpha_2 + 6\beta_2 + 36) = 0$$

or $42\beta_2 = -258$ and $\beta_2 = -43/7$. Substituting into Equation (14.9),

$$4\alpha_2 - (10)\left(\frac{43}{7}\right) + 46 = 0$$

$$4\alpha_2 = \frac{108}{7}$$

$$\alpha_2 = \frac{27}{7}$$

Substituting α_2 and β_2 into Equation (14.8), we have

$$\xi_{12} = \frac{27}{7}$$

$$\xi_{22} = -\frac{9}{7}$$

$$\xi_{32} = -\frac{39}{7}$$

$$\xi_{42} = \frac{21}{7}$$

Multiplying by $7/3$, we have

$$\xi'_{12} = 9$$
$$\xi'_{22} = -3$$
$$\xi'_{32} = -13$$
$$\xi'_{42} = 7$$

To obtain the cubic coefficients, we note that $\xi = \alpha_3 + \beta_3 X + \gamma_3 X^2 + X^3$. Then,

$$\xi_{13} = \alpha_3$$
(14.10)
$$\xi_{23} = \alpha_3 + \beta_3 + \gamma_3 + 1$$
$$\xi_{33} = \alpha_3 + 3\beta_3 + 9\gamma_3 + 27$$
$$\xi_{43} = \alpha_3 + 6\beta_3 + 36\gamma_3 + 216$$

Since the sum of the coefficients is zero,

(14.11) $$4\alpha_3 + 10\beta_3 + 46\gamma_3 + 244 = 0$$

Furthermore, we know that

(14.12) $$(\ \ 5)(\alpha_3) \mid (-3)(\alpha_3 + \beta_3 + \gamma_3 + 1) + (1)(\alpha_3 + 3\beta_3 + 9\gamma_3 + 27)$$
$$+ (7)(\alpha_3 \mid 6\beta_3 + 36\gamma_3 + 216) - 0$$

and

(14.13) $$(9)(\alpha_3) + (-3)(\alpha_3 + \beta_3 + \gamma_3 + 1) + (-13)(\alpha_3 + 3\beta_3 + 9\gamma_3 + 21)$$
$$+ (7)(\alpha_3 + 6\beta_3 + 36\gamma_3 + 216) = 0$$

The last two equations reduce to

(14.12′) $$42\beta_3 + 258\gamma + 1,536 = 0$$

and

(14.13′) $$132\gamma + 1,158 = 0$$

Solving Equation (14.13′), we obtain $\gamma_3 = -193/22$. Substituting in Equation (14.12′), we obtain $\beta_3 = 381/22$. Finally, we obtain from Equation (14.11) $\alpha_3 = -75/22$. Then

$$\xi_{13} = -\frac{75}{22}$$

$$\xi_{23} = \frac{135}{22}$$

$$\xi_{33} = -\frac{75}{22}$$

$$\xi_{43} = \frac{15}{22}$$

Multiplying by 22/15, we have

$$\xi'_{13} = -5$$
$$\xi'_{23} = 9$$
$$\xi'_{33} = -5$$
$$\xi'_{43} = 1$$

Our coefficients are

ξ'_1	ξ'_2	ξ'_3
−5	9	−5
−3	−3	9
1	−13	−5
7	7	1

To check our calculations, we compute $\sum_j \xi'_{jp}$ and $\sum_j \xi'_{jp}\xi_{jp'}$. We have

$$-5 - 3 + 1 + 7 = 0$$
$$9 - 3 - 13 + 7 = 0$$
$$-5 + 9 - 5 + 1 = 0$$

and

$$(-5)(9) + (-3)(-3) + (1)(-13) + (7)(7) = 58 - 58 = 0$$
$$(-5)(-5) + (-3)(9) + (1)(-5) + (7)(1) = 32 - 32 = 0$$
$$(9)(-5) + (-3)(9) + (-13)(-5) + (7)(1) = 72 - 72 = 0$$

The coefficients are orthogonal. They are used in formulas for sums of squares just as the tabled coefficients are.

14.5 CONCLUDING REMARKS

The analyses discussed in this chapter should never be routinely applied whenever one or more independent variables are quantitative. Any set of a data points can be fit by a polynomial of order $a - 1$, but if the population function is not polynomial (e.g., a sine curve), the polynomial analysis will be misleading. It is also dangerous to identify statistical components freely with psychological processes. It is one thing to postulate a cubic component of A, to test for it, and to find it significant, thus substantiating the theory. It is another matter to assign psychological meaning to a significant component which has not been postulated on a priori grounds. An unexpected significant component would be of interest and should alert the experimenter to the possible need to revise his behavioral hypotheses. However, remembering that the calculation of several polynomial F tests will increase the overall Type I error rate, significant results established on an a posteriori basis should require subsequent experimental validation before they are drawn into the body of scientific conclusions. With these caveats in mind, trend analysis can be a powerful tool for establishing the true shapes of data functions. As such, these methods of analyses should go hand in hand with the development of precise quantitative behavioral theories.

EXERCISES

14.1 In the following problem assume that the levels of A are equally spaced. Test the orthogonal polynomial components of A and AB (including single df components of AB). Assume that $n = 5$ and $MS_{S/AB} = .40$.

	A_1	A_2	A_3	A_4
B_1	15	5	5	15
B_2	24	18	12	26

14.2 Present a set of graphs compatible with the following results.

SV	df	F
A	2	*
lin	1	*
quad	1	*
B	3	—
C	1	—
AB	6	—
AC	2	*
lin $(A) \times C$	1	—
quad $(A) \times C$	1	*
BC	3	*
ABC	6	—

$* \, p < .01$

14.3 A conflict theorist has scaled TAT cards and has chosen seven that are equally spaced along a sexual content continuum. He predicts that low guilt subjects will give increasing numbers of sexual responses as sexual content increases, and that high guilt subjects will show the same number of responses to the low-sex-content cards but will inhibit responses to the high-sex-content cards. Assuming 20 subjects in each group (no counterbalance required), give the SV, df, and error terms, stating explicitly what terms should be significant according to the hypotheses and why.

14.4 Two hundred subjects are required to learn a list of paired associates. Incorrect responses are followed by one of five levels of shock, varying from 50 *ma* to 250 *ma* at equal intervals. Subjects are also subjected to one of the following levels of distraction, D: (1) continuous white noise, (2) noise presented only during the interval between stimulus and response, (3) noise presented only during the interval between trials, and (4) no noise. There are an equal number of subjects in each of the 20 cells of the design.

    The experimenter, after testing S, D, and $S \times D$ is interested in testing the following hypotheses:

    (1) The curve describing trials to criterion as a function of S is an inverted U.

    (2) The intermittent D groups perform differently from the non-intermittent groups.

    (3) The performance curve over level of shock will be flatter, i.e., less curved, for the intermittent noise groups and most curved for the no noise group.

(a) Present the computations required for the F tests appropriate to testing hypotheses (1), (2), and (3).

(b) What other independent comparisons could be made with this set of data?

14.5 In a recent experiment, per-cent *prediction* of an event was plotted as a function of the per-cent *occurrence* of the event. Theory led to a prediction of a straight line function with slope of 1.0.

(a) How would this theoretical formulation be tested?

(b) How would confidence limits on the true slope be obtained?

14.6   There are three training methods (T) and four amounts of practice (P) in a completely randomized design.   There are five subjects in each cell.   The total number of errors for each of the 12 groups are given below.

	P_1	P_2	P_3	P_4
T_1	9	5	3	4
T_2	6	8	5	4
T_3	5	4	6	3

The levels of P are so chosen as to be equally spaced (i.e., 1, 2, 3, and 4 hrs.).

(a) Find the sum of squares for the linear components of P and $P \times T$.
(b) We are interested in comparing the rate of learning under T_1 with the average of T_2 and T_3.   Compute the appropriate sum of squares.
(c) Suppose the subjects at each level of T went through all levels of P (P might be the stage of practice).   Give computational formulas for the error terms for the effects to be tested in (a) and (b).

APPENDIX TABLES

Line\Col.	(1)	(2)	(3)	(4)	(5)	(6)	(7)	(8)	(9)	(10)	(11)	(12)	(13)	(14)
1	10480	15011	01536	02011	81647	91646	69179	14194	62590	36207	20969	99570	91291	90700
2	22368	46573	25595	85393	30995	89198	27982	53402	93965	34095	52666	19174	39615	99505
3	24130	48360	22527	97265	76393	64809	15179	24830	49340	32081	30680	19655	63348	58629
4	42167	93093	06243	61680	07856	16376	39440	53537	71341	57004	00849	74917	97758	16379
5	37570	39975	81837	16656	06121	91782	60468	81305	49684	60672	14110	06927	01263	54613
6	77921	06907	11008	42751	27756	53498	18602	70659	90655	15053	21916	81825	44394	42880
7	99562	72905	56420	69994	98872	31016	71194	18738	44013	48840	63213	21069	10634	12952
8	96301	91977	05463	07972	18876	20922	94595	56869	69014	60045	18425	84903	42508	32307
9	89579	14342	63661	10281	17453	18103	57740	84378	25331	12566	58678	44947	05585	56941
10	85475	36857	53342	53988	53060	59533	38867	62300	08158	17983	16439	11458	18593	64952
11	28918	69578	88231	33276	70997	79936	56865	05859	90106	31595	01547	85590	91610	78188
12	63553	40961	48235	03427	49626	69445	18663	72695	52180	20847	12234	90511	33703	90322
13	09429	93969	52636	92737	88974	33488	36320	17617	30015	08272	84115	27156	30613	74952
14	10365	61129	87529	85689	48237	52267	67689	93394	01511	26358	85104	20285	29975	89868
15	07119	97336	71048	08178	77233	13916	47564	81056	97735	85977	29372	74461	28551	90707
16	51085	12765	51821	51259	77452	16308	60756	92144	49442	53900	70960	63990	75601	40719
17	02368	21382	52404	60268	89368	19885	55322	44819	01188	65255	64835	44919	05944	55157
18	01011	54092	33362	94904	31273	04146	18594	29852	71585	85030	51132	01915	92747	64951
19	52162	53916	46369	58586	23216	14513	83149	98736	23495	64350	94738	17752	35156	35749
20	07056	97628	33787	09998	42698	06691	76988	13602	51851	46104	88916	19509	25625	58104
21	48663	91245	85828	14346	09172	30168	90229	04734	59193	22178	30421	61666	99904	32812
22	54164	58492	22421	74103	47070	25306	76468	26384	58151	06646	21524	15227	96909	44592
23	32639	32363	05597	24200	13363	38005	94342	28728	35806	06912	17012	64161	18296	22851
24	29334	27001	87637	87308	58731	00256	45834	15398	46557	41135	10367	07684	36188	18510
25	02488	33062	28834	07351	19731	92420	60952	61280	50001	67658	32586	86679	50720	94953
26	81525	72295	04839	96423	24878	82651	66566	14778	76797	14780	13300	87074	79666	95725
27	29676	20591	68086	26432	46901	20849	89768	81536	86645	12659	92259	57102	80428	25280
28	00742	57392	39064	66432	84673	40027	32832	61362	98947	96067	64760	64584	96096	98253
29	05366	04213	25669	26422	44407	44048	37937	63904	45766	66134	75470	66520	34693	90449
30	91921	26418	64117	94305	26766	25940	39972	22209	71500	64568	91402	42416	07844	69618

TABLE A-1 (Continued)

Line\Col.	(1)	(2)	(3)	(4)	(5)	(6)	(7)	(8)	(9)	(10)	(11)	(12)	(13)	(14)
31	00582	04711	87917	77341	42206	35126	74087	99547	81817	42607	43808	76655	62028	76630
32	00725	69884	62797	56170	86324	88072	76222	36086	84637	93161	76038	65855	77919	88006
33	69011	65795	95876	55293	18988	27354	26575	08625	40801	59920	29841	80150	12777	48501
34	25976	57948	29888	88604	67917	48708	18912	82271	65424	69774	33611	54262	85963	03547
35	09763	83473	73577	12908	30883	18317	28290	35797	05998	41688	34952	37888	38917	88050
36	91567	42595	27958	30134	04024	86385	29880	99730	55536	84855	29080	09250	79656	73211
37	17955	56349	90999	49127	20044	59931	06115	20542	18059	02008	73708	83517	36103	42791
38	46503	18584	18845	49618	02304	51038	20655	58727	28168	15475	56942	53389	20562	87338
39	92157	89634	94824	78171	84610	82834	09922	25417	44137	48413	25555	21246	35509	20468
40	14577	62765	35605	81263	39667	47358	56873	56307	61607	49518	89656	20103	77490	18062
41	98427	07523	33362	64270	01638	92477	66969	98420	04880	45585	46565	04102	46880	45709
42	34914	63976	88720	82765	34476	17032	87589	40836	32427	70002	70663	88863	77775	69348
43	70060	28277	39475	46473	23219	53416	94970	25832	69975	94884	19661	72828	00102	66794
44	53976	54914	06990	67245	68350	82948	11398	42878	80287	88267	47363	46634	06541	97809
45	76072	29515	40980	07391	58745	25774	22987	80059	39911	96189	41151	14222	60697	59583
46	90725	52210	83974	29992	65831	38857	50490	83765	55657	14361	31720	57375	56228	41546
47	64364	67412	33339	31926	14883	24413	59744	92351	97473	89286	35931	04110	23726	51900
48	08962	00358	31662	25388	61642	34072	81249	35648	56891	69352	48373	45578	78547	81788
49	95012	68379	93526	70765	10592	04542	76463	54328	02349	17247	28865	14777	62730	92277
50	15664	10493	20492	38391	91132	21999	59516	81652	27195	48223	46751	22923	32261	85653
51	16408	81899	04153	53381	79401	21438	83035	92350	36693	31238	59649	91754	72772	02338
52	18629	81953	05520	91962	04739	13092	97662	24822	94730	06496	35090	04822	86774	98289
53	73115	35101	47498	87637	99016	71060	88824	71013	18735	20286	23153	72924	35165	43040
54	57491	16703	23167	49323	45021	33132	12544	41035	80780	45393	44812	12515	98931	91202
55	30405	83946	23792	14422	15059	45799	22716	19792	09983	74353	68668	30429	70735	25499
56	16631	35006	85900	98275	32388	52390	16815	69298	82732	38480	73817	32523	41961	44437
57	96773	20206	42559	78985	05300	22164	24369	54224	35083	19687	11052	91491	60383	19746
58	38935	64202	14349	82674	66523	44133	00697	35552	35970	19124	63318	29686	03387	59846
59	31624	76384	17403	53363	44167	64486	64758	75366	76554	31601	12614	33072	60332	92325
60	78919	19474	23632	27889	47914	02584	37680	20801	72152	39339	34806	08930	85001	87820

Abridged from "Table of 105,000 Random Decimal Digits," Statement 4914, Bureau of Transport Economics and Statistics, Interstate Commerce Commission, 1949.

TABLE A-2

Unit Normal Distribution

$$[P(z \leq z_{1-\alpha}) = 1 - \alpha]$$

$1 - \alpha$	$z_{1-\alpha}$	$1 - \alpha$	$z_{1-\alpha}$	$1 - \alpha$	$z_{1-\alpha}$
.50	0.00	.75	0.67	.950	1.645
.51	0.03	.76	0.71	.955	1.695
.52	0.05	.77	0.74	.960	1.751
.53	0.08	.78	0.77	.965	1.812
.54	0.10	.79	0.81	.970	1.881
.55	0.13	.80	0.84	.975	1.960
.56	0.15	.81	0.88	.980	2.054
.57	0.18	.82	0.92	.985	2.170
.58	0.20	.83	0.95	.990	2.326
.59	0.23	.84	0.99	.995	2.576
.60	0.25	.85	1.04	.996	2.652
.61	0.28	.86	1.08	.997	2.748
.62	0.30	.87	1.13	.998	2.878
.63	0.33	.88	1.17	.999	3.090
.64	0.36	.89	1.23		
.65	0.39	.90	1.28	.9995	3.291
.66	0.41	.91	1.34	.99995	3.891
.67	0.44	.92	1.41		
.68	0.47	.93	1.48	.999995	4.417
.69	0.50	.94	1.55		
				.9999995	5.327
.70	0.52				
.71	0.55				
.72	0.58				
.73	0.61				
.74	0.64				

TABLE A-3
Distribution of t

df	Probability												
	.9	.8	.7	.6	.5	.4	.3	.2	.1	.05	.02	.01	.001
1	.158	.325	.510	.727	1.000	1.376	1.963	3.078	6.314	12.706	31.821	63.657	636.619
2	.142	.289	.445	.617	.816	1.061	1.386	1.886	2.920	4.303	6.965	9.925	31.598
3	.137	.277	.424	.584	.765	.978	1.250	1.638	2.353	3.182	4.541	5.841	12.924
4	.134	.271	.414	.569	.741	.941	1.190	1.533	2.132	2.776	3.747	4.604	8.610
5	.132	.267	.408	.559	.727	.920	1.156	1.476	2.015	2.571	3.365	4.032	6.869
6	.131	.265	.404	.553	.718	.906	1.134	1.440	1.943	2.447	3.143	3.707	5.959
7	.130	.263	.402	.549	.711	.896	1.119	1.415	1.895	2.365	2.998	3.499	5.408
8	.130	.262	.399	.546	.706	.889	1.108	1.397	1.860	2.306	2.896	3.355	5.041
9	.129	.261	.398	.543	.703	.883	1.100	1.383	1.833	2.262	2.821	3.250	4.781
10	.129	.260	.397	.542	.700	.879	1.093	1.372	1.812	2.228	2.764	3.169	4.587
11	.129	.260	.396	.540	.697	.876	1.088	1.363	1.796	2.201	2.718	3.106	4.437
12	.128	.259	.395	.539	.695	.873	1.083	1.356	1.782	2.179	2.681	3.055	4.318
13	.128	.259	.394	.538	.694	.870	1.079	1.350	1.771	2.160	2.650	3.012	4.221
14	.128	.258	.393	.537	.692	.868	1.076	1.345	1.761	2.145	2.624	2.977	4.140
15	.128	.258	.393	.536	.691	.866	1.074	1.341	1.753	2.131	2.602	2.947	4.073
16	.128	.258	.392	.535	.690	.865	1.071	1.337	1.746	2.120	2.583	2.921	4.015
17	.128	.257	.392	.534	.689	.863	1.069	1.333	1.740	2.110	2.567	2.898	3.965
18	.127	.257	.392	.534	.688	.862	1.067	1.330	1.734	2.101	2.552	2.878	3.922
19	.127	.257	.391	.533	.688	.861	1.066	1.328	1.729	2.093	2.539	2.861	3.883
20	.127	.257	.391	.533	.687	.860	1.064	1.325	1.725	2.086	2.528	2.845	3.850

21	.127	.257	.391	.532	.686	.859	1.063	1.323	1.721	2.080	2.518	2.831	3.819
22	.127	.256	.390	.532	.686	.858	1.061	1.321	1.717	2.074	2.508	2.819	3.792
23	.127	.256	.390	.532	.685	.858	1.060	1.319	1.714	2.069	2.500	2.807	3.767
24	.127	.256	.390	.531	.685	.857	1.059	1.318	1.711	2.064	2.492	2.797	3.745
25	.127	.256	.390	.531	.684	.856	1.058	1.316	1.708	2.060	2.485	2.787	3.725
26	.127	.256	.390	.531	.684	.856	1.058	1.315	1.706	2.056	2.479	2.779	3.707
27	.127	.256	.389	.531	.684	.855	1.057	1.314	1.703	2.052	2.473	2.771	3.690
28	.127	.256	.389	.530	.683	.855	1.056	1.313	1.701	2.048	2.467	2.763	3.674
29	.127	.256	.389	.530	.683	.854	1.055	1.311	1.699	2.045	2.462	2.756	3.659
30	.127	.256	.389	.530	.683	.854	1.055	1.310	1.697	2.042	2.457	2.750	3.646
40	.126	.255	.388	.529	.681	.851	1.050	1.303	1.684	2.021	2.423	2.704	3.551
60	.126	.254	.387	.527	.679	.848	1.046	1.296	1.671	2.000	2.390	2.660	3.460
120	.126	.254	.386	.526	.677	.845	1.041	1.289	1.658	1.980	2.358	2.617	3.373
∞	.126	.253	.385	.524	.674	.842	1.036	1.282	1.645	1.960	2.326	2.576	3.291

This table is adapted from Table III of R. A. Fisher and F. Yates, *Statistical Tables for Biological, Agricultural and Medical Research*, Oliver and Boyd Ltd., Edinburgh, by permission of the authors and publishers.

TABLE A-4
Distribution of χ^2

df							Probability							
	.99	.98	.95	.90	.80	.70	.50	.30	.20	.10	.05	.02	.01	.001
1	$.0^3157$	$.0^3628$	.00393	.0158	.0642	.148	.455	1.074	1.642	2.706	3.841	5.412	6.635	10.827
2	.0201	.0404	.103	.211	.446	.713	1.386	2.408	3.219	4.605	5.991	7.824	9.210	13.815
3	.115	.185	.352	.584	1.005	1.424	2.366	3.665	4.642	6.251	7.815	9.837	11.345	16.266
4	.297	.429	.711	1.064	1.649	2.195	3.357	4.878	5.989	7.779	9.488	11.668	13.277	18.467
5	.554	.752	1.145	1.610	2.343	3.000	4.351	6.064	7.289	9.236	11.070	13.388	15.086	20.515
6	.872	1.134	1.635	2.204	3.070	3.828	5.348	7.231	8.558	10.645	12.592	15.033	16.812	22.457
7	1.239	1.564	2.167	2.833	3.822	4.671	6.346	8.383	9.803	12.017	14.067	16.622	18.475	24.322
8	1.646	2.032	2.733	3.490	4.594	5.527	7.344	9.524	11.030	13.362	15.507	18.168	20.090	26.125
9	2.088	2.532	3.325	4.168	5.380	6.393	8.343	10.656	12.242	14.684	16.919	19.679	21.666	27.877
10	2.558	3.059	3.940	4.865	6.179	7.267	9.342	11.781	13.442	15.987	18.307	21.161	23.209	29.588
11	3.053	3.609	4.575	5.578	6.989	8.148	10.341	12.899	14.631	17.275	19.675	22.618	24.725	31.264
12	3.571	4.178	5.226	6.304	7.807	9.034	11.340	14.011	15.812	18.549	21.026	24.054	26.217	32.909
13	4.107	4.765	5.892	7.042	8.634	9.926	12.340	15.119	16.985	19.812	22.362	25.472	27.688	34.528
14	4.660	5.368	6.571	7.790	9.467	10.821	13.339	16.222	18.151	21.064	23.685	26.873	29.141	36.123
15	5.229	5.985	7.261	8.547	10.307	11.721	14.339	17.322	19.311	22.307	24.996	28.259	30.578	37.697
16	5.812	6.614	7.962	9.312	11.152	12.624	15.338	18.418	20.465	23.542	26.296	29.633	32.000	39.252
17	6.408	7.255	8.672	10.085	12.002	13.531	16.338	19.511	21.615	24.769	27.587	30.995	33.409	40.790
18	7.015	7.906	9.390	10.865	12.857	14.440	17.338	20.601	22.760	25.989	28.869	32.346	34.805	42.312
19	7.633	8.567	10.117	11.651	13.716	15.352	18.338	21.689	23.900	27.204	30.144	33.687	36.191	43.820
20	8.260	9.237	10.851	12.443	14.578	16.266	19.337	22.775	25.038	28.412	31.410	35.020	37.566	45.315
21	8.897	9.915	11.591	13.240	15.445	17.182	20.337	23.858	26.171	29.615	32.671	36.343	38.932	46.797
22	9.542	10.600	12.338	14.041	16.314	18.101	21.337	24.939	27.301	30.813	33.924	37.659	40.289	48.268
23	10.196	11.293	13.091	14.848	17.187	19.021	22.337	26.018	28.429	32.007	35.172	38.968	41.638	49.728
24	10.856	11.992	13.848	15.659	18.062	19.943	23.337	27.096	29.553	33.196	36.415	40.270	42.980	51.179
25	11.524	12.697	14.611	16.473	18.940	20.867	24.337	28.172	30.675	34.382	37.652	41.566	44.314	52.620

df														
26	12.198	13.409	15.379	17.292	19.820	21.792	25.336	29.246	31.795	35.563	38.885	42.856	45.642	54.052
27	12.879	14.125	16.151	18.114	20.703	22.719	26.336	30.319	32.912	36.741	40.113	44.140	46.963	55.476
28	13.565	14.847	16.928	18.939	21.588	23.647	27.336	31.391	34.027	37.916	41.337	45.419	48.278	56.893
29	14.256	15.574	17.708	19.768	22.475	24.577	28.336	32.461	35.139	39.087	42.557	46.693	49.588	58.302
30	14.953	16.306	18.493	20.599	23.364	25.508	29.336	33.530	36.250	40.256	43.773	47.962	50.892	59.703
32	16.362	17.783	20.072	22.271	25.148	27.373	31.336	35.665	38.466	42.585	46.194	50.487	53.486	62.487
34	17.789	19.275	21.664	23.952	26.938	29.242	33.336	37.795	40.676	44.903	48.602	52.995	56.061	65.247
36	19.233	20.783	23.269	25.643	28.735	31.115	35.336	39.922	42.879	47.212	50.999	55.489	58.619	67.985
38	20.691	22.304	24.884	27.343	30.537	32.992	37.335	42.045	45.076	49.513	53.384	57.969	61.162	70.703
40	22.164	23.838	26.509	29.051	32.345	34.872	39.335	44.165	47.269	51.805	55.759	60.436	63.691	73.402
42	23.650	25.383	28.144	30.765	34.157	36.755	41.335	46.282	49.456	54.090	58.124	62.892	66.206	76.084
44	25.148	26.939	29.787	32.487	35.974	38.641	43.335	48.396	51.639	56.369	60.481	65.337	68.710	78.750
46	26.657	28.504	31.439	34.215	37.795	40.529	45.335	50.507	53.818	58.641	62.830	67.771	71.201	81.400
48	28.177	30.080	33.098	35.949	39.621	42.420	47.335	52.616	55.993	60.907	65.171	70.197	73.683	84.037
50	29.707	31.664	34.764	37.689	41.449	44.313	49.335	54.723	58.164	63.167	67.505	72.613	76.154	86.661
52	31.246	33.256	36.437	39.433	43.281	46.209	51.335	56.827	60.332	65.422	69.832	75.021	78.616	89.272
54	32.793	34.856	38.116	41.183	45.117	48.106	53.335	58.930	62.496	67.673	72.153	77.422	81.069	91.872
56	34.350	36.464	39.801	42.937	46.955	50.005	55.335	61.031	64.658	69.919	74.468	79.815	83.513	94.461
58	35.913	38.078	41.492	44.696	48.797	51.906	57.335	63.129	66.816	72.160	76.778	82.201	85.950	97.039
60	37.485	39.699	43.188	46.459	50.641	53.809	59.335	65.227	68.972	74.397	79.082	84.580	88.379	99.607
62	39.063	41.327	44.889	48.226	52.487	55.714	61.335	67.322	71.125	76.630	81.381	86.953	90.802	102.166
64	40.649	42.960	46.595	49.996	54.336	57.620	63.335	69.416	73.276	78.860	83.675	89.320	93.217	104.716
66	42.240	44.599	48.305	51.770	56.188	59.527	65.335	71.508	75.424	81.085	85.965	91.681	95.626	107.258
68	43.838	46.194	50.020	53.548	58.042	61.436	67.335	73.600	77.571	83.308	88.250	94.037	98.028	109.791
70	45.442	47.893	51.739	55.329	59.898	63.346	69.334	75.689	79.715	85.527	90.531	96.388	100.425	112.317

For odd values of df between 30 and 70, the means of the tabular values for $df-1$ and $df+1$ may be taken. For larger values of df, the expression $\sqrt{2\chi^2} - \sqrt{2df-1}$ may be used as a normal deviate with unit variance, remembering that the probability for χ^2 corresponds with that of a single tail of the normal curve.

This table is adapted from R. A. Fisher and F. Yates, *Statistical Tables for Biological, Agricultural and Medical Research*, Oliver and Boyd Ltd., Edinburgh, by permission of the authors and publishers.

TABLE A-5

Per Cent Points in the Distribution of F

df_2	df_1	1	2	3	4	5	6	8	12	24	∞
·1	0.1%	405284	500000	540379	562500	576405	585937	598144	610667	623497	636619
	0.5%	16211	20000	21615	22500	23056	23437	23925	24426	24940	25465
	1 %	4052	4999	5403	5625	5764	5859	5981	6106	6234	6366
	2.5%	647.79	799.50	864.16	899.58	921.85	937.11	956.66	976.71	997.25	1018.30
	5 %	161.45	199.50	215.71	224.58	230.16	233.99	238.88	243.91	249.05	254.32
	10 %	39.86	49.50	53.59	55.83	57.24	58.20	59.44	60.70	62.00	63.33
	20 %	9.47	12.00	13.06	13.73	14.01	14.26	14.59	14.90	15.24	15.58
2	0.1	998.5	999.0	999.2	999.2	999.3	999.3	999.4	999.4	999.5	999.5
	0.5	198.50	199.00	199.17	199.25	199.30	199.33	199.37	199.42	199.46	199.51
	1	98.49	99.00	99.17	99.25	99.30	99.33	99.36	99.42	99.46	99.50
	2.5	38.51	39.00	39.17	39.25	39.30	39.33	39.37	39.42	39.46	39.50
	5	18.51	19.00	19.16	19.25	19.30	19.33	19.37	19.41	19.45	19.50
	10	8.53	9.00	9.16	9.24	9.29	9.33	9.37	9.41	9.45	9.49
	20	3.56	4.00	4.16	4.24	4.28	4.32	4.36	4.40	4.44	4.48
3	0.1	167.5	148.5	141.1	137.1	134.6	132.8	130.6	128.3	125.9	123.5
	0.5	55.55	49.80	47.47	46.20	45.39	44.84	44.13	43.39	42.62	41.83
	1	34.12	30.81	29.46	28.71	28.24	27.91	27.49	27.05	26.60	26.12
	2.5	17.44	16.04	15.44	15.10	14.89	14.74	14.54	14.34	14.12	13.90
	5	10.13	9.55	9.28	9.12	9.01	8.94	8.84	8.74	8.64	8.53
	10	5.54	5.46	5.39	5.34	5.31	5.28	5.25	5.22	5.18	5.13
	20	2.68	2.89	2.94	2.96	2.97	2.97	2.98	2.98	2.98	2.98
4	0.1	74.14	61.25	56.18	53.44	51.71	50.53	49.00	47.41	45.77	44.05
	0.5	31.33	26.28	24.26	23.16	22.46	21.98	21.35	20.71	20.03	19.33
	1	21.20	18.00	16.69	15.98	15.52	15.21	14.80	14.37	13.93	13.46
	2.5	12.22	10.65	9.98	9.60	9.36	9.20	8.98	8.75	8.51	8.26
	5	7.71	6.94	6.59	6.39	6.26	6.16	6.04	5.91	5.77	5.63
	10	4.54	4.32	4.19	4.11	4.05	4.01	3.95	3.90	3.83	3.76
	20	2.35	2.47	2.48	2.48	2.48	2.47	2.47	2.46	2.44	2.43
5	0.1	47.04	36.61	33.20	31.09	29.75	28.84	27.64	26.42	25.14	23.78
	0.5	22.79	18.31	16.53	15.56	14.94	14.51	13.96	13.38	12.78	12.14
	1	16.26	13.27	12.06	11.39	10.97	10.67	10.29	9.89	9.47	9.02
	2.5	10.01	8.43	7.76	7.39	7.15	6.98	6.76	6.52	6.28	6.02
	5	6.61	5.79	5.41	5.19	5.05	4.95	4.82	4.68	4.53	4.36
	10	4.06	3.78	3.62	3.52	3.45	3.40	3.34	3.27	3.19	3.10
	20	2.18	2.26	2.25	2.24	2.23	2.22	2.20	2.18	2.16	2.13
6	0.1	35.51	27.00	23.70	21.90	20.81	20.03	19.03	17.99	16.89	15.75
	0.5	18.64	14.54	12.92	12.03	11.46	11.07	10.57	10.03	9.47	8.88
	1	13.74	10.92	9.78	9.15	8.75	8.47	8.10	7.72	7.31	6.88
	2.5	8.81	7.26	6.60	6.23	5.99	5.82	5.60	5.37	5.12	4.85
	5	5.99	5.14	4.76	4.53	4.39	4.28	4.15	4.00	3.84	3.67
	10	3.78	3.46	3.29	3.18	3.11	3.05	2.98	2.90	2.82	2.72
	20	2.07	2.13	2.11	2.09	2.08	2.06	2.04	2.02	1.99	1.95
7	0.1	29.22	21.69	18.77	17.19	16.21	15.52	14.63	13.71	12.73	11.69
	0.5	16.24	12.40	10.88	10.05	9.52	9.16	8.68	8.18	7.65	7.08
	1	12.25	9.55	8.45	7.85	7.46	7.19	6.84	6.47	6.07	5.65
	2.5	8.07	6.54	5.89	5.52	5.29	5.12	4.90	4.67	4.42	4.14
	5	5.59	4.74	4.35	4.12	3.97	3.87	3.73	3.57	3.41	3.23
	10	3.59	3.26	3.07	2.96	2.88	2.83	2.75	2.67	2.58	2.47
	20	2.00	2.04	2.02	1.99	1.97	1.96	1.93	1.91	1.87	1.83
8	0.1	25.42	18.49	15.83	14.39	13.49	12.86	12.04	11.19	10.30	9.34
	0.5	14.69	11.04	9.60	8.81	8.30	7.95	7.50	7.01	6.50	5.95
	1	11.26	8.65	7.59	7.01	6.63	6.37	6.03	5.67	5.28	4.86
	2.5	7.57	6.06	5.42	5.05	4.82	4.65	4.43	4.20	3.95	3.67
	5	5.32	4.46	4.07	3.84	3.69	3.58	3.44	3.28	3.12	2.93
	10	3.46	3.11	2.92	2.81	2.73	2.67	2.59	2.50	2.40	2.29
	20	1.95	1.98	1.95	1.92	1.90	1.88	1.86	1.83	1.79	1.74

This table is abridged from Table 5 of R. A. Fisher and F. Yates, *Statistical Tables for Biological, Agricultural and Medical Research*, Oliver and Boyd Ltd., Edinburgh, by permission of the authors and publishers. The 0.5% and 2.5% points are reprinted by permission from "Tables of Percentage Points of the Inverted Beta (F) Distribution," *Biometrika*, 33:73–88 (April 1943).

df_1 df_2		1	2	3	4	5	6	8	12	24	∞
9	0.1%	22.86	16.39	13.90	12.56	11.71	11.13	10.37	9.57	8.72	7.81
	0.5%	13.61	10.11	8.72	7.96	7.47	7.13	6.69	6.23	5.73	5.19
	1 %	10.56	8.02	6.99	6.42	6.06	5.80	5.47	5.11	4.73	4.31
	2.5%	7.21	5.71	5.08	4.72	4.48	4.32	4.10	3.87	3.61	3.33
	5 %	5.12	4.26	3.86	3.63	3.48	3.37	3.23	3.07	2.90	2.71
	10 %	3.36	3.01	2.81	2.69	2.61	2.55	2.47	2.38	2.28	2.16
	20 %	1.91	1.94	1.90	1.87	1.85	1.83	1.80	1.76	1.72	1.67
10	0.1	21.04	14.91	12.55	11.28	10.48	9.92	9.20	8.45	7.64	6.76
	0.5	12.83	9.43	8.08	7.34	6.87	6.54	6.12	5.66	5.17	4.64
	1	10.04	7.56	6.55	5.99	5.64	5.39	5.06	4.71	4.33	3.91
	2.5	6.94	5.46	4.83	4.47	4.24	4.07	3.85	3.62	3.37	3.08
	5	4.96	4.10	3.71	3.48	3.33	3.22	3.07	2.91	2.74	2.54
	10	3.28	2.92	2.73	2.61	2.52	2.46	2.38	2.28	2.18	2.06
	20	1.88	1.90	1.86	1.83	1.80	1.78	1.75	1.72	1.67	1.62
11	0.1	19.69	13.81	11.56	10.35	9.58	9.05	8.35	7.63	6.85	6.00
	0.5	12.23	8.91	7.60	6.88	6.42	6.10	5.68	5.24	4.76	4.23
	1	9.65	7.20	6.22	5.67	5.32	5.07	4.74	4.40	4.02	3.60
	2.5	6.72	5.26	4.63	4.28	4.04	3.88	3.66	3.43	3.17	2.88
	5	4.84	3.98	3.59	3.36	3.20	3.09	2.95	2.79	2.61	2.40
	10	3.23	2.86	2.66	2.54	2.45	2.39	2.30	2.21	2.10	1.97
	20	1.86	1.87	1.83	1.80	1.77	1.75	1.72	1.68	1.63	1.57
12	0.1	18.64	12.97	10.80	9.63	8.89	8.38	7.71	7.00	6.25	5.42
	0.5	11.75	8.51	7.23	6.52	6.07	5.76	5.35	4.91	4.43	3.90
	1	9.33	6.93	5.95	5.41	5.06	4.82	4.50	4.16	3.78	3.36
	2.5	6.55	5.10	4.47	4.12	3.89	3.73	3.51	3.28	3.02	2.72
	5	4.75	3.88	3.49	3.26	3.11	3.00	2.85	2.69	2.50	2.30
	10	3.18	2.81	2.61	2.48	2.39	2.33	2.24	2.15	2.04	1.90
	20	1.84	1.85	1.80	1.77	1.74	1.72	1.69	1.65	1.60	1.54
13	0.1	17.81	12.31	10.21	9.07	8.35	7.86	7.21	6.52	5.78	4.97
	0.5	11.37	8.19	6.93	6.23	5.79	5.48	5.08	4.64	4.17	3.65
	1	9.07	6.70	5.74	5.20	4.86	4.62	4.30	3.96	3.59	3.16
	2.5	6.41	4.97	4.35	4.00	3.77	3.60	3.39	3.15	2.89	2.60
	5	4.67	3.80	3.41	3.18	3.02	2.92	2.77	2.60	2.42	2.21
	10	3.14	2.76	2.56	2.43	2.35	2.28	2.20	2.10	1.98	1.85
	20	1.82	1.83	1.78	1.75	1.72	1.69	1.66	1.62	1.57	1.51
14	0.1	17.14	11.78	9.73	8.62	7.92	7.43	6.80	6.13	5.41	4.60
	0.5	11.06	7.92	6.68	6.00	5.56	5.26	4.86	4.43	3.96	3.44
	1	8.86	6.51	5.56	5.03	4.69	4.46	4.14	3.80	3.43	3.00
	2.5	6.30	4.86	4.24	3.89	3.66	3.50	3.29	3.05	2.79	2.49
	5	4.60	3.74	3.34	3.11	2.96	2.85	2.70	2.53	2.35	2.13
	10	3.10	2.73	2.52	2.39	2.31	2.24	2.15	2.05	1.94	1.80
	20	1.81	1.81	1.76	1.73	1.70	1.67	1.64	1.60	1.55	1.48
15	0.1	16.59	11.34	9.34	8.25	7.57	7.09	6.47	5.81	5.10	4.31
	0.5	10.80	7.70	6.48	5.80	5.37	5.07	4.67	4.25	3.79	3.26
	1	8.68	6.36	5.42	4.89	4.56	4.32	4.00	3.67	3.29	2.87
	2.5	6.20	4.77	4.15	3.80	3.58	3.41	3.20	2.96	2.70	2.40
	5	4.54	3.68	3.29	3.06	2.90	2.79	2.64	2.48	2.29	2.07
	10	3.07	2.70	2.49	2.36	2.27	2.21	2.12	2.02	1.90	1.76
	20	1.80	1.79	1.75	1.71	1.68	1.66	1.62	1.58	1.53	1.46
16	0.1	16.12	10.97	9.00	7.94	7.27	6.81	6.19	5.55	4.85	4.06
	0.5	10.58	7.51	6.30	5.64	5.21	4.91	4.52	4.10	3.64	3.11
	1	8.53	6.23	5.29	4.77	4.44	4.20	3.89	3.55	3.18	2.75
	2.5	6.12	4.69	4.08	3.73	3.50	3.34	3.12	2.89	2.63	2.32
	5	4.49	3.63	3.24	3.01	2.85	2.74	2.59	2.42	2.24	2.01
	10	3.05	2.67	2.46	2.33	2.24	2.18	2.09	1.99	1.87	1.72
	20	1.79	1.78	1.74	1.70	1.67	1.64	1.61	1.56	1.51	1.43
17	0.1	15.72	10.66	8.73	7.68	7.02	6.56	5.96	5.32	4.63	3.85
	0.5	10.38	7.35	6.16	5.50	5.07	4.78	4.39	3.97	3.51	2.98
	1	8.40	6.11	5.18	4.67	4.34	4.10	3.79	3.45	3.08	2.65
	2.5	6.04	4.62	4.01	3.66	3.44	3.28	3.06	2.82	2.56	2.25
	5	4.45	3.59	3.20	2.96	2.81	2.70	2.55	2.38	2.19	1.96
	10	3.03	2.64	2.44	2.31	2.22	2.15	2.06	1.96	1.84	1.69
	20	1.78	1.77	1.72	1.68	1.65	1.63	1.59	1.55	1.49	1.42

df_2	df_1	1	2	3	4	5	6	8	12	24	∞
18	0.1%	15.38	10.39	8.49	7.46	6.81	6.35	5.76	5.13	4.45	3.67
	0.5%	10.22	7.21	6.03	5.37	4.96	4.66	4.28	3.86	3.40	2.87
	1 %	8.28	6.01	5.09	4.58	4.25	4.01	3.71	3.37	3.00	2.57
	2.5%	5.98	4.56	3.95	3.61	3.38	3.22	3.01	2.77	2.50	2.19
	5 %	4.41	3.55	3.16	2.93	2.77	2.66	2.51	2.34	2.15	1.92
	10 %	3.01	2.62	2.42	2.29	2.20	2.13	2.04	1.93	1.81	1.66
	20 %	1.77	1.76	1.71	1.67	1.64	1.62	1.58	1.53	1.48	1.40
19	0.1	15.08	10.16	8.28	7.26	6.61	6.18	5.59	4.97	4.29	3.52
	0.5	10.07	7.09	5.92	5.27	4.85	4.56	4.18	3.76	3.31	2.78
	1	8.18	5.93	5.01	4.50	4.17	3.94	3.63	3.30	2.92	2.49
	2.5	5.92	4.51	3.90	3.56	3.33	3.17	2.96	2.72	2.45	2.13
	5	4.38	3.52	3.13	2.90	2.74	2.63	2.48	2.31	2.11	1.88
	10	2.99	2.61	2.40	2.27	2.18	2.11	2.02	1.91	1.79	1.63
	20	1.76	1.75	1.70	1.66	1.63	1.61	1.57	1.52	1.46	1.39
20	0.1	14.82	9.95	8.10	7.10	6.46	6.02	5.44	4.82	4.15	3.38
	0.5	9.94	6.99	5.82	5.17	4.76	4.47	4.09	3.68	3.22	2.69
	1	8.10	5.85	4.94	4.43	4.10	3.87	3.56	3.23	2.86	2.42
	2.5	5.87	4.46	3.86	3.51	3.29	3.13	2.91	2.68	2.41	2.09
	5	4.35	3.49	3.10	2.87	2.71	2.60	2.45	2.28	2.08	1.84
	10	2.97	2.59	2.38	2.25	2.16	2.09	2.00	1.89	1.77	1.61
	20	1.76	1.75	1.70	1.65	1.62	1.60	1.56	1.51	1.45	1.37
21	0.1	14.59	9.77	7.94	6.95	6.32	5.88	5.31	4.70	4.03	3.26
	0.5	9.83	6.89	5.73	5.09	4.68	4.39	4.01	3.60	3.15	2.61
	1	8.02	5.78	4.87	4.37	4.04	3.81	3.51	3.17	2.80	2.36
	2.5	5.83	4.42	3.82	3.48	3.25	3.09	2.87	2.64	2.37	2.04
	5	4.32	3.47	3.07	2.84	2.68	2.57	2.42	2.25	2.05	1.81
	10	2.96	2.57	2.36	2.23	2.14	2.08	1.98	1.88	1.75	1.59
	20	1.75	1.74	1.69	1.65	1.61	1.59	1.55	1.50	1.44	1.36
22	0.1	14.38	9.61	7.80	6.81	6.19	5.76	5.19	4.58	3.92	3.15
	0.5	9.73	6.81	5.65	5.02	4.61	4.32	3.94	3.54	3.08	2.55
	1	7.94	5.72	4.82	4.31	3.99	3.76	3.45	3.12	2.75	2.31
	2.5	5.79	4.38	3.78	3.44	3.22	3.05	2.84	2.60	2.33	2.00
	5	4.30	3.44	3.05	2.82	2.66	2.55	2.40	2.23	2.03	1.78
	10	2.95	2.56	2.35	2.22	2.13	2.06	1.97	1.86	1.73	1.57
	20	1.75	1.73	1.68	1.64	1.61	1.58	1.54	1.49	1.43	1.35
23	0.1	14.19	9.47	7.67	6.69	6.08	5.65	5.09	4.48	3.82	3.05
	0.5	9.63	6.73	5.58	4.95	4.54	4.26	3.88	3.47	3.02	2.48
	1	7.88	5.66	4.76	4.26	3.94	3.71	3.41	3.07	2.70	2.26
	2.5	5.75	4.35	3.75	3.41	3.18	3.02	2.81	2.57	2.30	1.97
	5	4.28	3.42	3.03	2.80	2.64	2.53	2.38	2.20	2.00	1.76
	10	2.94	2.55	2.34	2.21	2.11	2.05	1.95	1.84	1.72	1.55
	20	1.74	1.73	1.68	1.63	1.60	1.57	1.53	1.49	1.42	1.34
24	0.1	14.03	9.34	7.55	6.59	5.98	5.55	4.99	4.39	3.74	2.97
	0.5	9.55	6.66	5.52	4.89	4.49	4.20	3.83	3.42	2.97	2.43
	1	7.82	5.61	4.72	4.22	3.90	3.67	3.36	3.03	2.66	2.21
	2.5	5.72	4.32	3.72	3.38	3.15	2.99	2.78	2.54	2.27	1.94
	5	4.26	3.40	3.01	2.78	2.62	2.51	2.36	2.18	1.98	1.73
	10	2.93	2.54	2.33	2.19	2.10	2.04	1.94	1.83	1.70	1.53
	20	1.74	1.72	1.67	1.63	1.59	1.57	1.53	1.48	1.42	1.33
25	0.1	13.88	9.22	7.45	6.49	5.88	5.46	4.91	4.31	3.66	2.89
	0.5	9.48	6.60	5.46	4.84	4.43	4.15	3.78	3.37	2.92	2.38
	1	7.77	5.57	4.68	4.18	3.86	3.63	3.32	2.99	2.62	2.17
	2.5	5.69	4.29	3.69	3.35	3.13	2.97	2.75	2.51	2.24	1.91
	5	4.24	3.38	2.99	2.76	2.60	2.49	2.34	2.16	1.96	1.71
	10	2.92	2.53	2.32	2.18	2.09	2.02	1.93	1.82	1.69	1.52
	20	1.73	1.72	1.66	1.62	1.59	1.56	1.52	1.47	1.41	1.32
26	0.1	13.74	9.12	7.36	6.41	5.80	5.38	4.83	4.24	3.59	2.82
	0.5	9.41	6.54	5.41	4.79	4.38	4.10	3.73	3.33	2.87	2.33
	1	7.72	5.53	4.64	4.14	3.82	3.59	3.29	2.96	2.58	2.13
	2.5	5.66	4.27	3.67	3.33	3.10	2.94	2.73	2.49	2.22	1.88
	5	4.22	3.37	2.98	2.74	2.59	2.47	2.32	2.15	1.95	1.69
	10	2.91	2.52	2.31	2.17	2.08	2.01	1.92	1.81	1.68	1.50
	20	1.73	1.71	1.66	1.62	1.58	1.56	1.52	1.47	1.40	1.31

df_2	df_1	1	2	3	4	5	6	8	12	24	∞
27	0.1%	13.61	9.02	7.27	6.33	5.73	5.31	4.76	4.17	3.52	2.75
	0.5%	9.34	6.49	5.36	4.74	4.34	4.06	3.69	3.28	2.83	2.29
	1 %	7.68	5.49	4.60	4.11	3.78	3.56	3.26	2.93	2.55	2.10
	2.5%	5.63	4.24	3.65	3.31	3.08	2.92	2.71	2.47	2.19	1.85
	5 %	4.21	3.35	2.96	2.73	2.57	2.46	2.30	2.13	1.93	1.67
	10 %	2.90	2.51	2.30	2.17	2.07	2.00	1.91	1.80	1.67	1.49
	20 %	1.73	1.71	1.66	1.61	1.58	1.55	1.51	1.46	1.40	1.30
28	0.1	13.50	8.93	7.19	6.25	5.66	5.24	4.69	4.11	3.46	2.70
	0.5	9.28	6.44	5.32	4.70	4.30	4.02	3.65	3.25	2.79	2.25
	1	7.64	5.45	4.57	4.07	3.75	3.53	3.23	2.90	2.52	2.06
	2.5	5.61	4.22	3.63	3.29	3.06	2.90	2.69	2.45	2.17	1.83
	5	4.20	3.34	2.95	2.71	2.56	2.44	2.29	2.12	1.91	1.65
	10	2.89	2.50	2.29	2.16	2.06	2.00	1.90	1.79	1.66	1.48
	20	1.72	1.71	1.65	1.61	1.57	1.55	1.51	1.46	1.39	1.30
29	0.1	13.39	8.85	7.12	6.19	5.59	5.18	4.64	4.05	3.41	2.64
	0.5	9.23	6.40	5.28	4.66	4.26	3.98	3.61	3.21	2.76	2.21
	1	7.60	5.42	4.54	4.04	3.73	3.50	3.20	2.87	2.49	2.03
	2.5	5.59	4.20	3.61	3.27	3.04	2.88	2.67	2.43	2.15	1.81
	5	4.18	3.33	2.93	2.70	2.54	2.43	2.28	2.10	1.90	1.64
	10	2.89	2.50	2.28	2.15	2.06	1.99	1.89	1.78	1.65	1.47
	20	1.72	1.70	1.65	1.60	1.57	1.54	1.50	1.45	1.39	1.29
30	0.1	13.29	8.77	7.05	6.12	5.53	5.12	4.58	4.00	3.36	2.59
	0.5	9.18	6.35	5.24	4.62	4.23	3.95	3.58	3.18	2.73	2.18
	1	7.56	5.39	4.51	4.02	3.70	3.47	3.17	2.84	2.47	2.01
	2.5	5.57	4.18	3.59	3.25	3.03	2.87	2.65	2.41	2.14	1.79
	5	4.17	3.32	2.92	2.69	2.53	2.42	2.27	2.09	1.89	1.62
	10	2.88	2.49	2.28	2.14	2.05	1.98	1.88	1.77	1.64	1.46
	20	1.72	1.70	1.64	1.60	1.57	1.54	1.50	1.45	1.38	1.28
40	0.1	12.61	8.25	6.60	5.70	5.13	4.73	4.21	3.64	3.01	2.23
	0.5	8.83	6.07	4.98	4.37	3.99	3.71	3.35	2.95	2.50	1.93
	1	7.31	5.18	4.31	3.83	3.51	3.29	2.99	2.66	2.29	1.80
	2.5	5.42	4.05	3.46	3.13	2.90	2.74	2.53	2.29	2.01	1.64
	5	4.08	3.23	2.84	2.61	2.45	2.34	2.18	2.00	1.79	1.51
	10	2.84	2.44	2.23	2.09	2.00	1.93	1.83	1.71	1.57	1.38
	20	1.70	1.68	1.62	1.57	1.54	1.51	1.47	1.41	1.34	1.24
60	0.1	11.97	7.76	6.17	5.31	4.76	4.37	3.87	3.31	2.69	1.90
	0.5	8.49	5.80	4.73	4.14	3.76	3.49	3.13	2.74	2.29	1.69
	1	7.08	4.98	4.13	3.65	3.34	3.12	2.82	2.50	2.12	1.60
	2.5	5.29	3.93	3.34	3.01	2.79	2.63	2.41	2.17	1.88	1.48
	5	4.00	3.15	2.76	2.52	2.37	2.25	2.10	1.92	1.70	1.39
	10	2.79	2.39	2.18	2.04	1.95	1.87	1.77	1.66	1.51	1.29
	20	1.68	1.65	1.59	1.55	1.51	1.48	1.44	1.38	1.31	1.18
120	0.1	11.38	7.31	5.79	4.95	4.42	4.04	3.55	3.02	2.40	1.56
	0.5	8.18	5.54	4.50	3.92	3.55	3.28	2.93	2.54	2.09	1.43
	1	6.85	4.79	3.95	3.48	3.17	2.96	2.66	2.34	1.95	1.38
	2.5	5.15	3.80	3.23	2.89	2.67	2.52	2.30	2.05	1.76	1.31
	5	3.92	3.07	2.68	2.45	2.29	2.17	2.02	1.83	1.61	1.25
	10	2.75	2.35	2.13	1.99	1.90	1.82	1.72	1.60	1.45	1.19
	20	1.66	1.63	1.57	1.52	1.48	1.45	1.41	1.35	1.27	1.12
∞	0.1	10.83	6.91	5.42	4.62	4.10	3.74	3.27	2.74	2.13	1.00
	0.5	7.88	5.30	4.28	3.72	3.35	3.09	2.74	2.36	1.90	1.00
	1	6.64	4.60	3.78	3.32	3.02	2.80	2.51	2.18	1.79	1.00
	2.5	5.02	3.69	3.12	2.79	2.57	2.41	2.19	1.94	1.64	1.00
	5	3.84	2.99	2.60	2.37	2.21	2.09	1.94	1.75	1.52	1.00
	10	2.71	2.30	2.08	1.94	1.85	1.77	1.67	1.55	1.38	1.00
	20	1.64	1.61	1.55	1.50	1.46	1.43	1.38	1.32	1.23	1.00

Distribution of F_{max} Statistic

df for s_X^{2j}	$1 - \alpha$	a = number of variances								
		2	3	4	5	· 6	7	8	9	10
4	.95	9.60	15.5	20.6	25.2	29.5	33.6	37.5	41.4	44.6
	.99	23.2	37.	49.	59.	69.	79.	89.	97.	106.
5	.95	7.15	10.8	13.7	16.3	18.7	20.8	22.9	24.7	26.5
	.99	14.9	22.	28.	33.	38.	42.	46.	50.	54.
6	.95	5.82	8.38	10.4	12.1	13.7	15.0	16.3	17.5	18.6
	.99	11.1	15.5	19.1	22.	25.	27.	30.	32.	34.
7	.95	4.99	6.94	8.44	9.70	10.8	11.8	12.7	13.5	14.3
	.99	8.89	12.1	14.5	16.5	18.4	20.	22.	23.	24.
8	.95	4.43	6.00	7.18	8.12	9.03	9.78	10.5	11.1	11.7
	.99	7.50	9.9	11.7	13.2	14.5	15.8	16.9	17.9	18.9
9	.95	4.03	5.34	6.31	7.11	7.80	8.41	8.95	9.45	9.91
	.99	6.54	8.5	9.9	11.1	12.1	13.1	13.9	14.7	15.3
10	.95	3.72	4.85	5.67	6.34	6.92	7.42	7.87	8.28	8.66
	.99	5.85	7.4	8.6	9.6	10.4	11.1	11.8	12.4	12.9
12	.95	3.28	4.16	4.79	5.30	5.72	6.09	6.42	6.72	7.00
	.99	4.91	6.1	6.9	7.6	8.2	8.7	9.1	9.5	9.9
15	.95	2.86	3.54	4.01	4.37	4.68	4.95	5.19	5.40	5.59
	.99	4.07	4.9	5.5	6.0	6.4	6.7	7.1	7.3	7.5
20	.95	2.46	2.95	3.29	3.54	3.76	3.94	4.10	4.24	4.37
	.99	3.32	3.8	4.3	4.6	4.9	5.1	5.3	5.5	5.6
30	.95	2.07	2.40	2.61	2.78	2.91	3.02	3.12	3.21	3.29
	.99	2.63	3.0	3.3	3.4	3.6	3.7	3.8	3.9	4.0
60	.95	1.67	1.85	1.96	2.04	2.11	2.17	2.22	2.26	2.30
	.99	1.96	2.2	2.3	2.4	2.4	2.5	2.5	2.6	2.6
∞	.95	1.00	1.00	1.00	1.00	1.00	1.00	1.00	1.00	1.00
	.99	1.00	1.00	1.00	1.00	1.00	1.00	1.00	1.00	1.00

This table is abridged from Table 31 in *Biometrika Tables for Statisticians*, Vol. 1, 2d ed. (New York: Cambridge, 1958). Edited by E. S. Pearson and H. O. Hartley. Reproduced with the permission of E. S. Pearson and the trustees of *Biometrika*.

TABLE A-7

Critical Values for Cochran's Test for Homogeneity of Variance

$$C = (\text{largest } s^2)/(\sum s_j^2)$$

df for s_j^2	$1-\alpha$	a = number of variances										
		2	3	4	5	6	7	8	9	10	15	20
1	.95	.9985	.9669	.9065	.8412	.7808	.7271	.6798	.6385	.6020	.4709	.3894
	.99	.9999	.9933	.9676	.9279	.8828	.8376	.7945	.7544	.7175	.5747	.4799
2	.95	.9750	.8709	.7679	.6838	.6161	.5612	.5157	.4775	.4450	.3346	.2705
	.99	.9950	.9423	.8643	.7885	.7218	.6644	.6152	.5727	.5358	.4069	.3297
3	.95	.9392	.7977	.6841	.5981	.5321	.4800	.4377	.4027	.3733	.2758	.2205
	.99	.9794	.8831	.7814	.6957	.6258	.5685	.5209	.4810	.4469	.3317	.2654
4	.95	.9057	.7457	.6287	.5441	.4803	.4307	.3910	.3584	.3311	.2419	.1921
	.99	.9586	.8335	.7212	.6329	.5635	.5080	.4627	.4251	.3934	.2882	.2288
5	.95	.8772	.7071	.5895	.5065	.4447	.3974	.3555	.3286	.3029	.2195	.1735
	.99	.9373	.7933	.6761	.5875	.5195	.4659	.4226	.3870	.3572	.2593	.2048
6	.95	.8534	.6771	.5598	.4783	.4184	.3726	.3362	.3067	.2823	.2034	.1602
	.99	.9172	.7606	.6410	.5531	.4866	.4347	.3932	.3592	.3308	.2386	.1877
7	.95	.8332	.6530	.5365	.4564	.3980	.3535	.3185	.2901	.2666	.1911	.1501
	.99	.8988	.7335	.6129	.5259	.4608	.4105	.3704	.3378	.3106	.2228	.1748
8	.95	.8159	.6333	.5175	.4387	.3817	.3384	.3043	.2768	.2541	.1815	.1422
	.99	.8823	.7107	.5897	.5037	.4401	.3911	.3522	.3207	.2945	.2104	.1646
9	.95	.8010	.6167	.5017	.4241	.3682	.3259	.2926	.2659	.2439	.1736	.1357
	.99	.8674	.6912	.5702	.4854	.4229	.3751	.3373	.3067	.2813	.2002	.1567
16	.95	.7341	.5466	.4366	.3645	.3135	.2756	.2462	.2226	.2032	.1429	.1108
	.99	.7949	.6059	.4884	.4094	.3529	.3105	.2779	.2514	.2297	.1612	.1248
36	.95	.6602	.4748	.3720	.3066	.2612	.2278	.2022	.1820	.1655	.1144	.0879
	.99	.7067	.5153	.4057	.3351	.2858	.2494	.2214	.1992	.1811	.1251	.0960
144	.95	.5813	.4031	.3093	.2513	.2119	.1833	.1616	.1446	.1308	.0889	.0675
	.99	.6062	.4230	.3251	.2644	.2229	.1929	.1700	.1521	.1376	.0934	.0709

Adapted from C. Eisenhart, M. W. Hastay, and W. A. Wallis, eds., *Techniques of Statistical Analysis*, chap. 15 (New York: McGraw-Hill, 1947).

TABLE A-8

Power Function for Analysis of Variance Test

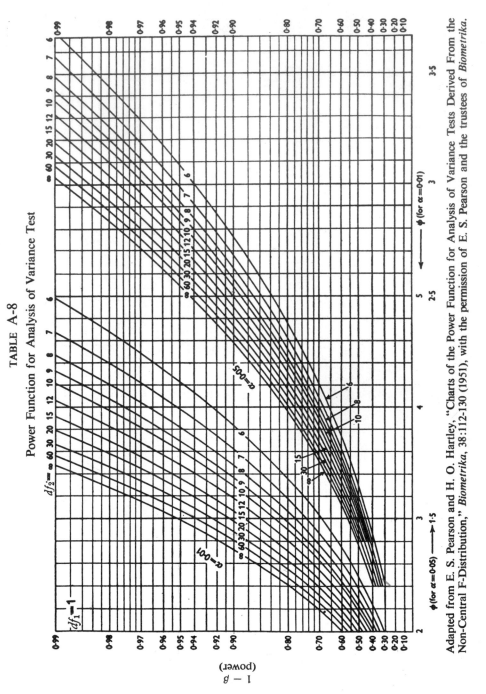

Adapted from E. S. Pearson and H. O. Hartley, "Charts of the Power Function for Analysis of Variance Tests Derived From the Non-Central F-Distribution," *Biometrika*, 38:112-130 (1951), with the permission of E. S. Pearson and the trustees of *Biometrika*.

390

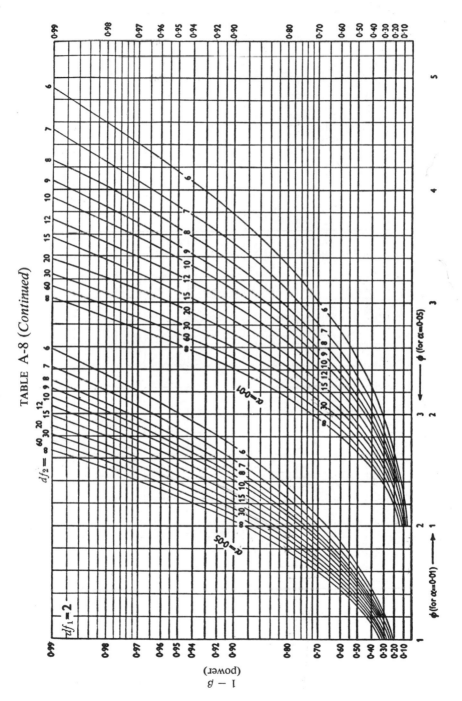

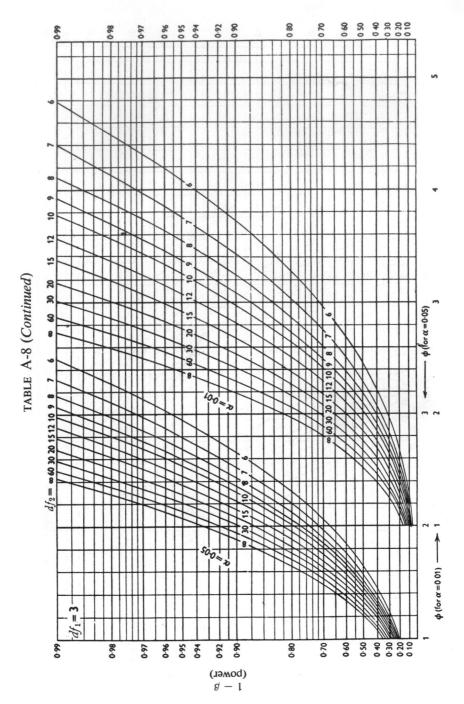

TABLE A-8 (*Continued*)

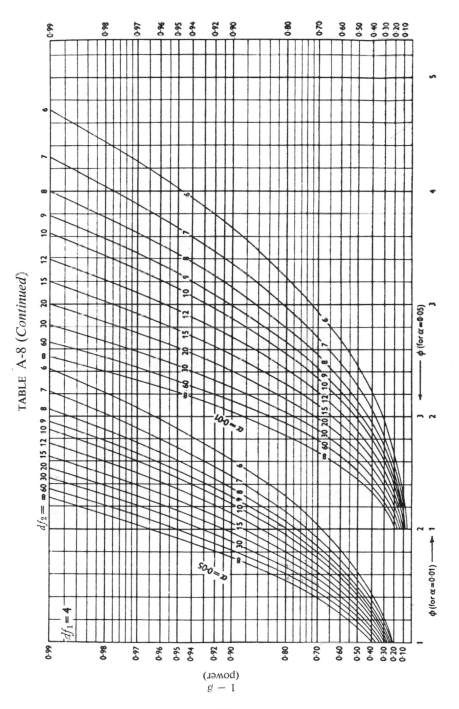

393

TABLE A-8 (Continued)

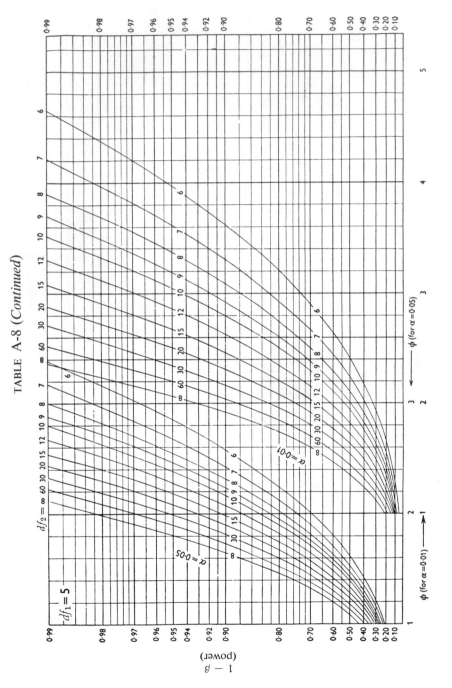

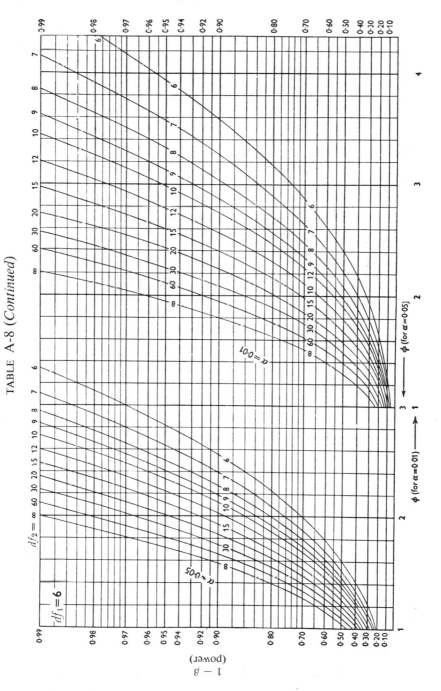

TABLE A-8 (Continued)

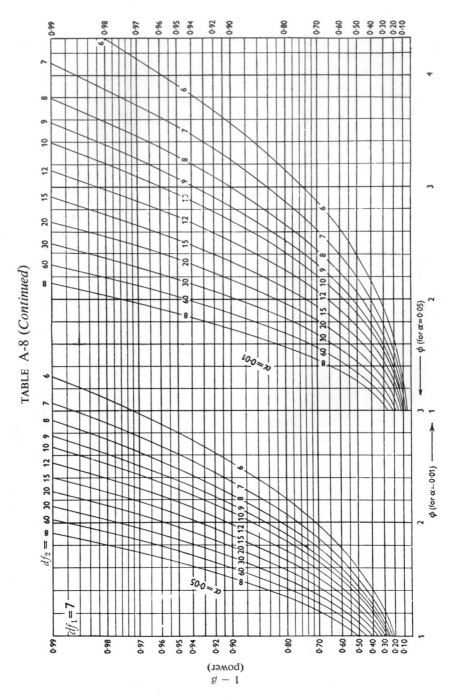

396

TABLE A-8 (Continued)

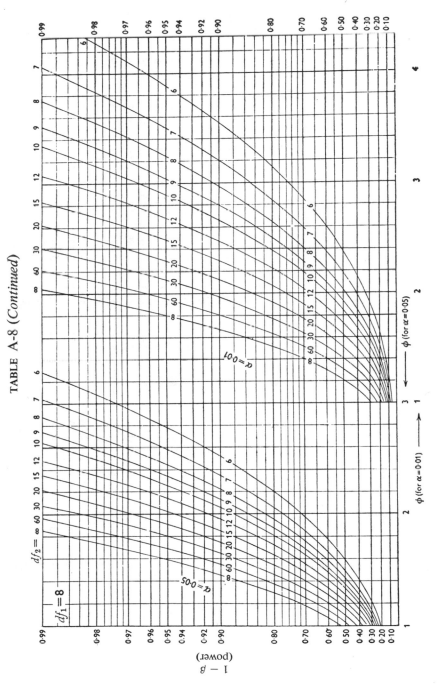

TABLE A-9
Distribution of the Studentized Range Statistic

| df for $s_{\overline{Y}}$ | $1-\alpha$ | \multicolumn{14}{c}{Number of steps between ordered means} | | | | | | | | | | | | | |
		2	3	4	5	6	7	8	9	10	11	12	13	14	15
1	.95	18.0	27.0	32.8	37.1	40.4	43.1	45.4	47.4	49.1	50.6	52.0	53.2	54.3	55.4
	.99	90.0	135	164	186	202	216	227	237	246	253	260	266	272	277
2	.95	6.09	8.3	9.8	10.9	11.7	12.4	13.0	13.5	14.0	14.4	14.7	15.1	15.4	15.7
	.99	14.0	19.0	22.3	24.7	26.6	28.2	29.5	30.7	31.7	32.6	33.4	34.1	34.8	35.4
3	.95	4.50	5.91	6.82	7.50	8.04	8.48	8.85	9.18	9.46	9.72	9.95	10.2	10.4	10.5
	.99	8.26	10.6	12.2	13.3	14.2	15.0	15.6	16.2	16.7	17.1	17.5	17.9	18.2	18.5
4	.95	3.93	5.04	5.76	6.29	6.71	7.05	7.35	7.60	7.83	8.03	8.21	8.37	8.52	8.66
	.99	6.51	8.12	9.17	9.96	10.6	11.1	11.5	11.9	12.3	12.6	12.8	13.1	13.3	13.5
5	.95	3.64	4.60	5.22	5.67	6.03	6.33	6.58	6.80	6.99	7.17	7.32	7.47	7.60	7.72
	.99	5.70	6.97	7.80	8.42	8.91	9.32	9.67	9.97	10.2	10.5	10.7	10.9	11.1	11.2
6	.95	3.46	4.34	4.90	5.31	5.63	5.89	6.12	6.32	6.49	6.65	6.79	6.92	7.03	7.14
	.99	5.24	6.33	7.03	7.56	7.97	8.32	8.61	8.87	9.10	9.30	9.49	9.65	9.81	9.95
7	.95	3.34	4.16	4.69	5.06	5.36	5.61	5.82	6.00	6.16	6.30	6.43	6.55	6.66	6.76
	.99	4.95	5.92	6.54	7.01	7.37	7.68	7.94	8.17	8.37	8.55	8.71	8.86	9.00	9.12
8	.95	3.26	4.04	4.53	4.89	5.17	5.40	5.60	5.77	5.92	6.05	6.18	6.29	6.39	6.48
	.99	4.74	5.63	6.20	6.63	6.96	7.24	7.47	7.68	7.87	8.03	8.18	8.31	8.44	8.55
9	.95	3.20	3.95	4.42	4.76	5.02	5.24	5.43	5.60	5.74	5.87	5.98	6.09	6.19	6.28
	.99	4.60	5.43	5.96	6.35	6.66	6.91	7.13	7.32	7.49	7.65	7.78	7.91	8.03	8.13
10	.95	3.15	3.88	4.33	4.65	4.91	5.12	5.30	5.46	5.60	5.72	5.83	5.93	6.03	6.11
	.99	4.48	5.27	5.77	6.14	6.43	6.67	6.87	7.05	7.21	7.36	7.48	7.60	7.71	7.81
11	.95	3.11	3.82	4.26	4.57	4.82	5.03	5.20	5.35	5.49	5.61	5.71	5.81	5.90	5.99
	.99	4.39	5.14	5.62	5.97	6.25	6.48	6.67	6.84	6.99	7.13	7.26	7.36	7.46	7.56

df															
12	.95	3.08	3.77	4.20	4.51	4.75	4.95	5.12	5.27	5.40	5.51	5.62	5.71	5.80	5.88
	.99	4.32	5.04	5.50	5.84	6.10	6.32	6.51	6.67	6.81	6.94	7.06	7.17	7.26	7.36
13	.95	3.06	3.73	4.15	4.45	4.69	4.88	5.05	5.19	5.32	5.43	5.53	5.63	5.71	5.79
	.99	4.26	4.96	5.40	5.73	5.98	6.19	6.37	6.53	6.67	6.79	6.90	7.01	7.10	7.19
14	.95	3.03	3.70	4.11	4.41	4.64	4.83	4.99	5.13	5.25	5.36	5.46	5.55	5.64	5.72
	.99	4.21	4.89	5.32	5.63	5.88	6.08	6.26	6.41	6.54	6.66	6.77	6.87	6.96	7.05
16	.95	3.00	3.65	4.05	4.33	4.56	4.74	4.90	5.03	5.15	5.26	5.35	5.44	5.52	5.59
	.99	4.13	4.78	5.19	5.49	5.72	5.92	6.08	6.22	6.35	6.46	6.56	6.66	6.74	6.82
18	.95	2.97	3.61	4.00	4.28	4.49	4.67	4.82	4.96	5.07	5.17	5.27	5.35	5.43	5.50
	.99	4.07	4.70	5.09	5.38	5.60	5.79	5.94	6.08	6.20	6.31	6.41	6.50	6.58	6.65
20	.95	2.95	3.58	3.96	4.23	4.45	4.62	4.77	4.90	5.01	5.11	5.20	5.28	5.36	5.43
	.99	4.02	4.64	5.02	5.29	5.51	5.69	5.84	5.97	6.09	6.19	6.29	6.37	6.45	6.52
24	.95	2.92	3.53	3.90	4.17	4.37	4.54	4.68	4.81	4.92	5.01	5.10	5.18	5.25	5.32
	.99	3.96	4.54	4.91	5.17	5.37	5.54	5.69	5.81	5.92	6.02	6.11	6.19	6.26	6.33
30	.95	2.89	3.49	3.84	4.10	4.30	4.46	4.60	4.72	4.83	4.92	5.00	5.08	5.15	5.21
	.99	3.89	4.45	4.80	5.05	5.24	5.40	5.54	5.56	5.76	5.85	5.93	6.01	6.08	6.14
40	.95	2.86	3.44	3.79	4.04	4.23	4.39	4.52	4.63	4.74	4.82	4.91	4.98	5.05	5.11
	.99	3.82	4.37	4.70	4.93	5.11	5.27	5.39	5.50	5.60	5.69	5.77	5.84	5.90	5.96
60	.95	2.83	3.40	3.74	3.98	4.16	4.31	4.44	4.55	4.65	4.73	4.81	4.88	4.94	5.00
	.99	3.76	4.28	4.60	4.82	4.99	5.13	5.25	5.36	5.45	5.53	5.60	5.67	5.73	5.79
120	.95	2.80	3.36	3.69	3.92	4.10	4.24	4.36	4.48	4.56	4.64	4.72	4.78	4.84	4.90
	.99	3.70	4.20	4.50	4.71	4.87	5.01	5.12	5.21	5.30	5.38	5.44	5.51	5.56	5.61
∞	.95	2.77	3.31	3.63	3.86	4.03	4.17	4.29	4.39	4.47	4.55	4.62	4.68	4.74	4.80
	.99	3.64	4.12	4.40	4.60	4.76	4.88	4.99	5.08	5.16	5.23	5.29	5.35	5.40	5.45

This table is abridged from Table II.2 in *The Probability Integrals of the Range and of the Studentized Range*, prepared by H. Leon Harter, Donald S. Clemm, and Eugene H. Guthrie. These tables are published in WADC tech. Rep. 58–484, vol. 2, 1959, Wright Air Development Center, and are reproduced with the permission of the authors.

Distribution of d Statistic in Comparing Treatment Means With a Control

df for MS_{error}	$1 - \alpha$	Number of means (including control)								
		2	3	4	5	6	7	8	9	10
5	.95	1.94	2.34	2.56	2.71	2.83	2.92	3.00	3.07	3.12
	.975	2.45	2.86	3.18	3.41	3.60	3.75	3.88	4.00	4.11
	.99	3.14	3.61	3.88	4.07	4.21	4.33	4.43	4.51	4.59
	.995	3.71	4.22	4.60	4.88	5.11	5.30	5.47	5.61	5.74
6	.95	1.89	2.27	2.48	2.62	2.73	2.82	2.89	2.95	3.01
	.975	2.36	2.75	3.04	3.24	3.41	3.54	3.66	3.76	3.86
	.99	3.00	3.42	3.66	3.83	3.96	4.07	4.15	4.23	4.30
	.995	3.50	3.95	4.28	4.52	4.17	4.87	5.01	5.13	5.24
7	.95	1.86	2.22	2.42	2.55	2.66	2.74	2.81	2.87	2.92
	.975	2.31	2.67	2.94	3.13	3.28	3.40	3.51	3.60	3.68
	.99	2.90	3.29	3.51	3.67	3.79	3.88	3.96	4.03	4.09
	.995	3.36	3.77	4.06	4.27	4.44	4.58	4.70	4.81	4.90
8	.95	1.83	2.18	2.37	2.50	2.60	2.68	2.75	2.81	2.86
	.975	2.26	2.61	2.86	3.04	3.18	3.29	3.39	3.48	3.55
	.99	2.82	3.19	3.40	3.55	3.66	3.75	3.82	3.89	3.94
	.995	3.25	3.63	3.90	4.09	4.24	4.37	4.48	4.57	4.65
9	.95	1.81	2.15	2.34	2.47	2.56	2.64	2.70	2.76	2.81
	.975	2.23	2.57	2.81	2.97	3.11	3.21	3.31	3.39	3.46
	.99	2.76	3.11	3.31	3.45	3.56	3.64	3.71	3.78	3.83
	.995	3.17	3.53	3.78	3.95	4.10	4.21	4.31	4.40	4.47
10	.95	1.80	2.13	2.31	2.44	2.53	2.60	2.67	2.72	2.77
	.975	2.20	2.53	2.76	2.92	3.05	3.15	3.24	3.31	3.38
	.99	2.72	3.06	3.25	3.38	3.48	3.56	3.63	3.69	3.74
	.995	3.11	3.45	3.68	3.85	3.98	4.09	4.18	4.26	4.33
11	.95	1.78	2.11	2.29	2.41	2.50	2.58	2.64	2.69	2.74
	.975	2.18	2.50	2.72	2.88	3.00	3.10	3.18	3.25	3.32
	.99	2.68	3.01	3.19	3.32	3.42	3.50	3.56	3.62	3.67
	.995	3.05	3.39	3.61	3.76	3.89	3.99	4.08	4.15	4.22
12	.95	1.77	2.09	2.27	2.39	2.48	2.55	2.61	2.66	2.71
	.975	2.16	2.48	2.69	2.84	2.96	3.06	3.14	3.21	3.27
	.99	2.65	2.97	3.15	3.27	3.37	3.44	3.51	3.56	3.61
	.995	3.01	3.33	3.54	3.69	3.81	3.91	3.99	4.06	4.13
13	.95	1.76	2.08	2.25	2.37	2.46	2.53	2.59	2.64	2.69
	.975	2.14	2.46	2.67	2.81	2.93	3.02	3.10	3.17	3.23
	.99	2.62	2.94	3.11	3.23	3.32	3.40	3.46	3.51	3.56
	.995	2.98	3.29	3.49	3.64	3.75	3.84	3.92	3.99	4.05

This table is adapted from "A Multiple Comparison Procedure for Comparing Several Treatments With a Control," *Journal of the American Statistical Association*, 50:1096–1121 (1955), with the permission of the author, C. W. Dunnett, and the editor.

df for MS_{error}	$1 - \alpha$	Number of means (including control)								
		2	3	4	5	6	7	8	9	10
14	.95	2.02	2.44	2.68	2.85	2.98	3.08	3.16	3.24	3.30
	.975	2.57	3.03	3.39	3.66	3.88	4.06	4.22	4.36	4.49
	.99	3.37	3.90	4.21	4.43	4.60	4.73	4.85	4.94	5.03
	.995	4.03	4.63	5.09	5.44	5.73	5.97	6.18	6.36	6.53
16	.95	1.75	2.06	2.23	2.34	2.43	2.50	2.56	2.61	2.65
	.975	2.12	2.42	2.63	2.77	2.88	2.96	3.04	3.10	3.16
	.99	2.58	2.88	3.05	3.17	3.26	3.33	3.39	3.44	3.48
	.995	2.92	3.22	3.41	3.55	3.65	3.74	3.82	3.88	3.93
18	.95	1.73	2.04	2.21	2.32	2.41	2.48	2.53	2.58	2.62
	.975	2.10	2.40	2.59	2.73	2.84	2.92	2.99	3.05	3.11
	.99	2.55	2.84	3.01	3.12	3.21	3.27	3.33	3.38	3.42
	.995	2.88	3.17	3.35	3.48	3.58	3.67	3.74	3.80	3.85
20	.95	1.72	2.03	2.19	2.30	2.39	2.46	2.51	2.56	2.60
	.975	2.09	2.38	2.57	2.70	2.81	2.89	2.96	3.02	3.07
	.99	2.53	2.81	2.97	3.08	3.17	3.23	3.29	3.34	3.38
	.995	2.85	3.13	3.31	3.43	3.53	3.61	3.67	3.73	3.78
24	.95	1.71	2.01	2.17	2.28	2.36	2.43	2.48	2.53	2.57
	.975	2.06	2.35	2.53	2.66	2.76	2.84	2.91	2.96	3.01
	.99	2.49	2.77	2.92	3.03	3.11	3.17	3.22	3.27	3.31
	.995	2.80	3.07	3.24	3.36	3.45	3.52	3.58	3.64	3.69
30	.95	1.70	1.99	2.15	2.25	2.33	2.40	2.45	2.50	2.54
	.975	2.04	2.32	2.50	2.62	2.72	2.79	2.86	2.91	2.96
	.99	2.46	2.72	2.87	2.97	3.05	3.11	3.16	3.21	3.24
	.995	2.75	3.01	3.17	3.28	3.37	3.44	3.50	3.55	3.59
40	.95	1.68	1.97	2.13	2.23	2.31	2.37	2.42	2.47	2.51
	.975	2.02	2.29	2.47	2.58	2.67	2.75	2.81	2.86	2.90
	.99	2.42	2.68	2.82	2.92	2.99	3.05	3.10	3.14	3.18
	.995	2.70	2.95	3.10	3.21	3.29	3.36	3.41	3.46	3.50
60	.95	1.67	1.95	2.10	2.21	2.28	2.35	2.39	2.44	2.48
	.975	2.00	2.27	2.43	2.55	2.63	2.70	2.76	2.81	2.85
	.99	2.39	2.64	2.78	2.87	2.94	3.00	3.04	3.08	3.12
	.995	2.66	2.90	3.04	3.14	3.22	3.28	3.33	3.38	3.42
120	.95	1.66	1.93	2.08	2.18	2.26	2.32	2.37	2.41	2.45
	.975	1.98	2.24	2.40	2.51	2.59	2.66	2.71	2.76	2.80
	.99	2.36	2.60	2.73	2.82	2.89	2.94	2.99	3.03	3.06
	.995	2.62	2.84	2.98	3.08	3.15	3.21	3.25	3.30	3.33
∞	.95	1.64	1.92	2.06	2.16	2.23	2.29	2.34	2.38	2.42
	.975	1.96	2.21	2.37	2.47	2.55	2.62	2.67	2.71	2.75
	.99	2.33	2.56	2.68	2.77	2.84	2.89	2.93	2.97	3.00
	.995	2.58	2.79	2.92	3.01	3.08	3.14	3.18	3.22	3.25

TABLE A-11

Coefficients of Orthogonal Polynomials

a	Polynomial	$X=1$	2	3	4	5	6	7	8	9	10	$\Sigma\,\xi'^2$	λ
3	Linear	-1	0	1								2	1
	Quadratic	1	-2	1								6	3
4	Linear	-3	-1	1	3							20	2
	Quadratic	1	-1	-1	1							4	1
	Cubic	-1	3	-3	1							20	$\frac{10}{3}$
5	Linear	-2	-1	0	1	2						10	1
	Quadratic	2	-1	-2	-1	2						14	1
	Cubic	-1	2	0	-2	1						10	$\frac{5}{6}$
	Quartic	1	-4	6	-4	1						70	$\frac{35}{12}$
6	Linear	-5	-3	-1	1	3	5					70	2
	Quadratic	5	-1	-4	-4	-1	5					84	$\frac{3}{2}$
	Cubic	-5	7	4	-4	-7	5					180	$\frac{5}{3}$
	Quartic	1	-3	2	2	-3	1					28	$\frac{7}{12}$
7	Linear	-3	-2	-1	0	1	2	3				28	1
	Quadratic	5	0	-3	-4	-3	0	5				84	1
	Cubic	-1	1	1	0	-1	-1	1				6	$\frac{1}{6}$
	Quartic	3	-7	1	6	1	-7	3				154	$\frac{7}{12}$
8	Linear	-7	-5	-3	-1	1	3	5	7			168	2
	Quadratic	7	1	-3	-5	-5	-3	1	7			168	1
	Cubic	-7	5	7	3	-3	-7	-5	7			264	$\frac{2}{3}$
	Quartic	7	-13	-3	9	9	-3	-13	7			616	$\frac{7}{12}$
	Quintic	-7	23	-17	-15	15	17	-23	7			2184	$\frac{7}{10}$
9	Linear	-4	-3	-2	-1	0	1	2	3	4		60	1
	Quadratic	28	7	-8	-17	-20	-17	-8	7	28		2772	3
	Cubic	-14	7	13	9	0	-9	-13	-7	14		990	$\frac{5}{6}$
	Quartic	14	-21	-11	9	18	9	-11	-21	14		2002	$\frac{7}{12}$
	Quintic	-4	11	-4	-9	0	9	4	-11	4		468	$\frac{3}{20}$
10	Linear	-9	-7	-5	-3	-1	1	3	5	7	9	330	2
	Quadratic	6	2	-1	-3	-4	-4	-3	-1	2	6	132	$\frac{1}{2}$
	Cubic	-42	14	35	31	12	-12	-31	-35	-14	42	8580	$\frac{5}{3}$
	Quartic	18	-22	-17	3	18	18	3	-17	-22	18	2860	$\frac{5}{12}$
	Quintic	-6	14	-1	-11	-6	6	11	1	-14	6	780	$\frac{1}{10}$

This table is adapted with permission from B. J. Winer, *Statistical Principles in Experimental Design* (New York: McGraw Hill, 1962).

INDEX